WORKED EXAMPLES
IN
STATISTICAL
INFERENCE

GW00391024

By

F. D. J. DUNSTAN, M.A., M.Sc., D.Phil.
A. B. J. NIX, B.Sc., Ph.D.
J. F. REYNOLDS, M.A., Ph.D.
R. J. ROWLANDS, B.Sc., Ph.D.

Lecturers at
University College, Cardiff

RND PUBLICATIONS

First published in 1984 by
RND PUBLICATIONS
6 The Avenue, Whitchurch, Cardiff CF4 2EG.

Copyright © 1984 RND PUBLICATIONS

CONTENTS

Preface

This book contains over 350 worked examples in statistical inference. The problems range from elementary exercises to those suitable for Scholarship and first-year University examinations, and are taken from the companion volume entitled Introductory Statistics Volume 2: Statistical Inference.

Each problem is solved in full detail and sometimes alternative solutions are given. The methods used for each solution are those appropriate to the relevant section of the companion volume.

A selection of tables reprinted from RND Statistical Tables is given at the end of the book.

Finally the authors are grateful to Chartwell Ltd., Jeymer Drive, Greenford, Middlesex for permission to include graphs drawn on their Poisson paper and arithmetic probability paper.

F.D.J.Dunstan
A.B.J.Nix
J.F.Reynolds
R.J.Rowlands
Cardiff, 1984

6

Sampling Theory

Exercises 6.2 Sampling Without Replacement from a Finite Population

1. In a money box there are one 5p, two 10p, one 20p and two 50p
    coins. Two coins are selected at random without replacement.
    Find the sampling distribution of their total value. What is
    the probability that the total value exceeds 30p?

¶   Let X_1, X_2 be the values of the selected coins. Below we list
    the possible pairs of values of X_1 and X_2, the corresponding
    value of $X_1 + X_2$, the total value, and the associated probabili-
    ties. In all there are $^6C_2 = 15$ possible combinations and so,
    for example, the probability that the values are 10 and 20 is
    2/15, since two of the possibilities consist of one 10p coin
    and one 20p coin.

Values	Total Value	Probability
5,10	15	2/15
5,20	25	1/15
5,50	55	2/15
10,10	20	1/15
10,20	30	2/15
10,50	60	4/15
20,50	70	2/15
50,50	100	1/15

The sampling distribution of the total value is therefore

Total value	15	20	25	30	55	60	70	100
Probability	2/15	1/15	1/15	2/15	2/15	4/15	2/15	1/15

The probability that the total value exceeds 30 is clearly
9/15 = 3/5.

2. Five cards numbered 1,2,3,4 and 5 are placed in a box and three of them are selected at random without replacement. Find, by enumeration, the sampling distributions of
   (i)   the median of the three numbers on the selected cards,
   (ii)   the smallest of these three numbers.

¶ There are $^5C_3$ = 10 possible combinations, all equally likely. They are listed below, along with the corresponding values of the median and the smallest chosen number.

Combination	Median	Smallest
123	2	1
124	2	1
125	2	1
134	3	1
135	3	1
145	4	1
234	3	2
235	3	2
245	4	2
345	4	3

Since each combination has probability 1/10, the required sampling distributions are as follows:

median	2	3	4
probability	3/10	4/10	3/10

smallest	1	2	3
probability	6/10	3/10	1/10

3. A subcommittee of three people is to be formed from a committee of six people. Of the six people on the committee, two are 30 years old, one is 32, two are 33 and one is 37. Obtain the sampling distributions of the mean and median age of the subcommittee if it is selected at random.

¶ Below we list the possible combinations of ages of the chosen subcommittee, the mean and median of the ages, and the probability of obtaining each combination. Note that there are $^6C_3$ = 20 possible combinations of people.

2

Combination	Mean	Median	Probability
30,30,32	$30\frac{2}{3}$	30	1/20
30,30,33	31	30	2/20
30,30,37	$32\frac{1}{3}$	30	1/20
30,32,33	$31\frac{2}{3}$	32	4/20
30,32,37	33	32	2/20
30,33,33	32	33	2/20
30,33,37	$33\frac{1}{3}$	33	4/20
32,33,33	$32\frac{2}{3}$	33	1/20
32,33,37	34	33	2/20
33,33,37	$34\frac{1}{3}$	33	1/20

The sampling distributions of the mean age and median age are thus

mean	$30\frac{2}{3}$	31	$31\frac{2}{3}$	32	$31\frac{1}{3}$	$32\frac{2}{3}$	33	$33\frac{1}{3}$	34	$34\frac{1}{3}$
probability	1/20	2/20	4/20	2/20	1/20	1/20	2/20	4/20	2/20	1/20

and

median	30	32	33
probability	4/20	6/20	10/20

4.   A bag contains two balls numbered 1, three numbered 2 and one numbered 5. Two balls are selected at random without replacement. Find the sampling distributions of S^2 and S. Verify that

$$E(S) \neq \sqrt{E(S^2)}$$

¶   The possible combinations of the numbers on the chosen balls are shown below, together with the associated probability and the corresponding values of S^2 and S. In all $^6C_2 = 15$ different pairs of balls can be chosen.

Combination	Probability	s^2	s
11	1/15	0	0
12	6/15	1/2	$1/\sqrt{2}$
15	2/15	8	$\sqrt{8}$
22	3/15	0	0
25	3/15	9/2	$3/\sqrt{2}$

Note that in the obvious notation,

$$s^2 = (x_1 - \frac{x_1+x_2}{2})^2 + (x_2 - \frac{x_1+x_2}{2})^2$$
$$= \tfrac{1}{2}(x_1-x_2)^2.$$

3

The sampling distributions of S^2 and S are thus

s^2	0	1/2	9/2	8
probability	4/15	6/15	3/15	2/15

and

s	0	$1/\sqrt{2}$	$3/\sqrt{2}$	$\sqrt{8}$
probability	4/15	6/15	3/15	2/15

Thus $E(S^2)$ $= 0 \times \dfrac{4}{15} + \dfrac{1}{2} \times \dfrac{6}{15} + \dfrac{9}{2} \times \dfrac{3}{15} + 8 \times \dfrac{2}{15}$

$= \dfrac{65}{30} = \dfrac{13}{6}$,

while

$E(S)$ $= 0 \times \dfrac{4}{15} + \dfrac{1}{\sqrt{2}} \times \dfrac{6}{15} + \dfrac{3}{\sqrt{2}} \times \dfrac{3}{15} + 8 \times \dfrac{2}{15}$

$= \dfrac{23\sqrt{2}}{30}$,

so that $\sqrt{E(S^2)} \neq E(S)$.

5. A small block of flats contains 6 families. One family has
    0 children, one family has 1 child, three families have 2
    children and one family has 3 children. A random sample of
    three families is selected without replacement.

    Let X_i denote the number of children in the ith selected
    family (i=1,2,3). Find, by enumeration, the distributions
    of the sample mean, sample variance and sample median of
    X_1, X_2 and X_3. Hence verify that Theorem 6.1 (Volume 2)
    holds in this case.

¶   Below are listed the possible combinations of values of
    X_1, X_2 and X_3, together with the associated probabilities
    and the corresponding values of the sample mean, sample
    variance and sample median.

Combination	Probability	Mean, $\bar{x}$	Variance, s^2	Median, m
0,1,2	3/20	1	1	1
0,1,3	1/20	4/3	7/3	1
0,2,2	3/20	4/3	4/3	2
0,2,3	3/20	5/3	7/3	2
1,2,2	3/20	5/3	1/3	2
1,2,3	3/20	2	1	2
2,2,2	1/20	2	0	2
2,2,3	3/20	7/3	1/3	2

The respective sampling distributions of the sample mean, sample variance and sample median are:

$\bar{x}$	1	4/3	5/3	2	7/3
prob	3/20	4/20	6/20	4/20	3/20

s^2	0	1/3	1	4/3	7/3
prob	1/20	6/20	6/20	3/20	4/20

m	1	2
prob	4/20	16/20

Therefore

$$E(\bar{X}) = 1 \times \frac{3}{20} + \frac{4}{3} \times \frac{4}{20} + \frac{5}{3} \times \frac{6}{20} + 2 \times \frac{4}{20} + \frac{7}{3} \times \frac{3}{20} = 5/3,$$

$$E(\bar{X}^2) = 1^2 \times \frac{3}{20} + \left(\frac{4}{3}\right)^2 \times \frac{4}{20} + \left(\frac{5}{3}\right)^2 \times \frac{6}{20} + 2^2 \times \frac{4}{20} + \left(\frac{7}{3}\right)^2 \times \frac{3}{20} = \frac{532}{180}$$

and $Var(\bar{X}) = \frac{532}{180} - \left(\frac{5}{3}\right)^2 = \frac{8}{45}$.

Now, for i=1,2 or 3,

$$E(X_i) = 0 \times \frac{1}{6} + 1 \times \frac{1}{6} + 2 \times \frac{3}{6} + 3 \times \frac{1}{6} = \frac{5}{3} = \mu, \text{ say,}$$

$$E(X_i^2) = 0^2 \times \frac{1}{6} + 1^2 \times \frac{1}{6} + 2^2 \times \frac{3}{6} + 3^2 \times \frac{1}{6} = \frac{11}{3}$$

and $Var(X_i) = \frac{11}{3} - \left(\frac{5}{3}\right)^2 = \frac{8}{9} = \sigma^2$ say.

In the notation of Theorem 6.1,

$$E(\bar{X}) = \frac{5}{3} = \mu,$$

$$\frac{N-n}{N-1} \cdot \frac{\sigma^2}{n} = \frac{6-3}{6-1} \times \frac{8}{9 \times 3} = \frac{8}{45} = Var(\bar{X})$$

and the Theorem holds here.

6. The following six cards are taken from a pack: the 2, 3 and 4 of Hearts and the 2, 3 and 4 of Spades. Three of the cards are selected at random without replacement. Find the sampling distributions of

(i) the highest value selected,

(ii) the difference between the highest and the lowest values selected.

¶ Below are listed the possible values of the selected cards together with the values of the highest value Z selected and the difference R between the highest and lowest values. There are $^6C_3 = 20$ possible combinations.

Combination	Probability	z	r
223	2/20	3	1
224	2/20	4	2
233	2/20	3	1
234	8/20	4	2
244	2/20	4	2
334	2/20	4	1
344	2/20	4	1

(i)   The sampling distribution of Z is

z	3	4
probability	4/20	16/20

(ii)   The sampling distribution of R is

r	1	2
probability	8/20	12/20

7.   A company has six employees. The amount of overtime worked per day by each employee is given in the following table:

Employee	A	B	C	D	E	F
Overtime (hours/day)	2	2	1	1	1	0

A random sample of n employees is selected without replacement, and the amount of overtime X_i worked per day by the ith member of the sample is recorded ($i=1,2,\ldots,n$). Find the sampling distribution of $\bar{X} = (X_1+X_2+\ldots+X_n)/n$ when (i) n=2, (ii) n=3. Hence calculate $E(\bar{X})$ and $Var(\bar{X})$ in each case. Use Theorem 6.1 (Volume 2) to check your results.

¶   Let X be the amount of overtime worked in a day by a randomly selected employee. X has the probability distribution

x	0	1	2
p_X	1/6	1/2	1/3

and has mean $\mu = 0 \times 1/6 + 1 \times 1/2 + 2 \times 1/3 = 7/6$, and variance $\sigma^2 = 0^2 \times 1/6 + 1^2 \times 1/2 + 2^2 \times 1/3 - (7/6)^2 = 17/36$.

Consider first the case n=2. The possible pairs of values x_1, x_2, together with the value of the sample mean and the associated probability, are shown below:

x_1, x_2	Probability	$\bar{x}$
0,1	3/15	1/2
1,1	3/15	1
0,2	2/15	1
1,2	6/15	3/2
2,2	1/15	2

The probabilities are calculated using the fact that there are $^6C_2$, that is 15, possible pairs of employees.

The sampling distribution of $\bar{X}$ is therefore

$\bar{x}$	1/2	1	3/2	2
probability	3/15	5/15	6/15	1/15

and $E(\bar{X}) = 7/6 = \mu$,

$$\text{Var}(\bar{X}) = \frac{17}{90} = \frac{\sigma^2}{2} \times \frac{6-2}{6-1} ,$$

in agreement with Theorem 6.1.

Similarly, if n=3 we obtain the following table:

x_1, x_2, x_3	Probability	$\bar{x}$
0,1,1	3/20	2/3
0,1,2	6/20	1
0,2,2	1/20	4/3
1,1,1	1/20	1
1,1,2	6/20	4/3
1,2,2	3/20	5/3

$\bar{X}$ now has the sampling distribution

$\bar{x}$	2/3	1	4/3	5/3
probability	3/20	7/20	7/20	3/20

We find that $E(\bar{X}) = 7/6 = \mu$,

and $\qquad \text{Var}(\bar{X}) = \frac{17}{180} = \frac{\sigma^2}{3} \times \frac{6-3}{6-1} ,$

again in agreement with Theorem 6.1.

8. A bag contains four discs of which one is numbered 0, one numbered 1 and two numbered 2. Calculate the population standard deviation σ. Suppose that a random sample of size three is taken from this population without replacement. Let X_1, X_2 and X_3 denote the numbers on the selected discs. Find the sampling distributions of the statistics

$$\frac{1}{3} \sum_{i=1}^{3} |x_i - \bar{x}| \qquad \text{and} \qquad S,$$

where $\bar{X}$ and S are the sample mean and sample standard deviation respectively. Obtain the means of these distributions and compare them with σ.

¶ Let X be the number on a randomly selected disc. Then X has the probability distribution

x	0	1	2
P_x	1/4	1/4	1/2

Thus $\quad E(X) = 5/4$

and $\qquad \sigma^2 = \text{Var}(X) = 0^2 \times \frac{1}{4} + 1^2 \times \frac{1}{4} + 2^2 \times \frac{1}{2} - (5/4)^2 = \frac{11}{16}$,

so that $\qquad \sigma = \sqrt{11}/4 = 0.8292$.

There are $^4C_3 = 4$ possible choices for the discs. Below are listed the possible combinations of values, together with the values of $\bar{X}$ and the two given statistics.

Combination	Probability	$\bar{x}$	s	$\frac{1}{3} \sum |x_i - \bar{x}|$
0,1,2	1/2	1	1	2/3
0,2,2	1/4	4/3	$\sqrt{12}/3$	8/9
1,2,2	1/4	5/3	$1/\sqrt{3}$	4/9

The sampling distribution of $\frac{1}{3} \sum_{i=1}^{3} |x_i - \bar{x}|$, the mean absolute deviation of the sample, is

value	4/9	2/3	8/9
probability	1/4	1/2	1/4

and its mean is $\frac{2}{3}$.

The sampling distribution of S is

s	$1/\sqrt{3}$	1	$\sqrt{12}/3$
probability	1/4	1/2	1/4

and $E(S) = \frac{1}{4}(2+\sqrt{3}) = 0.9330$.

We see that S tends to overestimate σ while the mean absolute deviation tends to underestimate σ.

9. A company is 10 years old and has 400 employees. The number of years that employees have been with the company has the following frequency distribution:

Years with company	1	2	3	4	5	6	7	8	9	10
Frequency	60	70	60	50	50	40	30	25	10	5

n employees are selected at random without replacement. Let X_i be the number of years that the ith member of the sample has been with the company (i=1,2,...,n). What is the smallest value of n for which the standard deviation of the sample mean

$$\bar{X} = (X_1 + X_2 + \ldots + X_n)/n$$

is less than (i) 6 months, (ii) 3 months?

¶   Let X be the number of years that a randomly selected employee has spent with the company. From the given frequency distribution, X has mean

$$\mu = \frac{1}{400} (1 \times 60 + 2 \times 70 + \ldots + 10 \times 5) = 4.05,$$

and variance

$$\sigma^2 = \frac{1}{400} (1^2 \times 60 + 2^2 \times 70 + \ldots + 10^2 \times 5) - 4.05^2 = \frac{2189}{400}.$$

Now

$$\text{Var}(\bar{X}) = \frac{\sigma^2}{n} \times \frac{400-n}{400-1}$$

$$= \frac{2189}{399 \times 400} \times \frac{400-n}{n}.$$

If the standard deviation of $\bar{X}$ is to be less than 1/2 year,

$$\frac{2189}{159600} \times \frac{400-n}{n} < \frac{1}{4},$$

i.e. $2189(400-n) < 39900\,n,$

or $n > \dfrac{2189 \times 400}{39900 + 2189} = 20.8.$

Therefore n must be at least 21.

If the standard deviation of $\bar{X}$ is to be less than 1/4 year,

$$\frac{2189}{159600} \times \frac{400-n}{n} < \frac{1}{16},$$

and n must be at least 72.

10. A characteristic X is distributed among the 26 members of a certain population with variance $\sigma^2 = 15$. A random sample of size <26 is taken without replacement from the population. A student uses the sampling distribution of $\bar{X}$ to calculate Var($\bar{X}$). The value he obtains is 2.35. Can this be correct?

¶   Let n be the size of the random sample. The sample mean $\bar{X}$ has variance

9

$$\frac{15}{n} \times \frac{26-n}{26-1} = \frac{390-15n}{25n} .$$

If this is calculated to be 2.35, then

$$\frac{390-15n}{25n} = 2.35$$

and
$$n = \frac{390}{15+25\times2.35} = 5.29.$$

This is obviously impossible and so 2.35 cannot be the correct figure.

Exercises 6.3 Sampling from a Distribution

1. A random sample of size two is obtained from the set $\{1,2,\ldots,6\}$ by tossing a fair die twice. Find the sampling distribution of the total score.

¶ There are 36 possible outcomes of this experiment. If Y denotes the total score then we have, for example,

$P(Y=6) = P$(outcome is one of $(5,1),(4,2),(3,3),(2,4),(1,5))$

in the obvious notation, and so

$P(Y=6) = 5/36.$

We calculate the probabilities of the other values in a similar way and obtain the following probability distribution.

y	2	3	4	5	6	7	8	9	10	11	12
p_y	1/36	2/36	3/36	4/36	5/36	6/36	5/36	4/36	3/36	2/36	1/36

2. A random sample can be taken either with or without replacement. Show that the ratio of the variances of $\bar{X}$ in the two cases is given by

$$(\frac{N-1}{N-n}).$$

Evaluate this ratio in the following cases:
  (a)   N=25; n=5,10,15,20,
  (b)   N=100; n=5,15,25,50,
  (c)   N=500; n=5,25,125,250.

Comment on your results.

¶ For sampling without replacement from a finite population of size N,

$$\text{Var}(\bar{X}) = \frac{\sigma^2}{n} \left(\frac{N-n}{N-1}\right)$$

where n is the sample size.

For sampling with replacement,

$$\text{Var}(\bar{X}) = \frac{\sigma^2}{n} \ .$$

The ratio of the second to the first is therefore

$$\frac{N-1}{N-n}$$

(a) N=25

n	5	10	15	20
ratio	1.2	1.6	2.4	4.8

(b) N=100

n	5	15	25	50
ratio	1.042	1.165	1.32	1.98

(c) N=500

n	5	25	125	250
ratio	1.008	1.051	1.331	1.996

We notice firstly that the ratio always exceeds 1. Secondly the
ratio increases with the sample size and decreases, for a given
sample size, with the population size. If the sample size is
small compared with the population size, then sampling without
replacement is almost equivalent to sampling with replacement.
If the sample size is nearly as large as the population size,
then there is very little variability in the sample mean when
sampling without replacement as almost all of the population
is examined. This explains the rapid increase in the ratio.

3. A factory produces a very large number of items each day. The
probability that an item selected at random will be found to be
defective is 0.04. A random sample of size 100 is taken from
the items produced during a particular day. Calculate the
variance of the proportion of defective items in the sample.

¶ If p denotes the population proportion then, if the population
is large, the number of defectives Y in the sample has a
binomial distribution B(100,p) with variance 100p(1-p).
The variance of the proportion of defectives, Y/100, is
therefore

$$\frac{p(1-p)}{100} \ .$$

As p=0.04, this is $\frac{0.04 \times 0.96}{100} = 0.000384.$

4. X_1, X_2 is a random sample of size 2 from the distribution

$$P_x = \frac{1}{3} \quad \text{if } x=1,2,3,$$
$$= 0 \quad \text{otherwise.}$$

Obtain the sampling distribution of $Y = \frac{X_1}{X_2}$. Is $E(Y)=E(X_1)/E(X_2)$?

¶ The possible pairs of values of X_1 and X_2, together with the corresponding value of Y and the associated probability, are given below

x_1, x_2	Probability	y
1,1	1/9	1
1,2	1/9	1/2
1,3	1/9	1/3
2,1	1/9	2
2,2	1/9	1
2,3	1/9	2/3
3,1	1/9	3
3,2	1/9	3/2
3,3	1/9	1

Thus Y has the probability distribution

y	1/3	1/2	2/3	1	3/2	2	3
probability	1/9	1/9	1/9	3/9	1/9	1/9	1/9

Hence $E(Y) = \frac{1}{9}(\frac{1}{3} + \frac{1}{2} + \frac{2}{3} + 3 + \frac{3}{2} + 2 + 3) = \frac{11}{9}$.

Now $E(X_1) = E(X_2)$, clearly, and so

$$E(X_1/X_2) \neq E(X_1)/E(X_2).$$

5. Consider an experiment where a fair coin is tossed n times. Let the random variable X_i take the value 1 if the ith toss results in a head but the value 0 if it results in a tail $(i=1,\ldots,n)$. Find the distribution of the sample mean $\bar{X}$ and hence calculate its mean and variance in the cases $n=2,3,4$. Use the results of Theorem 6.2 (Volume 2) to check your answers.

¶ Let $Y = \sum_{i=1}^{n} X_i.$

Since $X_i=1$ if the ith toss results in a head, Y is simply the total number of heads obtained and therefore has a binomial distribution B(n,1/2).

Therefore $\quad P(Y=y) = {}^{n}C_{y}(1/2)^{n}$.

Thus $\qquad P(\bar{X} = y/n) = \dfrac{{}^{n}C_{y}}{2^{n}}, \quad y=0,1,\ldots,n$.

Since $E(Y) = \dfrac{n}{2}, \quad \mathrm{Var}(Y) = n \times \dfrac{1}{2} \times \dfrac{1}{2} = \dfrac{n}{4}$,

$\qquad E(\bar{X}) = \dfrac{1}{2}, \quad \mathrm{Var}(\bar{X}) = \dfrac{1}{n^2} \times \mathrm{Var}(Y) = \dfrac{1}{4n}$.

		$E(\bar{X})$	$\mathrm{Var}(\bar{X})$
	2	1/2	1/8
n	3	1/2	1/12
	4	1/2	1/16

Now $E(X_i) = 1 \times 1/2 + 0 \times 1/2 = 1/2 = \mu$, say

and $E(X_i^2) = 1^2 \times 1/2 + 0^2 \times 1/2 = 1/2$,

so that $\qquad \sigma^2 = \dfrac{1}{2} - \left(\dfrac{1}{2}\right)^2 = 1/4$.

By Theorem 6.2, $\quad E(\bar{X}) = \mu$ and $\mathrm{Var}(\bar{X}) = \sigma^2/n$.

Clearly this gives identical results to those calculated above.

6. A coin, which is not necessarily fair, is tossed n times. What is the smallest value of n which ensures that the standard deviation of the proportion of 'heads' is no larger than 0.1?

¶ Let p be the probability of obtaining a head. Let Y be the number of heads obtained in n tosses. Then Y has a binomial distribution $B(n,p)$ and

$$\mathrm{Var}(Y) = np(1-p).$$

The variance of the proportion of heads, Y/n, is thus

$$\frac{p(1-p)}{n}.$$

If $\sqrt{\dfrac{p(1-p)}{n}} \leqslant 0.1$, then $\quad n \geqslant 100p(1-p)$.

This must be true for all values of p, and in particular for that value which maximises the right hand side. Now $p(1-p)$ is maximised by $p = 1/2$, as is readily checked by differentiation. Hence the maximum value of the right hand side is $100 \times \dfrac{1}{2} \times \dfrac{1}{2}$ and n must be at least 25.

7. A random variable X takes the values 0 and 2, each with probability $\frac{1}{2}$. A random sample $X_1, X_2, \ldots, X_n$ is taken from its distribution. Find the sampling distributions of the statistics

$$A = \frac{1}{n} \sum_{i=1}^{n} (X_i - \bar{X})^2, \quad B = \frac{1}{(n-1)} \sum_{i=1}^{n} (X_i - \bar{X})^2$$

in the cases n=2 and n=3. Determine the mean of each distribution and compare your values with the variance of X.

¶   The possible sample values in the case n=2 are listed below
together with the values of the two statistics A and B.

Sample values		$\bar{x}$	a	b
0	0	0	0	0
0	2	1	1	2
2	0	1	1	2
2	2	2	0	0

The sampling distribution of A is

a	0	1
p_a	1/2	1/2

while that of B is

b	0	2
p_b	1/2	1/2

Hence $E(A) = 1/2,$ $E(B) = 1$

Now $E(X) = 0 \times 1/2 + 2 \times 1/2 = 1,$
$\qquad\quad E(X^2) = 0^2 \times 1/2 + 2^2 \times 1/2 = 2$
and $Var(X) = E(X^2) - (E(X))^2 = 1.$

Therefore $E(B) = Var(X).$

The corresponding table in the case n=3 is shown below:

Sample values			$\bar{x}$	a	b
0	0	0	0	0	0
0	0	2	2/3	8/9	4/3
0	2	0	2/3	8/9	4/3
2	0	0	2/3	8/9	4/3
2	2	0	4/3	8/9	4/3
2	0	2	4/3	8/9	4/3
0	2	2	4/3	8/9	4/3
2	2	2	2	0	0

Hence A and B have sampling distributions

a	0	8/9
p_a	1/4	3/4

and

b	0	4/3
p_b	1/4	3/4

Therefore $E(A) = 2/3$, $E(B) = 1 = Var(X)$.

Thus in both cases, $E(B) = Var(X)$. Theorem 6.3 (Volume 2) tells us that this result is true for all values of n and for all distributions of X.

8. Let $X_1, X_2, \ldots, X_n$ be a random sample from the uniform distribution on $[0,a]$. Let R denote the range of the sample. Using the results of Example 6.15 (Volume 2) find an expression for $E(R)$ and show that its value approaches a as the sample size becomes large.

¶ The range $R = Z-W$, where Z and W are respectively the maximum and minimum of the sample.

Hence $E(R) = E(Z) - E(W)$.

If sampling is from a uniform distribution on $[0,a]$, then

$$E(Z) = \frac{n}{n+1}\, a, \qquad E(W) = \frac{1}{n+1}\, a.$$

Therefore $E(R) = \frac{n-1}{n+1}\, a \; = \; a - \frac{2a}{n+1}\,.$

As n becomes large, this approaches the value a.

9. A firm supplies 50 customers with a certain product. Let X_i denote the number of units of the product ordered by the ith customer during one week. The set of orders, $X_1, X_2, \ldots, X_{50}$, is a random sample from a distribution with probability function

$$p_x = 0.05\,(0.95)^x \qquad \text{if } x=0,1,2,\ldots,$$
$$= 0 \qquad\qquad\qquad \text{otherwise.}$$

The firm despatches the week's orders in boxes of various sizes. The maximum capacity of the largest type of box used by the firm is 100 units. Find the probability that at least one order has to be despatched in at least 2 boxes.

¶ Let $Z = \max(X_1, X_2, \ldots, X_{50})$ be the size of the largest order.
Then

$$\begin{aligned}
P(Z \leq z) &= P(X_i \leq z, \; i=1, \ldots, 50) \\
&= P(X_1 \leq z) \, P(X_2 \leq z) \, \ldots \, P(X_{50} \leq z) \\
&= (P(X_1 \leq z))^{50}.
\end{aligned}$$

Now
$$\begin{aligned}
P(X_1 \leq z) &= \sum_{x=0}^{z} (0.05)(0.95)^x \\
&= 0.05 \, \frac{(1-0.95^{z+1})}{1-0.95} \\
&= 1-0.95^{z+1}
\end{aligned}$$

Hence
$$P(Z \leq z) = (1-0.95^{z+1})^{50}.$$

At least one order has to be despatched in two boxes if the
size of the largest exceeds 100, the maximum capacity.
Therefore the required probability is

$$\begin{aligned}
P(Z > 100) &= 1-P(Z \leq 100) \\
&= 1 - (1-0.95^{101})^{50} \\
&= 0.2457.
\end{aligned}$$

10. A piece of electrical equipment consists of 5 identical
components placed in series. It can function only if all
the components are working. The lifetime T of each component
(in units of 1000 hours) has the probability density function

$$f(t) = \frac{2}{(1+t)^3} \quad \text{if } 0 \leq t < \infty,$$
$$ = 0 \quad \text{otherwise.}$$

Calculate the mean lifetime of the piece of equipment.

¶ The lifetime S of the piece of equipment is the time until
the first failure of a component.

Therefore $S = \min(T_1, T_2, T_3, T_4, T_5)$
where T_i is the lifetime of the i-th component.

Now, by Theorem 6.4 (Volume 2), S has the probability density
function
$$g(s) = 5f(s)(1-F(s))^4,$$
where f and F denote respectively the probability density
and cumulative distribution functions of T.

Here $F(t) = \int_{0}^{t} \frac{2}{(1+x)^3}\, dx$

$= \left[-\frac{1}{(1+x)^2} \right]_{0}^{t}$

$= 1 - \frac{1}{(1+t)^2}\, .$

Therefore

$g(s) = 5 \cdot \frac{2}{(1+s)^3} \cdot \frac{1}{(1+s)^8}$

$= \frac{10}{(1+s)^{11}}$

Hence

$E(S) = \int_{0}^{\infty} \frac{10s}{(1+s)^{11}}\, ds$

$= 10 \int_{1}^{\infty} \frac{(u-1)}{u^{11}}\, du \qquad \text{where } 1+s = u$

$= 10 \left[-\frac{1}{9u^9} + \frac{1}{10u^{10}} \right]_{1}^{\infty}$

$= \frac{1}{9}$

and the mean lifetime of the piece of equipment is $1000/9 = 111.1$ hours.

Exercises 6.4 Distribution of the Sample Mean

1.   A random sample of size n is obtained from a normal distribution $N(\mu, \sigma^2)$. How large must n be to ensure that the sample
mean $\bar{X}$ lies within 0.25σ of μ with probability at least 0.95?

¶ $\bar{X}$ has a normal distribution $N(\mu, \sigma^2/n)$.   We want to choose n
so that

$P(|\bar{X}-\mu| \leq 0.25\sigma) \geq 0.95.$

The left hand side is

$P(\mu-0.25\sigma \leq \bar{X} \leq \mu+0.25\sigma)$

$= \Phi\left(\frac{\mu+0.25\sigma-\mu}{\sigma/\sqrt{n}}\right) - \Phi\left(\frac{\mu-0.25\sigma-\mu}{\sigma/\sqrt{n}}\right)$

$= \Phi(0.25\sqrt{n}) - \Phi(-0.25\sqrt{n})$

$= 2\Phi(0.25\sqrt{n}) - 1.$

Hence $\Phi(0.25\sqrt{n}) \geqslant 0.975$

so that $0.25\sqrt{n} \geqslant 1.96$

i.e. $n \geqslant (4 \times 1.96)^2 = 61.4656.$

Thus the smallest possible value of n is 62.

2.   The weights of sacks of potatoes are normally distributed with
     mean 25 kg and standard deviation 1 kg. The breaking strengths
     of ropes are normally distributed with mean 235 kg and standard
     deviation 4 kg. Nine sacks of potatoes are put in a sling which
     is raised by a rope. Find the probability that the rope will
     break.

¶   Let $X_1, X_2, \ldots, X_9$ be the weights of the nine sacks and let
     Y be the breaking strength of the rope. Assume that Y and
     the X's are independent random variables.

     We require
     $$P\left(\sum_1^9 X_i - Y > 0\right),$$
     since the rope breaks if the total weight exceeds the breaking
     strength.

     Now $\sum_1^9 X_i$ is $N(9 \times 25, 9 \times 1)$, i.e. $N(225, 9)$.

     Hence $\sum_1^9 X_i - Y$ is $N(225-235, 9+16)$, i.e. $N(-10, 25)$.

     The required probability is thus

     $$1 - \Phi\left(\frac{0+10}{5}\right) = 1 - \Phi(2) = 0.02275.$$

3.   To complete a certain job, two tasks have to be performed,
     one after the other.   The time (in hours) required to
     complete the first task has a N(4,2) distribution and that
     to complete the second is N(3,0.25). If the times required
     are independent, find the probability that the job will be
     completed within an 8 hour working day.

¶   Let X and Y be the times required for the first and second
     tasks.

     X + Y, the total time, has a normal distribution N(4+3,2+0.25) and the required probability is

$$P(X+Y \leq 8) = \Phi(\frac{8-7}{\sqrt{2.25}}) = \Phi(2/3) = 0.74750.$$

4. A man wishes to catch the 9 a.m. train. At 8.30 a.m. he takes a taxi whose travelling time to the station is normally distributed with mean 24 minutes and standard deviation $\sqrt{3}$ minutes. The time taken to buy a ticket and reach the platform is normally distributed with mean 4 minutes and standard deviation 1 minute. Find the probability that he catches the train if

(i) the train always leaves on time,

(ii) the train leaves at Y minutes after 9 a.m., where Y is normally distributed with mean 3 minutes and standard deviation 1 minute.

¶ Let X_1 be the travelling time of the taxi and X_2 be the time taken to buy a ticket. Assume that X_1 and X_2 are independent. If the train leaves at 9 a.m. he will catch it if

$$X_1 + X_2 \leq 30.$$

Now X_1+X_2 has a normal distribution $N(24+4,3+1)$, i.e. $N(28,4)$, and so the probability that he catches the train is

$$\Phi(\frac{30-28}{\sqrt{4}}) = \Phi(1) = 0.84134.$$

If the train leaves at Y minutes after 9 a.m., then he catches the train if

$$X_1 + X_2 \leq 30+Y.$$

Now X_1+X_2-Y is normally distributed with mean 24+4-3 and variance 3+1+1. Thus the probability that he catches the train is

$$\Phi(\frac{30-25}{\sqrt{5}}) = \Phi(\sqrt{5}) = 0.98733.$$

5. A firm sells two products A and B at £3 and £2 per item respectively. Let X denote the number of items of A and Y the number of items of B sold in a week. X and Y are independent and normally distributed, X being $N(450,2100)$ and Y being $N(510,1800)$. The total Z of the overheads for the week is independent of X and Y and has a $N(2000,1125)$ distribution. Find the expected profit and the probability that the profit exceeds £300.

¶   The profit is   R = 3X + 2Y - Z.

Now $E(R)$ = $3E(X) + 2E(Y) - E(Z)$
$$= 3 \times 450 + 2 \times 510 - 2000 = 370.$$

Also $Var(Z)$ = $9 Var(X) + 4 Var(Y) + Var(Z)$
$$= 9 \times 2100 + 4 \times 1800 + 1125$$
$$= 27225.$$

$$P(R > 300) = 1 - \Phi(\frac{300-370}{\sqrt{27225}}) = \Phi(\frac{70}{165}) = 0.6643.$$

6.   The weights of turkeys on a turkey farm have mean 7 kg and
standard deviation 1.5 kg. Use the Central Limit Theorem to
find an approximation for the probability that the mean weight
of a random sample of 100 turkeys will lie between 6.75 kg
and 7.25 kg.

¶   Let $X_1, X_2, \ldots, X_{100}$ be the weights of the turkeys in the
random sample. By the Central Limit Theorem the average
weight $\bar{X}$ has approximately a normal distribution with mean
7 and variance $1.5^2/100$.

Therefore the required probability is
$$P(6.75 \leq \bar{X} \leq 7.25) = \Phi(\frac{7.25-7}{1.5/10}) - \Phi(\frac{6.75-7}{1.5/10})$$
$$= \Phi(1.\dot{6}) - \Phi(-1.\dot{6})$$
$$= 2\Phi(1.\dot{6}) - 1$$
$$= 0.90442.$$

7.   The times that patients spend in a doctor's consulting room
have mean 5 minutes and standard deviation 2 minutes. The
doctor sees 30 patients during his surgery which starts
at 4.30 p.m. Find approximately the probability that he
finishes with his last patient before 6.50 p.m. What
assumptions need to be made in order to solve this problem?

¶   Let the times spent by the patients be $X_1, X_2, \ldots, X_{30}$ and
assume that they are independent and identically distributed.
Then, by the Central Limit Theorem, the total time
$$T = \sum_{1}^{30} X_i$$

is approximately normally distributed with mean 30×5 and variance 30×2^2.

He finishes before 6.50 p.m. if T < 140 and the probability of this is
$$\Phi(\frac{140-150}{\sqrt{120}}) = 0.18066.$$

8. The volume V of wine contained in a randomly chosen bottle of nominal volume 1 litre has probability density function

$$f(v) = 29v^{28} \quad \text{if } 0 \leqslant v \leqslant 1,$$
$$= 0 \qquad \text{otherwise.}$$

Find approximately the probability that 10000 such bottles contain a total of 9675 litres of wine or more.

¶   Let V_i be the volume of wine in the i-th bottle, i=1,...,10,000. Then
$$E(V_i) = \int_0^1 29v^{29} \, dv = \frac{29}{30} = 0.9\dot{6}$$

$$E(V_i^2) = \int_0^1 29v^{30} \, dv = \frac{29}{31}$$

and $\text{Var}(V_i) = \frac{29}{31} - (\frac{29}{30})^2 = \frac{29}{31 \times 30^2} = 0.0010394.$

By the Central Limit Theorem, the total volume X has a distribution which is approximately normal with mean $9666.\dot{6}$ and variance 10.3943.   Thus

$$P(X \geqslant 9675) = 1-\Phi(\frac{9675-9666.\dot{6}}{\sqrt{10.3943}})$$

$$= 1-\Phi(2.5848)$$
$$= 0.00487.$$

9. The number of typing errors made on a page by a typist is Poisson distributed with mean 2. Use the Central Limit Theorem to calculate approximately the probability that he makes more than 950 typing errors in a 450-page book. (It may be assumed that the numbers of errors made on different pages are statistically independent.)

¶ Let X_i be the number of errors on the i-th page, i=1,...,450. The total number of errors is

$$T = \sum_1^{450} X_i$$

and since $E(X_i) = Var(X_i) = 2$,

$$E(T) = 900, \quad Var(T) = 900.$$

By the Central Limit Theorem, T is approximately normally distributed and, since T is discrete, we use a continuity correction.
In fact

$$P(T > 950) \approx P(Y > 950.5)$$

where Y is N(900,900).

Therefore $P(T > 950) \approx 1-\Phi(\frac{950.5-900}{\sqrt{900}})$

$$= 1-\Phi(1.68\dot{3})$$
$$= 0.04616.$$

(We obtain 0.04779 if the continuity correction is not used.)

10. Authors can sometimes be characterized by the lengths of their sentences. It is found that in manuscripts known to have been written by author A, the mean and standard deviation of the number of words per sentence are 20 and 7 respectively. A manuscript of unknown authorship contains 100 sentences. Assuming that it was written by author A, find approximately the probability that the mean number of words per sentence exceeds 21. What assumptions need to be made in order to solve this problem?

¶ We require the probability that the total number T of words in the manuscript exceeds 2100. Assuming that the numbers of words in different sentences are independent and identically distributed with mean 20 and standard deviation 7, T is approximately N(2000,4900) and, using a continuity correction, we have

$$P(T > 2100) \approx 1 - \Phi\left(\frac{2100.5 - 2000}{\sqrt{4900}}\right)$$

$$= 1 - \Phi(1.4357)$$

$$= 0.07554.$$

(We obtain 0.07656 if the continuity correction is not used.)

Exercises 6.5 Techniques of Sampling

1. Use Table 11 to generate a random sample of size 5 from

    (i)   the distribution of X, where

    $$p_X = \frac{1}{5} \text{ if } x = -2,-1,0,1,2,$$

    $$= 0 \text{ otherwise,}$$

    (ii)   the distribution of $Y = X^2$, where X is as in (i),

    (iii)   the binomial distribution with $n=5$ and $p=0.3$,

    (iv)   the Poisson distribution with mean 2.

¶   (i)   Let u be a sample value of a uniform distribution
             on $[0,1]$ and let
             $$x = -2 \text{ if } 0 \leqslant u \leqslant 0.2,$$
             $$= -1 \text{ if } 0.2 < u \leqslant 0.4,$$
             $$= 0 \text{ if } 0.4 < u \leqslant 0.6,$$
             $$= 1 \text{ if } 0.6 < u \leqslant 0.8,$$
             $$= 2 \text{ if } 0.8 < u \leqslant 1.$$

    Then x will be a sample value of X.

    The first 5 numbers in the first column of the table
    are   43980   82570   86570   86204   12949, and the
    corresponding u values are

    $$0.43980, 0.82570, 0.86570, 0.86204, 0.12949.$$

    By the rule above, these lead to the sample values
    $$0, 2, 2, 2, -2.$$

    (ii)   Y has probability function

y	0	1	4
p_y	0.2	0.4	0.4

    Now we take $y = 0$ if $0 \leqslant u \leqslant 0.2$,
    $$= 1 \text{ if } 0.2 < u \leqslant 0.6,$$
    $$= 4 \text{ if } 0.6 < u \leqslant 1.$$

The next 5 sample values u, using the first column, are   0.36327, 0.11115, 0.57252, 0.49019, 0.45769. These lead to the following values of Y:

$$1, 0, 1, 1, 1.$$

(iii)   The distribution B(5,0.3) has probability function

x	0	1	2	3	4	5
p_x	0.16807	0.36015	0.3087	0.1323	0.02835	0.00243

using the formula $p_x = {}^5C_x(0.3)^x(0.7)^{5-x}$.

Thus the rule becomes

$$x = 0 \text{ if } 0 \leqslant u \leqslant 0.16807,$$
$$= 1 \text{ if } 0.16807 < u \leqslant 0.52822,$$
$$= 2 \text{ if } 0.52882 < u \leqslant 0.83692,$$
$$= 3 \text{ if } 0.83692 < u \leqslant 0.96922,$$
$$= 4 \text{ if } 0.96922 < u \leqslant 0.99757,$$
$$= 5 \text{ if } 0.99757 < u \leqslant 1.$$

The next 5 values in the first column of the table give values of u as follows:

$$0.80783, 0.39706, 0.83671, 0.52143, 0.75534.$$

These lead to x-values of   2,1,2,1 and 2.

(iv)   The Poisson distribution of mean 2 has probability function

x	0	1	2	3	4	5	6	7	etc
p_x	0.1353	0.2707	0.2707	0.1804	0.0902	0.0361	0.0120	0.0034	

The cumulative probabilities are

p	0	1	2	3	4	5	6	etc
$P(X \leqslant x)$	0.1353	0.4060	0.6767	0.8571	0.9473	0.9834	0.9955	

Using the next 5 sample values from the table, that is

$$0.76046, 0.05176, 0.71183, 0.97846 \text{ and } 0.69296,$$

we obtain the x-values

$$3, 0, 3, 5, 3.$$

2.   Explain how a table of random digits can be used to simulate an experiment in which a fair coin is tossed until a head is obtained. Simulate the experiment 50 times and, each time, record the number of throws taken. Calculate the relative frequency distribution of the results and compare it with the theoretical distribution.

¶   Consider a table of random digits. The probability that a digit is at most 4 is 1/2. Thus the single tossing of a fair coin can be simulated by choosing a random digit and calling the result 'heads' if the digit is at most 4 and 'tails' otherwise. The simulation required here is performed by doing this until a digit of at most 4 is obtained. For example the sequence of digits 9783 corresponds to T,T,T,H and 4 tosses are required.

Taking the random digits in Table 11, starting in the first row and taking them individually, the first 10 are 4,3,9,8,0,2,5,8,6,3 corresponding to H,H,T,T,H,H,T,T,T,H. The numbers of tosses to obtain a head are therefore 1,1,3,1,4.

Continuing in this way, the 50 sample values are
1,1,3,1,4,1,2,1,5,2,3,2,1,3,1,2,3,1,1,1,1,1,1,1,4,3,2,3,1,1,2,2,
4,3,1,3,5,4,2,1,1,1,1,1,3,1,1,2,4,6.

The frequency distribution is

Number	1	2	3	4	5	6	>6
Frequency	24	9	9	5	2	1	0

The relative frequencies, obtained by dividing by 50, are

       0.48, 0.18, 0.18, 0.10, 0.04, 0.02, 0

compared with the theoretical values

       0.50, 0.25, 0.125, 0.0625, 0.03125, 0.015625, 0.015625

obtained from $P_x = (\frac{1}{2})^x$ (x=1,2,...).

3.   A cell of a certain type, when subjected to a particular treatment, dies with probability $\frac{1}{4}$ or splits into two cells similar to the original with probability $\frac{3}{4}$. Distinct cells react independently to the treatment. A single cell is subjected to the treatment and, if it splits, the two new cells are treated in the same way. No further treatments are applied. Use a table of random numbers to simulate the whole experiment 30 times and, each time, record the value of X, the final number of living cells. Find the relative frequency distribution of the results and compare it with the theoretical probability function of X.

¶   Consider a pair of random digits. The range of values is 00-99 and so the probability that the number formed by the pair is at most 24 is $\frac{1}{4}$. We can simulate each stage by choosing a pair of digits. If the result is at most 24, the cell dies. Otherwise it splits.

For example consider the sequence of digits 3 5 0 2 7 8. The first pair is 35 and the cell splits. The next is 0 2 and the first new cell dies. The next pair is 7 8 and the other new cell splits, leaving 2 living cells.

If we do this, taking pairs of random digits starting in the 10th row of Table 11, the final numbers of cells are

4 0 2 2 4 2 0 4 0 0 4 4 2 4 0
0 4 2 2 4 4 2 2 0 2 0 2 4 0 0

The relative frequency distribution of these results is

0	1	2
1/3	1/3	1/3

Let X' and X denote the numbers of cells alive at the first and second stages. Then

$$P(X'=0) = \frac{1}{4}, \quad P(X'=2) = \frac{3}{4},$$

and $\quad P(X=0|X'=2) = \left(\frac{1}{4}\right)^2$ (as both must die).

Therefore $\quad P(X=0) = P(X=0|X'=0)P(X'=0) + P(X=0|X'=2)P(X'=2)$

$$= 1 \times \frac{1}{4} + \left(\frac{1}{4}\right)^2 \times \frac{3}{4}$$

$$= \frac{19}{64}.$$

$$P(X=4) = P(3 \text{ splits}) = \left(\frac{3}{4}\right)^3 = \frac{27}{64}.$$

Hence $\quad P(X=2) = 1 - \frac{19}{64} - \frac{27}{64} = \frac{18}{64}.$

Thus the probability distribution of X, the final number of living cells, is

x	0	2	4
P_x	$\frac{19}{64}$	$\frac{18}{64}$	$\frac{27}{64}$

The relative frequency distribution above agrees reasonably well with this, considering that 30 is a small sample size.

4. Suppose that Y is uniformly distributed on [0,1]. Use the result of Example 6.27 (Volume 2) to show that

$$X = -\frac{1}{\lambda} \log_e Y \text{ is exponentially distributed with mean } \frac{1}{\lambda}.$$

¶   In Example 6.27 we saw that if Y is uniformly distributed on [0,1] then $-\frac{1}{\lambda} \log_e(1-Y)$ has an exponential distribution with mean $1/\lambda$.

Let Z = 1-Y

Then Z has probability density function

$$g(z) = f(y)\left|\frac{dy}{dz}\right| \quad \text{as Z is a decreasing function of Y}$$

$$= 1 \times 1$$

$$= 1 \quad (0 \leq z \leq 1)$$

and so Z is uniformly distributed on [0,1].

Therefore $-\frac{1}{\lambda}\log_e(1-Z)$ has an exponential distribution with mean $1/\lambda$. Since 1-Z=Y this is the required result.

5. Use a table of random digits to generate a random sample of size 5 from the continuous distribution with probability density function f(x) in the following cases:

(i) $f(x) = \frac{1}{5}e^{-x/5}$ if $0 \leq x < \infty$,

        $= 0$ otherwise,

(ii) $f(x) = \frac{2}{3}\cos(x-\frac{\pi}{6})$ if $0 \leq x \leq \frac{2}{3}\pi$,

        $= 0$ otherwise,

(iii) $f(x) = \frac{1}{\pi(1+x^2)}$ $-\infty < x < \infty$,

(iv) $f(x) = (x\log_e 2)^{-1}$ if $1 \leq x \leq 2$,

        $= 0$ otherwise,

(v) $f(x) = 2xe^{-x^2}$ if $0 \leq x < \infty$,

        $= 0$ otherwise.

¶   (i)   Using the random numbers in the second column of Table 11, the first five are

            0.25863, 0.23905, 0.38795, 0.32327, 0.66813.

        Applying the transformation of Question 4 above with $\lambda = 1/5$, we obtain

            6.762, 7.155, 4.734, 5.646, 2.016

        and this is a random sample from an exponential distribution with mean 5 as required.

    (ii) We find the cumulative distribution function F(x) and its inverse $F^{-1}(y)$ and then use the result that if Y is uniformly distributed on [0,1] then $X=F^{-1}(Y)$ has the required distribution. (See Theorem 6.9, Volume 2.)

$$F(x) = \frac{2}{3} \int_0^x \cos(z - \frac{\pi}{6}) \, dz$$

$$= \frac{2}{3} [\sin(z - \frac{\pi}{6})]_0^x$$

$$= \frac{1}{3} + \frac{2}{3} \sin(x - \frac{\pi}{6}),$$

$$F^{-1}(y) = \frac{\pi}{6} + \sin^{-1}(\frac{3y-1}{2}).$$

The next five Y-values from the second column of Table 11 are
0.78695, 0.79150, 0.32787, 0.58557, 0.51728.
Applying the transformation we obtain the following X-values.
1.272, 1.281, 0.515, 0.912, 0.803 (in radians).
This is a random sample from the given distribution.

(iii) $\quad F(x) = \frac{1}{\pi} \int_{-\infty}^x \frac{dz}{1+z^2} = \frac{1}{\pi} [\tan^{-1}z]_{-\infty}^x = \frac{1}{2} + \frac{1}{\pi} \tan^{-1}x,$

$F^{-1}(y) = \tan(\pi(y - \frac{1}{2})).$

The next five Y-values are
0.24880, 0.03400, 0.15701, 0.47457, 0.73652.
These lead to the X-values
-1.008, -9.326, -1.860, -0.080, 0.919.

(iv) $\quad F(x) = \int_1^x \frac{1}{z \, \log_e 2} \, dz = \left[\frac{\log_e z}{\log_e 2}\right]_1^x = \frac{\log_e x}{\log_e 2},$

$F^{-1}(y) = e^{y \, \log_e 2}.$

The next five Y-values are
0.98360, 0.24211, 0.84148, 0.23697, 0.23855.
These lead to the X-values
1.977, 1.183, 1.792, 1.179, 1.180.

(v) $\quad F(x) = \int_0^x 2ze^{-z^2} \, dz = \left[-e^{-z^2}\right]_0^x = 1 - e^{-x^2},$

$F^{-1}(y) = \sqrt{-\log_e(1-y)}.$

The next five Y-values are
0.89963, 0.21542, 0.48961, 0.19008, 0.07942.
These lead to the X-values
1.516, 0.493, 0.820, 0.459, 0.288.

6. A pedestrian wishes to cross a one-way street. He arrives at a point A on the kerb and crosses on the first occasion that the nearest approaching vehicle is 5 seconds or more away.

The time which elapses between the arrival at A of the pedestrian and that of the first approaching vehicle is exponentially distributed with mean 5 seconds. Using a table of random digits, estimate the probability that the pedestrian does not have to wait at the kerb before he crosses the street. Base the estimate on 100 simulations and compare the result with the true value of the probability.

Assuming that the interarrival times of vehicles at A are exponentially distributed with mean 5 seconds, explain how a simulation method can be used to estimate the probability that the pedestrian must wait more than 6 seconds before he can cross the street.

¶   Let X have an exponential distribution of mean 5 seconds. If we obtain a sample value of X which is less than 5, then we can regard this as corresponding to the arrival of a car within 5 seconds of the arrival of the pedestrian, resulting in the pedestrian having to wait. Thus if we obtain 100 sample values of X, the number of values which exceed 5 represents the number of pedestrians who do not have to wait.

We know that if Y is uniformly distributed on [0,1], then
$$X = -5 \log_e Y$$
has the required exponential distribution. (See Question 4 above.) We do not need the actual sample values - only whether they are less than 5 or not. Since
$$X > 5 \iff -5 \log_e Y > 5$$
$$\iff -\log_e Y > 1$$
$$\iff Y < e^{-1} = 0.367879,$$
we can look at 100 sample values of Y and count how many are less than 0.367879.

Using the first two columns of Table 11, 34 of the one hundred Y-values are less than 0.367879. Thus our estimate of the required probability is 34/100 i.e. 0.34. The true probability is
$$P(X>5) = P(Y<e^{-1}) = e^{-1} = 0.367879.$$

Now let X_1 be the time between the arrivals of the pedestrian and the first car, X_2 that between the arrivals of the first and second cars and so on. It is given that the sequence $X_1, X_2, X_3, \ldots$ is a random sample from an exponential distribution with mean 5. To see if the pedestrian waits for more than 6 seconds we generate a sequence of sample values $x_1, x_2, x_3, \ldots$ from this distribution until one exceeds 5 or the sum of those generated exceeds 6. If we carry out a series of simulations in this way we can count the number of times that the pedestrian must wait more than 6 seconds and so estimate the required probability. For example, taking the second last column of Table 11, we obtain the sample values

7.757, 22.271, 2.405, 1.710, 4.668, 1.309, 4.800, etc.

The first gap is 7.757 and the pedestrian crosses immediately. The second gap is 22.271 and again the pedestrian does not wait. For the third simulation the gaps are 2.405, 1.710 and 4.668. These are all less than 5 but the sum exceeds 6 and the pedestrian must wait more than 6 seconds. For the fourth simulation the gaps are 1.309 and 4.800 and so the pedestrian cannot cross for at least 6.109 seconds. The estimate so far is 2/4, i.e. 0.5. An accurate estimate may be obtained by performing many more such simulations.

N.B. Whenever a simulation ends because a sample value exceeds 5, the pedestrian waits for 6 seconds at most. For example, the waiting time for the sequence 1.210, 2.372, 5.645 is

1.210 + 2.372 = 3.582 seconds.

7. For each of the following probability density functions, plot a graph of the cumulative distribution function and hence use Table 11 to obtain a random sample of size 5.

(i) $f(x) = 6x(1-x)$ if $0 \le x \le 1$,
      $= 0$ otherwise,

(ii) $f(x) = \frac{5}{8}(1-x^4)$ if $-1 \le x \le 1$,
      $= 0$ otherwise,

(iii) $f(x) = \frac{1}{2}$ if $0 \le x \le 1$ or $2 \le x \le 3$,
      $= 0$ otherwise.

¶   In each case let $F(x)$ denote the cumulative distribution function and let Y be uniformly distributed on $[0,1]$. We obtain a Y-value y from Table 11 and read off the value x such that $F(x) = y$ from the graph of $F(x)$.

(i) $F(x) = \int_0^x 6z(1-z)\ dz$

$= 3x^2 - 2x^3$ $(0 \leq x \leq 1)$.

Its graph is plotted in the figure. The sample values of Y, starting at the bottom of the first column and working upwards, are

0.36433, 0.41664, 0.63689, 0.90391, 0.16902.

From the graph, the corresponding X-sample is

0.41, 0.44, 0.60, 0.82, 0.27.

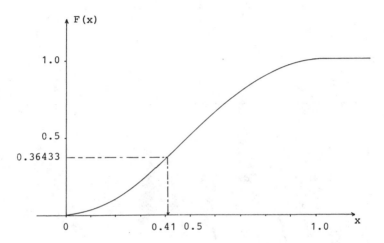

(ii) $F(x) = \frac{5}{8} \int_{-1}^x (1-z^4)\ dz$

$= \frac{5}{8}\ [z - z^5/5]_{-1}^x$

$= \frac{5}{8}(x - x^5/5) + \frac{1}{2}$ $(-1 \leq x \leq 1)$.

The next five Y-values are

0.95500, 0.36256, 0.48656, 0.61670, 0.22944.

From the graph of F(x), the corresponding X-sample is

0.82, -0.20, -0.01, 0.21, -0.41.

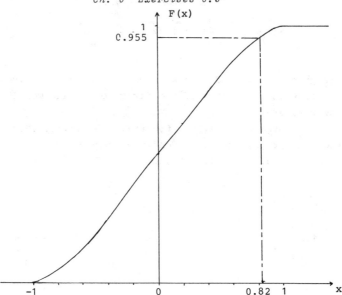

(iii) If $0 \leqslant x \leqslant 1$,

$$F(x) = \int_0^x \frac{1}{2} \, dz = \frac{x}{2} \, .$$

If $2 \leqslant x \leqslant 3$,

$$F(x) = \int_0^1 \frac{1}{2} \, dz + \int_2^x \frac{1}{2} \, dz$$

$$= \frac{1}{2} + (x-2)/2$$

$$= (x-1)/2.$$

The graph of $F(x)$ is shown below.

The next five sample values of Y are

$$0.60210, \ 0.62917, \ 0.84778, \ 0.49185, \ 0.59515.$$

From the graph, the corresponding X-sample is

$$2.20, \ 2.26, \ 2.70, \ 0.98 \text{ and } 2.19.$$

N.B. In contrast to cases (i) and (ii), the inversion could
      easily be carried out analytically here to give more
      accurate results. The only difficulty is that $F^{-1}(\frac{1}{2})$
      is undefined but, since Y takes the value $\frac{1}{2}$ with
      probability zero, we are free to define $F^{-1}(\frac{1}{2})$ to be 1,

for example. With this choice

$$F^{-1}(y) = 2y \quad \text{if } 0 \leq y < \frac{1}{2}$$

$$= 1 \quad \text{if } y = \frac{1}{2}$$

$$= 2y+1 \text{ if } \frac{1}{2} < y \leq 1.$$

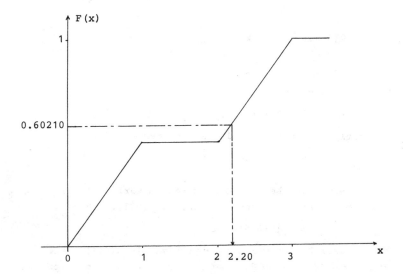

8. Use a table of random numbers, together with a table of the standard normal cumulative distribution function, to generate a random sample of size 4 from the normal distribution with mean 6 and standard deviation 2.

¶ Let X be N(6,4). Then

$$Z = \frac{X-6}{2}$$

has a standard normal distribution with cumulative distribution function $\Phi(z)$.

Therefore $\quad\quad Y = \Phi(Z)$
is uniformly distributed on [0,1],
$$Z = \Phi^{-1}(Y)$$
and $\quad X = 6 + 2\Phi^{-1}(Y).$

If we have a sample value y of Y we find $\Phi^{-1}(y)$ using a table of Φ and apply the above result.

Taking the third column of Table 11, the first four sample values are

$$0.26439, \quad 0.35993, \quad 0.84683, \quad 0.46960.$$

We require $\Phi^{-1}(0.26439)$ i.e. the value of z such that

$$\Phi(z) = 0.26439 = 1 - \Phi(-z).$$

Thus $\Phi(-z) = 0.73561.$

Now $\Phi(0.63) = 0.73565$

and so $0.63 \approx \Phi^{-1}(0.73561),$

$-0.63 \approx \Phi^{-1}(0.26439).$

Thus the sample value of X is

$$6 + 2 \times (-0.63) = 4.74.$$

Similarly, the other sample values lead to

$$5.28, \quad 8.04, \quad \text{and} \quad 5.85.$$

9.   Let $U_1, U_2, \ldots, U_n$ be independent random variables which are uniformly distributed on the interval [0,1]. Then

$$Z = (\bar{U} - 0.5)\sqrt{12n}$$

has a distribution which is approximately $N(0,1)$ – see Example 6.18, Volume 2. Use this result, with $n=6$, to obtain a random sample of size 4 from (i) a $N(0,1)$ distribution and (ii) a $N(1,4)$ distribution.

¶   (i)   Choosing 6 numbers at a time from the fourth column of Table 11, the 4 values of $\bar{U}$ are

$$0.63049, \quad 0.49376, \quad 0.67442, \quad 0.69788$$

The corresponding values of

$$Z = \sqrt{72}(\bar{U} - 0.5)$$

are $1.107, \quad -0.053, \quad 1.480, \quad 1.679.$

(ii)   If X is $N(1,4)$ then

$$Z = (X-1)/2$$

is $N(0,1)$. Having obtained a value of Z, we use the formula $2z+1=x$ to obtain a value of X.

Using the above values of Z we obtain the sample values

$$3.214, \ 0.894, \ 3.960, \ 4.358.$$

10. The random variable Y is uniformly distributed between 0 and 1. Show that the random variable X defined by

$$X = \log_e(2Y) \qquad \text{if } 0 < Y \leqslant \tfrac{1}{2},$$

$$= -\log_e(2(1-Y)) \qquad \text{if } \tfrac{1}{2} < Y < 1$$

has the Laplace distribution with probability density function

$$f(x) = \tfrac{1}{2}e^{-|x|} \qquad -\infty < x < \infty.$$

Use this result, together with random number tables, to generate a random sample of size 5 from this distribution.

¶ Let X have cumulative distribution function F(x).

If $x \leqslant 0$,
$$\begin{aligned} F(x) &= P(X \leqslant x) \\ &= P(\log_e 2Y \leqslant x) \\ &= P(Y \leqslant \tfrac{1}{2}e^x) \\ &= \tfrac{1}{2}e^x \quad \text{as Y is uniform on } [0,1]. \end{aligned}$$

If $x > 0$,
$$\begin{aligned} F(x) &= P(X \leqslant x) \\ &= 1 - P(X > x) \\ &= 1 - P(-\log_e 2(1-Y) > x) \\ &= 1 - P(2(1-Y) < e^{-x}) \\ &= 1 - P(Y > 1 - \tfrac{1}{2}e^{-x}) \\ &= 1 - \tfrac{1}{2}e^{-x}. \end{aligned}$$

Differentiating, the probability density function is

$$\begin{aligned} f(x) &= \tfrac{1}{2}e^x \text{ if } x \leqslant 0, \\ &= \tfrac{1}{2}e^{-x} \text{ if } x > 0 \end{aligned}$$

i.e. $f(x) = \tfrac{1}{2}e^{-|x|} \quad -\infty < x < \infty.$

Taking 5 sample values of the uniform distribution from column six of Table 11, we obtain

$$0.32750, \ 0.84788, \ 0.22119, \ 0.31757, \ 0.63380.$$

As $0.32750 < \tfrac{1}{2}$, the corresponding X-value is

$$\log_e(2 \times 0.32750) = -0.4231.$$

As $0.84788 > \tfrac{1}{2}$, the X-value is

$$-\log_e(2(1-0.84788)) = 1.1899.$$

Similarly the other three values lead to −0.8156, −0.4539 and 0.3114.

11. A sample is to be obtained without replacement from a population of 100 items, numbered from 1 to 100. Use Table 11 to choose
>   (a) a simple random sample of size 8,
>   (b) a systematic sample of size 10,
>   (c) a systematic sample of size 8.

The population is divided into three groups. The first contains items numbered 1 to 20, the second contains items numbered 21 to 50, while the third group contains the remaining items. Choose a stratified random sample of size 10 in which the number chosen from each stratum is proportional to the size of the stratum.

¶ (a) We first obtain a random sample from the uniform distribution on [0,1]. Starting in the fourth row of Table 11, we have

>   0.86204, 0.32327, 0.46960, 0.31019, 0.89194,
>   0.31757, 0.47078, 0.83503, 0.71038, ...

Multiplying by 100, rounding to the nearest integer above and ignoring repetitions, we select the items numbered

>   87, 33, 47, 32, 90, 48, 84, 72.

(See the next Exercise and also Miscellaneous Problem 5 of this chapter for alternative methods of selecting simple random samples without replacement.)

(b) As the sampling interval is 100/10, i.e. 10, we choose an integer between 1 and 10 by selecting a random digit. This will be the required integer unless the digit is 0, in which case the required integer is 10. Taking the first digit in the fourth row of Table 11 we obtain 8 and select the items numbered

>   8, 18, 28, 38, 48, 58, 68, 78, 88, 98.

(c) The sampling interval is 100/8 = 12.5. We first choose an integer at random between 1 and 12; this is the number of the first item to be selected. Considering non-overlapping pairs of digits in Table 11, starting with the fourth row, we obtain

>   86   20   43   23   27   46   96   03.

We ignore the first seven pairs as they exceed 12 and choose the eighth. Thus item 3 is the first to be chosen. The

remaining ones are of the form
$$3 + [k \times 12.5],$$
where [x] denotes the integer part of x, (k=1,...,7).
Thus we obtain the systematic sample
$$3, \ 15, \ 28, \ 40, \ 53, \ 65, \ 78, \ 90.$$
To obtain a stratified random sample of the kind specified,
we must select two items at random from the first group,
three items at random from the second group, and five items
at random from the third group. Using the fifth row of
Table 11, we obtain three independent random samples of
sizes 2, 3 and 5 from the uniform distribution on [0,1],
namely
$$0.12949, \ 0.66813;$$
$$0.52110, \ 0.86683, \ 0.64116;$$
$$0.63380, \ 0.19737, \ 0.27269, \ 0.39312, \ 0.47588.$$
We now select the items numbered
$$[20 \times 0.12949] + 1 = 3$$
and
$$[20 \times 0.66813] + 1 = 14$$
from the first group, the items numbered
$$[30 \times 0.52110] + 21 = 36,$$
$$[30 \times 0.86683] + 21 = 47$$
and
$$[30 \times 0.64116] + 21 = 40$$
from the second group and the items numbered
$$[50 \times 0.63380] + 51 = 82,$$
$$[50 \times 0.19737] + 51 = 60,$$
$$[50 \times 0.27269] + 51 = 64,$$
$$[50 \times 0.39312] + 51 = 70$$
and
$$[50 \times 0.47588] + 51 = 74$$
from the third group.

12. The following table gives the marks obtained in an examination
by 24 school-children. The sex (M-male, F-female) and the
junior school attended by each child (A,B or C) are also given.

Child	1	2	3	4	5	6	7	8	9	10	11	12
Sex	M	M	M	M	F	M	M	M	M	F	M	M
School	B	A	C	A	B	A	A	C	B	C	A	A
Mark	42	68	38	83	62	70	69	49	59	60	51	76
Child	13	14	15	16	17	18	19	20	21	22	23	24
Sex	M	F	M	F	M	M	M	F	M	F	M	M
School	B	A	A	B	C	A	B	A	C	A	A	C
Mark	70	81	49	56	40	66	40	78	38	63	68	45

Calculate (i) the mean mark of all 24 children, (ii) the mean mark for males and the mean mark for females, (iii) the mean marks for children from each of the three schools.

Use a table of random numbers to obtain without replacement (a) a simple random sample of 8 children, (b) a stratified sample of 8 children reflecting the sex structure of the population, (c) a stratified sample of 8 children reflecting the proportions attending each school. Calculate the sample means of your three samples and comment on your results.

¶ (i)   The mean mark of all children is 1421/24 = 59.2083.

(ii)   The mean mark for males is 1021/18 = 56.72.
That for females is 400/6 = 66.6.

(iii) The mean for children from A is 822/12 = 68.5.
That for children from B is 329/6 = 54.83
and for those from C is 270/6 = 45.

(a)   To choose a simple random sample we can use the following method. Choose a pair of digits from Table 11 and then choose the child according to the table below.

Digits	00–03	04–07	08–11	....	92–95
Child	1	2	3	....	24

(The pairs 96, 97, 98, 99 are discarded whenever they occur.)

Taking the final row of Table 11, the pairs of digits are

    34, 43, 36, 63, 62, 26, 48, 22, 21, 58, 57, 38, 03
leading to
    10, 11, 10, 16, 16, 7, 13, 6, 6, 15, 15, 10, 1.
Ignoring repetitions, we choose the children numbered
    10, 11, 16, 7, 13, 6, 15, 1.

(b)   As there are 18 males and 6 females, we choose 6 males and 2 females. For the males, we can use the above method with groupings 00–04, 05–09,...,85–89 (ignoring pairs from 90 to 99). Taking the second last row in Table 11, the pairs are

    41, 66, 49, 56, 82, 62,
leading to the numbers
    9, 14, 10, 12, 17, 13.

Converting these numbers, we choose the children numbered
11, 18, 12, 15, 23, 17.   (For example, the ninth male is
child number eleven.)

For the females we can simply choose two single random digits,
ignoring 0,7,8 and 9. Continuing along the second last row
we find the sequence
$$7, 9, 5, 0, 5, 6, \ldots$$
and so the fifth and sixth females are chosen, i.e. the
children whose numbers are 20 and 22. The stratified
sample consists, therefore, of the children numbered
$$11, 18, 12, 15, 23, 17, 20, 22.$$

(c)   The numbers from schools A, B and C are 12, 6 and 6 and
so we select 4 children from A and 2 each from B and C.
Taking the third last row of Table 11, we have the pairs of
digits
$$63, 68, 90, 70, 60, 58, 80$$
and, using the above method with groupings 00-07, 08-15,
..., 88-95, we obtain the numbers
$$8, \quad 9, \quad 12, \quad 9, \quad 8, \quad 8, \quad 11.$$
Thus we choose the 8th, 9th, 12th and 11th from school A,
i.e. the children numbered 15, 18, 23, 22. For schools B
and C we follow the method used for the females. The next
digits in the row are
$$2, \quad 0, \quad 7, \quad 5, \quad 9, \quad 0, \quad 3, \quad 6.$$
Thus we take the 2nd and 5th from school B and the 3rd and
6th from school C, i.e. the children numbered 5, 16, 10, 24.
The stratified sample consists, therefore, of the children
numbered
$$15, 18, 23, 22, \quad 5, 16, 10, 24.$$
In (a) the sample mean mark is
$$\tfrac{1}{8}(60 + 51 + 56 + 69 + 70 + 70 + 49 + 42) = 58.375.$$
In (b) the sample mean mark is
$$\tfrac{1}{8}(51 + 66 + 76 + 49 + 68 + 40 + 78 + 63) = 61.375.$$
In (c) the sample mean mark is
$$\tfrac{1}{8}(49 + 66 + 68 + 63 + 62 + 56 + 60 + 45) = 58.625.$$
We see that, compared with the sample means in (a) and (c),
the value of the sample mean in (b) differs considerably
from 59.0283, the value of the population mean. The purpose

of stratification is to reduce the chance of obtaining an unrepresentative sample but the sample in (b) is stratified only with respect to sex and, by chance, it contains a disproportionately large number of children from school A, inflating the sample mean. We could have used 6 strata, classifying the population both by sex and by school attended. This would have been worthwhile because, as the calculations in (ii) and (iii) show, there are considerable differences between the sexes and between the schools.

13. A gardener has 12 gooseberry bushes in his garden, 5 in a row at one end of the garden and 7 in a row at the other end. The 5 at one end produced yields of 550, 610, 640, 705 and 810 grams, while those at the other end produced yields of 795, 820, 840, 845, 865, 870 and 905 grams.

    Suppose that a simple random sample of size 5 is taken from the set of 12 bushes. Find the mean and standard deviation of the sample mean.

    Suppose instead that a stratified random sample of size 5 is obtained by choosing 2 bushes at random from the 5 bushes at one end of the garden and 3 bushes at random from the 7 bushes at the other end of the garden. Find the mean and standard deviation of the stratified mean, $\bar{X}_w$.

¶ Let $\bar{X}$ be the mean of the simple random sample. Then
$$E(\bar{X}) = \mu, \ Var(\bar{X}) = \frac{\sigma^2}{5} \left(\frac{12-5}{12-1}\right),$$
where μ and σ^2 are the population mean and variance. We find that
$$\mu = 771.25, \ \sigma^2 = 12300.52.$$
Therefore
$$E(\bar{X}) = 771.25, \ \ SD(\bar{X}) = 39.57.$$

Consider now the two strata
$$A : 550, 610, 640, 705, 810;$$
$$B : 795, 820, 840, 845, 865, 870, 905.$$

In the obvious notation,
$$\mu_a = 663, \ \ \sigma_a^2 = 7896,$$
$$\mu_b = 848.57, \ \sigma_b^2 = 1097.96.$$

As two sample values are chosen at random from A,

$$E(\bar{X}_a) = 663, \quad Var(\bar{X}_a) = \frac{7896}{2} \times \frac{5-2}{5-1} = 2961,$$

where $\bar{X}_a$ is the mean of this sample.

Similarly,

$$E(\bar{X}_b) = 848.57, \quad Var(\bar{X}_b) = \frac{1097.96}{3} \times \frac{7-3}{7-1} = 243.99.$$

Now $\quad \bar{X}_w = \frac{5}{12} \bar{X}_a + \frac{7}{12} \bar{X}_b.$

Therefore $\quad E(\bar{X}_w) = (5 \times 663 + 7 \times 848.57)/12 = 771.25$

and $\quad Var(\bar{X}_w) = \frac{25}{144} \times 2961 + \frac{49}{144} \times 243.99 = 597.09$

so that $\quad SD(\bar{X}_w) = 24.435.$

Thus $\bar{X}$ and $\bar{X}_w$ have the same means, but $\bar{X}_w$ has a much smaller standard deviation than $\bar{X}$.

One of the main reasons for sampling randomly is that the reliability of estimators based on random samples can be assessed by calculating their variance or standard deviation. The danger with random samples is that they can be unrepresentative of the sampled population. Stratification reduces the chance that the random sample is unrepresentative and this is reflected in the fact that $SD(\bar{X}_w)$ is smaller than $SD(\bar{X})$.

14. Describe how you would carry out a national survey to find out which television programmes are most popular.

¶ There is no single correct method for carrying out a survey. Below are listed some of the main points which must be considered in designing a survey and some comments on them in this context.

Method of survey   In this case selected people will either receive questionnaires or be interviewed face-to-face.

Sampling frame   Unless the type of programme is specified the sampling frame will consist of all people who watch television programmes. There is no convenient listing of all such people and in practice the survey might be carried out by random interviewing on the street. This excludes disabled people who probably watch television a lot.

<u>Choice of Sample Size</u>   This is impossible to specify without
further information and without knowing the required degree
of accuracy. It must, however, be specified.

<u>Method of Sampling</u>
If the population is not homogeneous, dividing it into strata
will generally be a sensible procedure. We could divide the
population by sex, age and socio-economic group into
different classes and conduct a sample in each group. Since
no list of people in each category exists, it is not easy to
do this. In practice, people might be selected for interview
and then rejected if the quota for their category has been
exceeded.

An alternative method, though one which would not be suitable
for a single survey, is to install special equipment in a
number of chosen homes. This monitors the programmes which
have been watched. The problem of choosing the homes remains
and there is no check, of course, on which programmes are
watched by individual family members.

15.   The Civil Aviation Authority is proposing to enlarge the
airport of a certain city. The local authority, worried about
public reaction, commissions a survey to find out if the
inhabitants are in favour of this development. How would you
design such a survey?

¶   The design of the survey includes the choice of the questions
asked and the form of questioning. We will consider here
only the sampling methods involved.

Firstly a sampling frame must be chosen. One possibility is
the electoral roll for the areas concerned. There are two
obvious disadvantages. Firstly those under 18 are excluded
and secondly organisations such as local firms, possibly
situated near the airport, are not explicitly included,
though some of their individual members would be.

One way of trying to overcome these deficiencies would be
to use cluster sampling. From a list of properties used by
the local authority for the purpose of collecting rates,

a number could be chosen and then a fixed percentage of the
occupants, whether it be a private house, a school or a
factory, would be questioned.

In either case a stratification based on area would seem
appropriate since those living near the airport may well
hold different views from those living further away.

Miscellaneous Problems

1.   In a large college, the ages of the students range from 16
     to 19 inclusive;   40% are 16, 30% are 17, 15% are 18 and 15%
     are 19. A sample of two students is selected at random.
     Let X_1 and X_2 denote their ages. Regarding the sample as
     being taken with replacement, find the sampling distributions
     of $\bar{X}$ and S^2. Hence calculate $E(\bar{X})$, $Var(\bar{X})$ and $E(S^2)$. Use
     the formulae of Theorems 6.2 and 6.3 (Volume 2) to check your
     results.

¶ X_1 and X_2 have the following probability distribution.

x	16	17	18	19
P_x	0.4	0.3	0.15	0.15

Thus $\mu = E(X_1) = 17.05$, $\sigma^2 = Var(X_1) = 1.1475$.
The various possible sample values are shown below.

Sample Values	Probability	$\bar{x}$	s^2
16,16	0.16	16	0
16,17	0.24	16.5	0.5
16,18	0.12	17	2
16,19	0.12	17.5	4.5
17,17	0.09	17	0
17,18	0.09	17.5	0.5
17,19	0.09	18	2
18,18	0.0225	18	0
18,19	0.045	18.5	0.5
19,19	0.0225	19	0

The sampling distributions of $\bar{X}$ and S^2 are as follows:

$\bar{x}$	16	16.5	17	17.5	18	18.5	19
Prob	0.16	0.24	0.21	0.21	0.1125	0.045	0.0225

s^2	0	0.5	2	4.5
Prob	0.295	0.375	0.21	0.12

From these we find that

$E(\bar{X}) = 17.05$, $Var(\bar{X}) = 0.57375$, $E(S^2) = 1.1475$.

Therefore $E(\bar{X}) = \mu$, $Var(\bar{X}) = \sigma^2/2$ and $E(S^2) = \sigma^2$

as predicted by theory.

2.   A wholesaler obtains items of a certain product from supplier A and an equal number of the same item from supplier B. Six per cent of the items from B are defective. Only two per cent of the items from A are defective. An unmarked crate containing a large number of items is delivered to the wholesaler. He selects 50 of the items at random and tests them. Write down an approximation for the sampling distribution of the number of defective items in the sample assuming that the crate came from (i) supplier A, (ii) supplier B. Hence calculate an approximation for the probability that the crate came from supplier B, given that only 2 of the 50 items inspected were defective.

¶   The number X of defective items has approximately a binomial distribution since, although the items are selected without replacement, they come from a large set.

If the supplier is A, then X is B(50,0.02), while if the supplier is B, X is B(50,0.06).

Denoting by SB and SA the events that the supplier is B and A respectively, Bayes' Theorem gives

$$P(SB|2 \text{ defectives}) = \frac{P(2 \text{ defectives}|SB)\,P(SB)}{P(2 \text{ defectives}|SA)\,P(SA) + P(2 \text{ defectives}|SB)\,P(SB)}$$

$$= \frac{{}^{50}C_2(0.06)^2(0.94)^{48} \times \frac{1}{2}}{{}^{50}C_2(0.02)^2(0.98)^{48}\times\frac{1}{2} + {}^{50}C_2(0.06)^2(0.94)^{48}\times\frac{1}{2}}$$

$$= 0.549.$$

3.   In a pack of playing cards, 13 of the 52 cards are spades. A card is selected at random and the random variable X is defined as follows:

$$X = 1 \quad \text{if the card is a spade,}$$
$$= 0 \quad \text{if not.}$$

Show that

$$E(X) = \frac{1}{4}, \quad Var(X) = \frac{3}{16}.$$

A random sample of 5 cards is taken from the full pack without replacement. Let

$$Y_i = 1 \quad \text{if the ith card is a spade,}$$
$$= 0 \quad \text{if not} \quad (i=1,2,3,4,5).$$

Find the sampling distribution of

$$\bar{Y} = \frac{1}{5} \sum_{i=1}^{5} Y_i$$

and verify Theorem 6.1, Volume 2. (You are advised not to enumerate all possible samples as there are 2,598,960 of them.)

¶ $P(X=1) = 13/52 = 1/4$ and $P(X=0) = 3/4$.

Hence $E(X) = \frac{1}{4}$, $E(X^2) = \frac{1}{4}$, $Var(X) = \frac{3}{16}$.

Let

$$Z = \sum_{1}^{5} Y_i.$$

Then $$P(Z=z) = \frac{^{13}C_z \times {}^{39}C_{5-z}}{^{52}C_5} \quad (z=0,1,\ldots,5).$$

Evaluating this we find that Z has the sampling distribution

z	0	1	2	3	4	5
p_z	0.22153	0.41142	0.27428	0.08154	0.01073	0.00050

Thus $\bar{Y}$ has the sampling distribution

$\bar{y}$	0	1/5	2/5	3/5	4/5	1
Prob	0.22153	0.41142	0.27428	0.08154	0.01073	0.00050

From this we find that

$$E(\bar{Y}) = 0.25, \quad Var(\bar{Y}) = 0.03456.$$

Thus $$E(\bar{Y}) = E(X)$$

and $$\frac{Var(X)}{5} \times \frac{52-5}{52-1} = 0.03456 = Var(\bar{Y}),$$

agreeing with the theoretical results.

4.   The random variable X has the probability distribution

$$P_X = \frac{1}{4} \quad \text{if } x=1,$$
$$= \frac{1}{2} \quad \text{if } x=2,$$
$$= \frac{1}{4} \quad \text{if } x=3,$$
$$= 0 \quad \text{otherwise.}$$

Calculate σ^2, the variance of X.

A random sample of size two is taken from this distribution.
Find the sampling distributions of S^2 and S. Verify that
$E(S^2)=\sigma^2$ but show that $E(S) \neq \sigma$.

¶ $E(X) = 1 \times 1/4 + 2 \times 1/2 + 3 \times 1/4 = 2,$
$\sigma^2 = Var(X) = 1/4(1-2)^2 + 1/2(2-2)^2 + 1/4(3-2)^2 = 1/2.$

The following table gives the possible sample values and the
resulting values of S and S^2.

Sample Values	Probability	s^2	s
1,1	1/16	0	0
1,2	1/4	1/2	$1/\sqrt{2}$
1,3	1/8	2	$\sqrt{2}$
2,2	1/4	0	0
2,3	1/4	1/2	$1/\sqrt{2}$
3,3	1/16	0	0

Thus S^2 has the sampling distribution

s^2	0	1/2	2
Prob	3/8	1/2	1/8

while that of S is

s	0	$1/\sqrt{2}$	$\sqrt{2}$
Prob	3/8	1/2	1/8

Thus $E(S^2) = 1/2 = \sigma^2$

but $E(S) = 3\sqrt{2}/8 \neq \sigma.$

5.   Use the following 'rejection method' to obtain a simple random
sample of size 6 without replacement from a population of size
60. Allocate 'sampling numbers' 00 to 59 to the members of
the population and consider successive non-overlapping pairs
of digits in a table of random numbers. If the number formed

by the pair is less than or equal to 59, select the member
with that sampling number. Make no selection if the number
is greater than 59 and go to the next pair. Continue until
6 different members have been selected.

Explain how a similar method can be used to select a simple
random sample without replacement from (a) a population of
size 995, (b) a population of size 1005. Why is the method
less convenient to use in case (b) than in case (a)?

¶ Taking the tenth row of Table 11, the pairs of digits are

45 76 95 17 28 50 10 96 49.

Discarding those over 59 we select the members with sampling
numbers

45 17 28 50 10 49.

If the size of the population is 995 we choose 3 digits at
a time. Those between 000 and 994 correspond to the population
members and the rest are discarded.

If the population size is 1005 the digits have to be taken
four at a time. Those between 0000 and 1004 are allocated to
the members and the rest are discarded. This is very
inefficient and a better method is to let numbers 0000-0008
correspond to the first member, 0009-0017 correspond to the
second member and so on, with 9036-9044 corresponding to the
1005th member. More concisely, if the 4-digit number is m
then choose the member whose sampling number is the integer
part of m/9.

6. A university extra-mural class has 40 students, whose ages are
given below.

42	29	30	52	38	60	26	52	46	38
36	28	64	42	28	29	22	42	53	36
52	26	30	48	51	62	28	43	36	53
62	41	32	29	37	56	42	52	29	40

Calculate the mean age of this population.

Allocate sampling numbers 00 to 39 to these data and hence
use random number tables to obtain 8 random samples of 4
without replacement.

Calculate the mean age for each sample and the mean of the sample means. Compare these means with the population mean and comment on your results.

¶ The mean age is 41.05 years.

Starting in the fifth row of Table 11, the pairs of digits are

    12   94   96   68   13   52   11   08

Those between 00 and 39 are 12, 13, 11 and 08 and these are chosen. The corresponding ages are 64, 42, 28 and 46 (numbering the students in the first row from 0 to 9, those in the second from 10 to 19, and so on). The mean age of the sample is 45.

We obtain seven further samples from rows 6-12 and the results are as follows:

Sample Numbers				Ages				Mean
12	13	11	08	64	42	28	46	45.0
36	32	30	27	42	32	62	43	44.75
11	31	04	05	28	41	38	60	41.75
25	23	27	26	62	48	43	28	45.25
01	18	22	26	29	53	30	28	35.00
17	28	10	23	42	36	36	48	40.50
32	09	03	39	32	38	52	40	40.50
39	34	00	23	40	37	42	48	41.75

The mean of these means is 41.8125. Note that although some of the sample means differ considerably from 41.05, the population mean, their mean is quite close to it.

7. Use Table 11 to simulate the dealing of 4 hands of 13 cards from a pack of 52.

¶ In order to simulate this, we must first label the cards. We assign a two digit number to each as follows. First the clubs are given numbers 00,01,...,12 with 00 being the Ace, 01 the two, and so on, with 12 being the King.

Similarly, 13,14,...,25 are allocated to Diamonds, 26,27,...,38 to Hearts and 39,40,...,51 to Spades.

We choose two digits from Table 11. If the pair is between 00 and 51 then we identify it with the corresponding card.

If not, we reject it and choose another.

Starting in the first row, the first seven pairs are

43, 98, 02, 58, 63, 26, 43.

The pair 43 represents the 5 of Spades, 02 the 3 of Clubs, 26 the Ace of Hearts. Pairs 98, 58 and 63 are rejected and 43 is also rejected as it has already been chosen.

Continuing in this way, the first 13 cards, using the obvious notation, are

5S, 3C, AH, 10S, 9C, 2H, QS, AS, 3D, 2D, 6H, 9D, 7D.

Similarly the second hand is

4H, 6C, 10H, KH, 9S, 7S, QC, JC, 2C, 4D, 5D, 4C, 5H

and the third is

10D, 8D, JD, 8S, 8C, KC, AD, 8H, QD, JH, 7H, 4S, 2S.

This leaves 13 cards for the fourth hand, namely

AC, 5C, 7C, 10C, 6D, KD, 3H, 9H, QH, 3S, 6S, JS, KS.

8. A rugby club is sent three grandstand tickets for an international match. Ten members would like a ticket and four of these have the surname Jones. To decide which three members are given tickets, the names of the ten members are put in a hat and a random selection of three names is made without replacement.

Let X_i = 1 if the ith name selected is Jones,

= 0 otherwise (i=1,2,3).

Write down the distribution of X_1. Using the Law of Total Probability, deduce the distributions of X_2 and X_3. Explain in words why these three distributions are identical.

¶ Clearly $P(X_1=1) = \frac{4}{10}$, $P(X_1=0) = \frac{6}{10}$.

Using the Law of Total Probability,

$P(X_2=1) = P(X_2=1|X_1=1) \, P(X_1=1) + P(X_2=1|X_1=0) \, P(X_1=0)$

$\qquad = \frac{3}{9} \times \frac{4}{10} + \frac{4}{9} \times \frac{6}{10} = \frac{4}{10}$,

since, for example, $P(X_2=1|X_1=1) = 3/9$ as of the 9 names left, 3 are Jones.

Clearly $P(X_2=0) = 6/10$.

49

Finally, $P(X_3=1) = P(X_3=1|X_1=X_2=1)P(X_1=X_2=1)$
$$+P(X_3=1|X_1=1,X_2=0)P(X_1=1,X_2=0)$$
$$+P(X_3=1|X_1=0,X_2=1)P(X_1=0,X_2=1)$$
$$+P(X_3=1|X_1=X_2=0)P(X_1=X_2=0)$$
$$= \frac{2}{8} \times \frac{3}{9} \times \frac{4}{10} + \frac{3}{8} \times \frac{6}{9} \times \frac{4}{10} + \frac{3}{8} \times \frac{4}{9} \times \frac{6}{10}$$
$$+ \frac{4}{8} \times \frac{5}{9} \times \frac{6}{10}$$
$$= 4/10$$

and $\qquad P(X_3=0) = 6/10.$

The distributions of X_1, X_2 and X_3 are identical because each of the ten names in the hat have an equal chance of being the ith selected and so the unconditional probability that the ith name selected is Jones is independent of i.

9. A coin is selected at random from a large population of coins in which 90% are fair and 10% have probability 1 of falling 'heads'. The coin is tossed twice and the random variables X_1, X_2 are defined as follows:

$\qquad X_i = 1 \qquad$ if the ith toss falls 'heads',
$\qquad \quad = 0 \qquad$ otherwise.

Determine the sampling distribution of $\bar{X} = (X_1+X_2)/2$.

¶ $\quad P(X_i=1) = P(X_i=1|\text{coin is fair}) \; P(\text{coin is fair})$
$$+P(X_i=1|\text{coin is not fair}) \; P(\text{coin is not fair})$$
$$= \frac{1}{2} \times \frac{9}{10} + 1 \times \frac{1}{10} = \frac{11}{20} \; .$$

Thus $P(\bar{X}=0) = P(X_1=0, \; X_2=0) = (\frac{9}{20})^2 = \frac{81}{400}$,

$\qquad P(\bar{X}=1) = P(X_1=1, \; X_2=1) = (\frac{11}{20})^2 = \frac{121}{400}$,

$\qquad P(\bar{X}=1/2) = 1 - \frac{81}{400} - \frac{121}{400} = \frac{198}{400}$.

10. A lift in a new office block has a maximum load of 1000 kg. Assuming that the masses of potential users are normally distributed with mean 80 kg and standard deviation 10 kg, find the probability that the lift is overloaded with 12 people in it.

It is decided, in the interests of safety, to impose an upper limit k to the number of people allowed to use the lift at any one time. It is stipulated that if k people are in the lift, the probability that their total mass exceeds 1000 kg must be no more than 0.0001. Find the required value of k.

¶   Let $X_1, X_2, \ldots, X_{12}$ denote the masses of the 12 people.
Let
$$Y = \sum_1^{12} X_i.$$

Then Y is normal with mean 960 and variance 1200. Therefore the probability that the lift is overloaded is

$$P(Y > 1000) = 1 - \Phi\left(\frac{1000-960}{\sqrt{1200}}\right)$$

$$= 1 - \Phi(1.1547) = 0.12411.$$

Now let W be the total mass of k people. Then the distribution of W is normal with mean 80k and variance 100k.

We require
$$P(W > 1000) \leq 0.0001.$$
But
$$P(W > 1000) = 1 - \Phi\left(\frac{1000-80k}{\sqrt{100k}}\right)$$

and so
$$\Phi\left(\frac{1000-80k}{\sqrt{100k}}\right) \geq 0.9999.$$
Therefore
$$\frac{1000-80k}{\sqrt{100k}} \geq 3.72.$$

If k=11 the left hand side is 3.62 while if k=10 the left hand side is 6.32. Therefore the appropriate value of k is 10.

11. The fractional parts of 100 numbers are distributed uniformly between 0 and 1. The numbers are first rounded to the nearest integer and then added. Find an approximation for the probability that the error in the sum due to rounding lies between −0.5 and 0.5.

¶   Since the numbers are rounded to the nearest integer, the rounding errors lie between −0.5 and 0.5 and are uniformly distributed on this interval. Thus if X_i denotes the rounding error in the i-th number,

$$E(X_i) = 0, \quad Var(X_i) = 1/12.$$

Let
$$Y = \sum_1^{100} X_i.$$

Y is the error in the sum due to rounding and, by the Central Limit Theorem, it has a distribution which is approximately

$$N(0,100/12).$$

Therefore

$$P(-0.5 \leq Y \leq 0.5) \approx \Phi(\frac{0.5}{\sqrt{100/12}}) - \Phi(\frac{-0.5}{\sqrt{100/12}})$$

$$= 2\Phi(\frac{0.5}{\sqrt{100/12}}) - 1$$

$$= 2\Phi(0.1732) - 1$$

$$= 0.13750.$$

12. A coach company can run 'mini' tours or 'safari' tours. Customers pay £10 each for a mini tour and £20 each for a safari tour. The number of customers who take any tour is normally distributed with mean 40 and standard deviation 5. On a certain day the company can run either two mini tours or one safari tour and will make a profit provided the takings for the day exceed £700. If the most important consideration is not to make a loss, should the company run the safari tour or the two mini tours?

¶ Suppose that the company runs the two mini tours. Let X_1 and X_2 be the numbers of customers who take the tours and let Y be the profit. Then

$$Y = 10(X_1+X_2) - 700.$$

As X_1 and X_2 are both $N(40,25)$, X_1+X_2 is $N(80,50)$. Therefore Y is $N(100,5000)$ and

$$P(Y \geq 0) = \Phi(\frac{100}{\sqrt{5000}}) = \Phi(1.4142) = 0.92135.$$

Suppose now that the company runs the safari tour. Let X be the number of customers who take the tour and let Y again denote the profit. Then

$$Y = 20X - 700.$$

As X is $N(40,25)$, Y is $N(100,10000)$ and

$$P(Y \geqslant 0) = \Phi(\frac{100}{\sqrt{10000}}) = \Phi(1) = 0.84134.$$

Therefore the company should run the two mini tours.

13. A new building has 500 single-bulb light fittings. The number of times that the bulb in a fitting must be replaced during a year is a random variable with mean 1.05 and variance 2.12. How many spare bulbs should be purchased so that the probability that the supply lasts for at least one year is 0.95?

¶ Let X_i be the number of times the i-th bulb is replaced during a year and let
$$Y = \sum_{1}^{500} X_i.$$

Then Y is the number of spare bulbs required.

By the Central Limit Theorem, Y is approximately normally distributed with mean 500 × 1.05 and variance 500 × 2.12. Let n be the number of bulbs purchased. We require that

$$P(Y \leqslant n) \geqslant 0.95.$$

But $\quad\quad P(Y \leqslant n) = \Phi(\frac{n-524.5}{\sqrt{1060}})\quad$ (applying a continuity correction)

and so $\quad\quad \Phi(\frac{n-524.5}{\sqrt{1060}}) \geqslant 0.95.$

Hence $\quad\quad \frac{n-524.5}{\sqrt{1060}} \geqslant 1.645$

and $\quad\quad n \geqslant 578.06.$

Thus at least 579 spare bulbs should be purchased.

14. Train A arrives at Platform 1 X minutes after 6 p.m. and train B arrives at Platform 5 Y minutes after 6 p.m. Assume that X and Y are independent random variables and that X is N(12,4) while Y is N(10,5). Train A waits for 5 minutes and train B waits for 6 minutes. Calculate the probability that the trains stand together in the station for at least one minute.

¶ Train A is in the station between X and X+5 minutes after 6 p.m. while B is there between Y and Y+6. The trains stand together for at least one minute if and only if A arrives at least one minute before B leaves, i.e. $X \leq Y+5$, and B arrives at least one minute before A leaves, i.e. $Y \leq X+4$. Combining these inequalities we have

$$X-5 \leq Y \leq X+4$$

i.e. $$-5 \leq Y-X \leq 4.$$

Now Y-X is $N(-2,9)$. Therefore the probability that the trains stand together for at least one minute is

$$P(-5 \leq Y-X \leq 4) = \Phi(\frac{4+2}{3}) - \Phi(\frac{-5+2}{3})$$

$$= \Phi(2) - \Phi(-1)$$

$$= 0.81859.$$

15. Let $X_1, X_2, \ldots, X_n$ be a random sample from a distribution with probability density function

$$f(x) = \lambda e^{-\lambda x} \quad \text{if } x \geq 0,$$
$$= 0 \quad \text{otherwise.}$$

Let $$Z = \max(X_1, X_2, \ldots, X_n), \quad W = \min(X_1, X_2, \ldots, X_n).$$

Show that the sampling distribution of Z has probability density function

$$g(z) = n\lambda e^{-\lambda z}(1-e^{-\lambda z})^{n-1} \quad \text{if } z \geq 0,$$
$$= 0 \quad \text{otherwise.}$$

and that the sampling distribution of W has probability density function $$h(w) = n\lambda e^{-n\lambda w} \quad \text{if } w \geq 0,$$
$$= 0 \quad \text{otherwise.}$$

¶ Let G(z) be the cumulative distribution function of Z. Then

$$G(z) = P(Z \leq z)$$
$$= P(\max(X_1, X_2, \ldots, X_n) \leq z)$$
$$= P(X_1 \leq z, X_2 \leq z, \ldots, X_n \leq z)$$
$$= P(X_1 \leq z) P(X_2 \leq z)\ldots P(X_n \leq z) \quad \text{(by independence)}$$

For $z \geq 0$
$$P(X_1 \leq z) = \int_0^z \lambda e^{-\lambda x} \, dx$$

$$= [-e^{-\lambda x}]_0^z$$

$$= 1-e^{-\lambda z}$$

and $$G(z) = (1-e^{-\lambda z})^n.$$

Differentiating,

$$g(z) = \frac{d}{dz} G(z) = n\lambda e^{-\lambda z}(1-e^{-\lambda z})^{n-1}.$$

Let H(w) be the cumulative distribution function of W.
Then

$$1-H(w) = P(W \geq w)$$

$$= P(\min(X_1,\ldots,X_n) \geq w)$$

$$= P(X_1 \geq w, X_2 \geq w,\ldots,X_n \geq w)$$

$$= P(X_1 \geq w) P(X_2 \geq w)\ldots P(X_n \geq w).$$

Now $P(X_i \geq w) = 1-P(X_i \leq w)$

$$= e^{-\lambda w}, \qquad \text{if } w \geq 0.$$

Hence $1-H(w) = e^{-n\lambda w}$,

$$H(w) = 1-e^{-n\lambda w}.$$

Differentiating,

$$h(w) = n\lambda e^{-n\lambda w}, \qquad w \geq 0.$$

16.   A company manufactures electronic calculators. Each calculator
uses an integrated circuit which is obtained from a supplier.
One in five of the circuits are either unusable when supplied
or are damaged beyond repair when the calculator is assembled.
Find approximately the probability that in order to manufacture
10000 calculators, between 12400 and 12600 integrated circuits
must be obtained from the supplier.

¶   Let M_i be the number of circuits required to manufacture the
ith calculator (i=1,...,10000).

Then
$$P(M_i=m) = (0.2)^{m-1}0.8 \qquad (m=1,2,\ldots).$$

This is a geometric distribution with mean

$$\frac{1}{0.8} = \frac{5}{4}$$

and variance $\dfrac{0.2}{0.8^2} = \dfrac{5}{16}$.

Let
$$N = \sum_{i=1}^{10000} M_i .$$

Then N is the number required to produce 10000 calculators.
By the Central Limit Theorem, the distribution of N is
approximately $N(\frac{50000}{4}, \frac{50000}{16})$. Therefore, applying a
continuity correction because the geometric distribution
is discrete,

$$P(12400 \leq N \leq 12600) \approx \Phi(\frac{12600.5-12500}{\sqrt{50000/16}}) - \Phi(\frac{12399.5-12500}{\sqrt{50000/16}})$$

$$= 2\Phi(1.7978) - 1$$
$$= 0.9278.$$

(The approximation is 0.9264 without the continuity
correction.)

17. Ten cars enter a one-hour race. Each car drives at a constant
speed for the whole hour. The speeds of the cars form a random
sample from a distribution with probability density function

$$f(x) = \alpha x e^{-\alpha x^2/2} \quad \text{if } x \geq 0.$$

Find the probability density function of the distance travelled
by the slowest car and show that its mean is $\sqrt{\pi/20\alpha}$. Find
also the probability density function of the total distance
travelled by the winner.

(Assume that $\int_0^\infty e^{-x^2/2} dx = \sqrt{\pi/2}$.)

¶ Let X_i be the speed of the ith car, $i=1,2,\ldots,10$. The
slowest car has speed

$$W = \min(X_1, X_2, \ldots, X_{10}).$$

Since the race lasts for one hour, W is also the distance
travelled by the slowest car.

For any i,

$$P(X_i \geq w) = \int_w^\infty \alpha x e^{-\alpha x^2/2} dx$$

$$= [-e^{-\alpha x^2/2}]_w^\infty$$

$$= e^{-\alpha w^2/2}$$

Thus, following the analysis in the solution of Problem 15,

$$P(W \geq w) = P(X_1 \geq w) P(X_2 \geq w) \ldots P(X_{10} \geq w)$$
$$= e^{-10\alpha w^2/2}$$

and differentiating, W has the probability density function

$$h(w) = 10\alpha w e^{-5\alpha w^2}, \quad w \geq 0.$$

Integrating by parts,

$$\begin{aligned}
E(W) &= \int_0^\infty 10\alpha w^2 e^{-5\alpha w^2} \, dw \\
&= [w(-e^{-5\alpha w^2})]_0^\infty + \int_0^\infty e^{-5\alpha w^2} \, dw \\
&= 0 + \int_0^\infty e^{-y^2/2} \, \frac{dy}{\sqrt{10\alpha}} \qquad (y = w\sqrt{10\alpha}) \\
&= \frac{1}{\sqrt{10\alpha}} \cdot \sqrt{\frac{\pi}{2}} \\
&= \sqrt{\frac{\pi}{20a}},
\end{aligned}$$

as required.

The speed of the winner is

$$Z = \max(X_1, X_2, \ldots, X_{10})$$

This is also the distance travelled by the winner.

Now $P(Z \leq z) = P(X_1 \leq z) \, P(X_2 \leq z) \ldots P(X_{10} \leq z)$
$$= (1 - e^{-\alpha z^2/2})^{10}, \quad z \geq 0.$$

Therefore Z has the probability density function

$$g(z) = 10\alpha z e^{-\alpha z^2/2} (1 - e^{-\alpha z^2/2})^9, \quad z \geq 0.$$

18. The random variable X is uniformly distributed on $[0,1]$.
     Let Z denote the sample maximum when a random sample of
     size 10 is obtained from the distribution of X. A random
     sample $Z_1, Z_2, \ldots, Z_{100}$ is obtained from the distribution of
     Z by drawing 100 independent random samples of size 10
     from the distribution of X. Find the probability that
     $\bar{Z} \geq 0.90$.

¶   Let $X_1, X_2, \ldots, X_{10}$ be a random sample from the distribution
     of X. Then for each i,

$$P(X_i \leq z) = x, \quad 0 \leq x \leq 1.$$

Following the method of Problem 15,

$$\begin{aligned}
P(Z \leq z) &= P(X_1 \leq z) \ldots P(X_{10} \leq z) \\
&= z^{10}
\end{aligned}$$

and so Z has probability density function

$$g(z) = 10z^9, \quad 0 \le z \le 1.$$

Therefore $\quad E(Z) = \displaystyle\int_0^1 10z^{10}\, dz = 10/11,$

$$E(Z^2) = \int_0^1 10z^{11}\, dz = 10/12$$

and $\quad \mathrm{Var}(Z) = \dfrac{10}{12} - \left(\dfrac{10}{11}\right)^2$

$$= \frac{1210-1200}{12 \times 11^2} = \frac{10}{1452}.$$

By the Central Limit Theorem, $\bar{Z}$ has a distribution which is approximately normal, with mean $E(Z) = 10/11$ and variance $\mathrm{Var}(Z)/100 = 1/14520$. Therefore

$$P(\bar{Z} \ge 0.9) \approx 1-\Phi\left(\frac{9/10-10/11}{\sqrt{1/14520}}\right)$$

$$= \Phi(1.095)$$
$$= 0.863.$$

19. Two bags contain discs numbered 1,2 or 3. Bag I contains five 1's, two 2's and five 3's, while Bag II contains three 1's, six 2's and three 3's. A bag is selected at random and two discs are chosen at random from the bag. Let X_1 and X_2 denote the numbers of the selected discs. Find the sampling distributions of $\bar{X}$ and S^2.

Consider the ratio

$$\frac{P(\text{Bag I selected}\,|A)}{P(\text{Bag II selected}\,|A)}$$

where A is an event associated with the chosen discs. Evaluate this if A is the event that

    (i)   the outcome is (2,2),

    (ii)   the sample mean is 2,

   (iii)   the sample variance is 0.

Comment on the use of this ratio as a method for deciding which bag was the selected one.

¶   The following table gives the values of

$$\bar{X} = \frac{X_1+X_2}{2} \quad\text{and}\quad S^2 = \tfrac{1}{2}(X_1-X_2)^2,$$

together with the associated probabilities, for the different possible pairs of sample values.

Sample Values	Probability	$\bar{x}$	s^2
1,1	13/132	1	0
1,2	28/132	3/2	1/2
1,3	34/132	2	2
2,2	16/132	2	0
2,3	28/132	5/2	1/2
3,3	13/132	3	0

For example, the probability of obtaining a 1 and a 2 is 28/132 as

$$P(X_1=2,X_2=1) = P(X_1=1,X_2=2)$$
$$= P(X_1=1,X_2=2|Bag\ I)\ P(Bag\ I)$$
$$+ P(X_1=1,X_2=2|Bag\ II)\ P(Bag\ II)$$
$$= \frac{5}{12} \times \frac{2}{11} \times \frac{1}{2} + \frac{3}{12} \times \frac{6}{11} \times \frac{1}{2} = \frac{14}{132} .$$

It follows that the sampling distribution of $\bar{X}$ is

$\bar{x}$	1	3/2	2	5/2	3
Prob	13/132	28/132	50/132	28/132	13/132

and that of S^2 is

s^2	0	1/2	2
Prob	42/132	56/132	34/132

(i) $P(Bag\ I|(2,2)) = P((2,2)|Bag\ I)\ P(Bag\ I)/P((2,2))$
$$= \frac{2/12 \times 1/11 \times 1/2}{16/132} = \frac{1}{16}.$$

Therefore $P(Bag\ II|(2,2)) = 1 - \frac{1}{16} = \frac{15}{16} .$

The value of the ratio is 1/15, suggesting strongly that Bag II was selected.

(ii) $P(\bar{X}=2\ |Bag\ I) = 2 \times \frac{5}{12} \times \frac{5}{11} + \frac{2}{12} \times \frac{1}{11} = \frac{52}{132} .$

Therefore
$$P(Bag\ I|\bar{X}=2) = P(\bar{X}=2|Bag\ I)P(Bag\ I)/P(\bar{X}=2)$$
$$= \frac{52/132 \times 1/2}{50/132} = \frac{13}{25}$$

and $P(Bag\ II|\bar{X}=2) = \frac{12}{25} .$

The value of the ratio is 13/12, suggesting marginally that
Bag I was selected.

(iii) $P(S^2=0 \,|\, \text{Bag I}) = \frac{5}{12} \times \frac{4}{11} + \frac{2}{12} \times \frac{1}{11} + \frac{5}{12} \times \frac{4}{11} = \frac{42}{132}$.

Therefore

$$P(\text{Bag I} \,|\, S^2=0) = P(S^2=0 \,|\, \text{Bag I}) \, P(\text{Bag I}) / P(S^2=0)$$

$$= \frac{42/132 \times 1/2}{42/132} = \frac{1}{2} \; ,$$

$$P(\text{Bag II} \,|\, S^2=0) = \frac{1}{2}$$

and the value of the ratio is 1. The interpretation is that
being told that the sample variance is zero conveys no
information about which bag was selected.

20. n points, $P_1, P_2, \ldots, P_n$ are randomly positioned in a plane in
such a way that the coordinates (X_i, Y_i) of the point
$P_i \,(i=1,2,\ldots,n)$ with respect to an origin O are independent
$N(0,1)$ random variables. If R_i denotes the length of OP_i,
show that

$$E(R_i^2) = 2$$

and $$\text{Var}(R_i^2) = 4 .$$

(You may assume that if Z is $N(0,1)$, then $E(Z^4)=3$.)

Let a,b be constants and define

$$V = \frac{1}{n} \sum_{i=1}^{n} R_i^2 \; .$$

Assuming that n is large, use the Central Limit Theorem to
obtain an approximation for $P(a \leq V \leq b)$ in terms of Φ,
the standard normal cumulative distribution function.
Hence calculate approximately the probability that the root
mean square distance $\sqrt{V}$ lies between 1.4 and 1.6 if there
are 36 points in all.

¶

$$R_i^2 = X_i^2 + Y_i^2 \; .$$

Therefore $E(R_i^2) = E(X_i^2) + E(Y_i^2)$

and $\text{Var}(R_i^2) = \text{Var}(X_i^2) + \text{Var}(Y_i^2)$

as X_i and Y_i are independent.

Now $\quad E(X_i^2) = Var(X_i) + (E(X_i))^2 = 1+0=1.$

Similarly $\quad E(Y_i^2) = 1.$

Hence $\quad E(R_i^2) = 2.$

Using $E(X_i^4) = 3,$

$$Var(X_i^2) = E(X_i^4) - (E(X_i^2))^2 = 2.$$

Similarly, $\quad Var(Y_i^2) = 2.$

Hence $\quad Var(R_i^2) = 4.$

By the Central Limit Theorem, V is approximately distributed with mean 2 and variance $4/n$.

Therefore
$$P(a \leqslant V \leqslant b) \approx \Phi(\frac{(b-2)\sqrt{n}}{2}) - \Phi(\frac{(a-2)\sqrt{n}}{2}) \ .$$
and, if n = 36,

$$P(1.4 \leqslant \sqrt{V} \leqslant 1.6) = P(1.96 \leqslant V \leqslant 2.56)$$

$$= \Phi(\frac{(2.56-2)\times 6}{2}) - \Phi(\frac{(1.96-2)\times 6}{2})$$

$$= \Phi(1.68) - \Phi(-0.12)$$

$$= 0.50128.$$

21. In an experiment, a variable y is related to a controllable variable x by the equation
$$y = a+bx$$
where a and b are constants to be determined. The experimenter measures y when x=1 and when x=5. Let y_1 and y_2 be the respective measurements. The relationship between y and x is estimated by drawing a line through the points $A=(1,y_1)$ and $B=(5,y_2)$; its slope being an estimate of b and its intercept being an estimate of a. Suppose that the measurements are subject to error and that, for a given value of x, the possible y-measurements are 2x, 2x+1, 2x+2 with respective probabilities $\frac{1}{4}$, $\frac{1}{2}$, $\frac{1}{4}$. Find the sampling distributions of the slope and intercept of the line AB and show that the mean slope is 2 and the mean intercept is 1.

¶ The slope of the line drawn is $(y_2-y_1)/4$ and its intercept is $(5y_1-y_2)/4$.

The possible values of y_1 are 2,3 and 4 while those of y_2 are 10, 11 and 12.

Below are listed the possible values of (y_1,y_2), the associated probabilities, and the values of the slope and intercept.

y_1,y_2	Probability	$(y_2-y_1)/4$	$(5y_1-y_2)/4$
2,10	1/16	2	0
2,11	2/16	9/4	-1/4
2,12	1/16	10/4	-2/4
3,10	2/16	7/4	5/4
3,11	4/16	2	1
3,12	2/16	9/4	3/4
4,10	1/16	6/4	10/4
4,11	2/16	7/4	9/4
4,12	1/16	2	2

The sampling distribution of the slope is

slope	6/4	7/4	2	9/4	10/4
prob	$\frac{1}{16}$	$\frac{4}{16}$	$\frac{6}{16}$	$\frac{4}{16}$	$\frac{1}{16}$

and this has mean 2.

The sampling distribution of the intercept is

intercept	-2/4	-1/4	0	3/4	1	5/4	2	9/4	10/4
prob	$\frac{1}{16}$	$\frac{2}{16}$	$\frac{1}{16}$	$\frac{2}{16}$	$\frac{4}{16}$	$\frac{2}{16}$	$\frac{1}{16}$	$\frac{2}{16}$	$\frac{1}{16}$

and this has mean 1.

22. One thousand numbers are selected at random from the interval [0,1]. For i=1,2,...,1000, define

$$X_i = [10Y_i+0.5]/10$$

where Y_i is the ith random number selected. Thus X_i is the result of rounding Y_i to the first decimal place. Find the mean and variance of X_i and hence obtain an approximation for the probability that the sum of the X_i's is at least 510. (Use a continuity correction.) Compare this with the probability that the sum of one thousand unrounded random numbers from [0,1] is 510 or more.

¶   If $X_i = [10Y_i+0.5]/10$

where [x] denotes the largest integer less than or equal to x,
then

$$P(X_i = 0) = P(X_i = 1) = 0.05$$

and for k=1,2,...,9

$$P(X_i = k/10) = 0.1.$$

For example,

$$P(X_i = 0) = P(10Y_i+0.5 < 1) = P(Y_i < 0.05) = 0.05$$

and $P(X_i = 0.1) = P(1 \leq 10Y_i+0.5 < 2) = P(0.05 \leq Y_i < 0.15) = 0.1$.

Thus
$$E(X_i) = 0 \times 0.05 + 0.1 \times 0.1 + \ldots + 0.9 \times 0.1 + 1 \times 0.05$$

$$= 0.5,$$

$$E(X_i^2) = 0^2 \times 0.05 + 0.1^2 \times 0.1 + \ldots + 0.9^2 \times 0.1 + 1^2 \times 0.05$$

$$= 0.335$$

and
$$Var(X_i) = 0.335 - 0.5^2 = 0.085.$$

Let $$Y = \sum_{1}^{1000} X_i.$$

Then $E(Y) = 500$, $Var(Y) = 85$

and, by the Central Limit Theorem, the distribution of Y is
approximately normal.

Hence $P(Y \geq 510) \approx 1-\Phi\left(\dfrac{509.95-500}{\sqrt{85}}\right)$

$$= 1-\Phi(1.0792)$$

$$= 0.14025.$$

(Note that the possible values of Y are ...,509.8, 509.9,
510.0,... so that the continuity correction involves the
midpoint of the interval [509.9, 510.0].)

If the numbers are unrounded then each has mean $\frac{1}{2}$ and
variance $\frac{1}{12}$, using the standard results on the uniform
distribution. Then Y has mean 500 and variance 1000/12
and the required probability is

$$1-\Phi\left(\frac{510-500}{\sqrt{1000/12}}\right) = 1-\Phi(1.0954) = 0.13668.$$

23. A drug company sells medication in the form of capsules. Each capsule contains 300 small tablets, each tablet being identical in size and shape but weighing 1, 1.2 or 1.5 units. Each capsule should contain 100 tablets of each weight. A large container is filled with an equal number of each type of tablet. These are thoroughly mixed and each capsule is filled by selecting 300 tablets at random from the container. The company sells the capsules in boxes, each holding 1000 capsules. Calculate the probability that the contents of a randomly selected box weighs more than 370100 units.

¶   Let X_i be the weight of the i-th tablet chosen.

Then $E(X_i) = \frac{1}{3} \times 1 + \frac{1}{3} \times 1.2 + \frac{1}{3} \times 1.5 = 1.23\dot{}$

and $E(X_i^2) = \frac{1}{3} \times 1^2 + \frac{1}{3} \times 1.2^2 + \frac{1}{3} \times 1.5^2 = 1.56\dot{3}$

so that $Var(X_i) = 1.56\dot{3} - 1.23^2 = 0.04\dot{2}$.

The weight of a capsule is

$$Y = \sum_{1}^{300} X_i$$

and has approximately a normal distribution with mean 370 and variance $12.\dot{6}$. The weight W of a box is the sum of 1000 random variables with this distribution and so is approximately normal with mean 370,000 and variance $12666.\dot{6}$.

Thus $P(W > 3701000) \approx 1-\Phi(\frac{370100-370000}{\sqrt{12666.6}})$

$$= 1-\Phi(0.8885)$$

$$= 0.1871.$$

24. Let a random sample of size n be taken from the uniform distribution on $[0,\theta]$. It can be shown that R, the range of the sample, has the probability density function

$g(r) = n(n-1)r^{n-2}(\theta-r)/\theta^n$ if $0 \leq r \leq \theta$,

$\quad\quad = 0$ otherwise.

Deduce that
$E(R) = \frac{n-1}{n+1}\theta$, $Var(R) = \frac{2(n-1)\theta^2}{(n+1)^2(n+2)}$.

64

Hence show that the covariance of Z, the sample maximum, and W, the sample minimum, is given by

$$\text{Cov}(Z,W) = \frac{\theta^2}{(n+1)^2(n+2)} \cdot$$

¶

$$E(R) = \int_0^\theta rg(r)\ dr$$

$$= \frac{n(n-1)}{\theta^n} \int_0^\theta r^{n-1}(\theta-r)\ dr$$

$$= \frac{n(n-1)}{\theta^n} \left[\frac{\theta r^n}{n} - \frac{r^{n+1}}{n+1}\right]_0^\theta$$

$$= \frac{n-1}{n+1}\ \theta\ .$$

$$E(R^2) = \frac{n(n-1)}{\theta^n} \int_0^\theta r^n(\theta-r)\ dr$$

$$= \frac{n(n-1)}{\theta^n} \left[\frac{\theta r^{n+1}}{n+1} - \frac{r^{n+2}}{n+2}\right]_0^\theta$$

$$= \frac{n(n-1)\ \theta^2}{(n+1)(n+2)}\ ,$$

so that

$$\text{Var}(R) = \frac{n(n-1)\ \theta^2}{(n+1)(n+2)} - \left(\frac{n-1}{n+1}\right)^2 \theta^2$$

$$= \frac{(n-1)\ \theta^2}{(n+1)^2(n+2)}\ (n(n+1) - (n+2)(n-1))$$

$$= \frac{2(n-1)\ \theta^2}{(n+1)^2(n+2)} \cdot$$

But $$\text{Var}(R) = \text{Var}(Z-W)$$
$$= \text{Var}(Z) + \text{Var}(W) - 2\,\text{Cov}(Z,W)$$

Now Z has the probability density function

$$f(z) = nz^{n-1}\ \theta^{-n} \quad (0 \le z \le \theta)$$

(see Example 6.15, Volume 2) so that

$$\text{Var}(Z) = \frac{n\theta^2}{(n+1)^2(n+2)} \cdot$$

Similarly $\quad \text{Var}(W) = \dfrac{n\theta^2}{(n+1)^2(n+2)}$.

Hence $\quad \text{Cov}(Z,W) = \dfrac{n\theta^2}{(n+1)^2(n+2)} - \dfrac{(n-1)\ \theta^2}{(n+1)^2(n+2)}$

$$= \frac{\theta^2}{(n+1)^2(n+2)}\ .$$

25. A sequence of independent random variables $X_1, X_2, \ldots, X_n$ is such that X_i is $N(\mu_i, \sigma_i^2)$ $(i=1,2,\ldots,n)$, and

$$Y = \sum_{i=1}^{n} a_i X_i,$$

where $a_1, a_2, \ldots, a_n$ are constants.

Using the identity

$$E(\exp(t\sum_{1}^{n} a_i X_i)) = \prod_{i=1}^{n} E(e^{a_i t X_i}),$$

show that Y is normally distributed with mean $\displaystyle\sum_{i=1}^{n} a_i \mu_i$ and variance $\displaystyle\sum_{i=1}^{n} a_i^2 \sigma_i^2$.

(It may be assumed that the moment generating function of a random variable X with the distribution $N(\mu, \sigma^2)$ is given by

$$E(e^{tX}) = e^{\mu t + \frac{1}{2}\sigma^2 t^2}$$

and that no other distribution has this moment generating function.)

¶ The moment generating function of Y is

$$M(t) = E(e^{tY}) = E(\exp(t\sum_{1}^{n} a_i X_i))$$

$$= \prod_{i=1}^{n} E(e^{a_i t X_i})$$

But $\quad E(e^{a_i t X_i}) = M_i(a_i t),$

where $M_i(t)$ is the moment generating function of X_i.

We are given that

$$M_i(t) = e^{\mu_i t + \frac{1}{2}\sigma_i^2 t^2}$$

Thus

$$M(t) = \prod_{i=1}^{n} (e^{\mu_i a_i t + \frac{1}{2}\sigma_i^2 a_i^2 t^2})$$

$$= \exp(t \sum \mu_i a_i + \frac{1}{2} t^2 \sum a_i^2 \sigma_i^2).$$

This is the moment generating function of a normal distribution with mean $\sum_1^n \mu_i a_i$ and variance $\sum_1^n a_i^2 \sigma_i^2$, as required.

7

Estimation

Miscellaneous Problems

1. A random sample of size 25 from a distribution of unknown
    mean μ and unknown variance σ^2 gave sample values
    $x_1, \ldots, x_{25}$ such that

    $$\sum_{i=1}^{25} x_i = 340.2, \qquad \sum_{i=1}^{25} x_i^2 = 4921.85.$$

    Find unbiased estimates of μ and σ^2.

¶   Unbiased estimates of μ and σ^2 are given by

    $$\bar{x} = \frac{1}{25} \sum_{i=1}^{25} x_i = \frac{340.2}{25} = 13.608$$

    and $\quad s^2 = \frac{1}{24} \left(\sum_{i=1}^{25} x_i^2 - 25\bar{x}^2 \right)$

    $$= \frac{1}{24} (4921.85 - 25 \times (13.608)^2)$$

    $$= 12.1837$$

    respectively.

2. A thousand boxes are stored in a warehouse. A quarter weigh
    2 kg each, a half weigh 3 kg each and the remainder weigh
    4 kg each. Three boxes are chosen at random and weighed.

Let $\bar{X}$ and M denote respectively the mean and the median of
the weights of these three boxes. Find the sampling distributions of $\bar{X}$ and M and show that $1000\bar{X}$ and $1000M$ are unbiased
estimators of the total weight of all the boxes. Which is
the better estimator? (Since the population size is large
compared with the sample size, sampling with replacement can
be used as an approximation to sampling without replacement.)

¶ Let X_1, X_2, X_3 denote the weights of the chosen boxes. Below
we list the possible combinations of values, the corresponding
values of $\bar{X}$ and M, and the probabilities of obtaining these
combinations. The probabilities are calculated as if the
selection had been performed with replacement. This is only
an approximation but because of the large number of boxes, it
has only a very small effect on the values obtained.

Combination	$\bar{x}$	$\underline{m}$	Probability
222	2	2	1/64
223	7/3	2	6/64
224	8/3	2	3/64
233	8/3	3	12/64
234	3	3	12/64
244	10/3	4	3/64
333	3	3	8/64
334	10/3	3	12/64
344	11/3	4	6/64
444	4	4	1/64

For example the probability of the combination 233 is
$3 \times 1/4 \times 1/2 \times 1/2 = 12/64$.

The sampling distributions of $\bar{X}$ and M are thus

$\bar{x}$	2	7/3	8/3	3	10/3	11/3	4
$P_{\bar{X}}$	1/64	6/64	15/64	20/64	15/64	6/64	1/64

and

m	2	3	4
P_m	10/64	44/64	10/64

$$E(\bar{X}) = 2 \times \frac{1}{64} + \frac{7}{3} \times \frac{6}{64} + \ldots + 4 \times \frac{1}{64} = 3 \ ,$$

$$E(M) = 2 \times \frac{10}{64} + 3 \times \frac{44}{64} + 4 \times \frac{10}{64} = 3$$

so that $E(1000\bar{X}) = E(1000M) = 3000.$

Since the total weight is 3000 kg, $1000\bar{X}$ and $1000M$ are both unbiased estimators.

Now

$$\text{Var}(\bar{X}) = \frac{1}{64} \times (2-3)^2 + \frac{6}{64} \times (\frac{7}{3} - 3)^2 + \ldots + \frac{1}{64} \times (4-3)^2$$

$$= 1/6$$

and $\text{Var}(M) = \frac{10}{64} \times (2-3)^2 + \frac{44}{64} \times (3-3)^2 + \frac{10}{64} \times (4-3)^2 = \frac{20}{64} \ .$

Since $\text{Var}(\bar{X}) < \text{Var}(M)$, $\text{Var}(1000\bar{X}) < \text{Var}(1000M)$
and $1000\bar{X}$ is the better estimator.

3. A random sample of 10 boys and 10 girls from a large sixth
    form college were weighed with the following results.

Boy's weight (kg)	77	67	65	60	71	62	67	58	65	81
Girl's weight (kg)	42	57	46	49	64	61	52	50	44	59

Find

(a) unbiased estimates of μ_b and σ_b^2, the mean and variance
     of the weights of the boys;

(b) unbiased estimates of μ_g and σ_g^2, the mean and variance
     of the weights of the girls;

(c) an unbiased estimate of $\mu_b - \mu_g$.

Assuming that $\sigma_b^2 = \sigma_g^2 = \sigma^2$, calculate an unbiased estimate
of σ^2 using both sets of weights.

¶ (a) An unbiased estimate of μ_b is given by the mean weight
        of the boys,

$$\hat{\mu}_b = \frac{1}{10} (77+67+\ldots+81) = 67.3 \ .$$

An unbiased estimate of σ_b^2 is the sample variance of
the weights of the boys,

$$\hat{\sigma}_b^2 = ((77^2+\ldots+81^2)-10\hat{\mu}_b^2)/9$$
$$= 52.6\dot{7}$$

(b) Similarly, unbiased estimates of μ_g and σ_g^2 are

$$\hat{\mu}_g = \frac{1}{10}\ (42+57+\ldots+59)\ =\ 52.4,$$

$$\hat{\sigma}_g^2 = ((42^2+57^2+\ldots+59^2)-10\hat{\mu}_g^2)/9$$
$$= 56.7\dot{1}.$$

(c) An unbiased estimate of $\mu_b-\mu_g$ is

$$\hat{\mu}_b-\hat{\mu}_g = 67.3\ -\ 52.4\ =\ 14.9$$

$$E(\hat{\sigma}_b^2)\ =\ E(\hat{\sigma}_g^2)\ =\ \sigma^2\quad\text{and so}$$

$$E(\frac{\hat{\sigma}_b^2\ +\ \hat{\sigma}_g^2}{2})\ =\ \sigma^2\ .$$

Therefore an unbiased estimate of σ^2 which uses both sets of weights is

$$\frac{1}{2}(\hat{\sigma}_b^2+\hat{\sigma}_g^2)\ =\ \frac{1}{2}(52.6\dot{7}\ +\ 56.7\dot{1})$$

$$=\ 54.69\dot{4}\ .$$

4. A factory produces a large number of items which are classified as either perfect or defective. A quality control inspector, after testing a random sample of the items, reported that his estimate of the proportion of defectives was 0.05 with an estimated standard error of $10^{-2}\times\sqrt{4.75}$. Unfortunately the record of the size of his sample is lost. Find the size of the sample which led to these results.

¶ Let p be the proportion of defectives. The sample proportion $\hat{p}$, used as estimator of p, has standard error $\sqrt{p(1-p)/n}$ and an estimate of this is

$$\sqrt{\frac{\hat{p}(1-\hat{p})}{n}}\ .$$

Now $\hat{p} = 0.05$ and so

$$\sqrt{\frac{0.05 \times 0.95}{n}} = 0.01 \sqrt{4.75} .$$

Therefore, squaring both sides,

$$\frac{0.05 \times 0.95}{n} = 0.0001 \times 4.75$$

$$\text{and } n = 100.$$

5. A bag contains a large number of discs of which 20% are numbered '2', 40% are numbered '3' and the rest are numbered '4'. If X denotes the number on a randomly chosen disc, calculate μ, the mean of X.

If a random sample of size two is taken from the population, find the sampling distribution of the sample mean $\bar{X}$. Answer the following.

(a) Is $\bar{X}$ an unbiased estimator for μ?

(b) Is $1/\bar{X}$ an unbiased estimator for $1/\mu$?

(c) Is $\bar{X}^2$ an unbiased estimator for μ^2?

(d) Is $a\bar{X}+b$ an unbiased estimator for $a\mu+b$?

¶ $\mu = 2 \times \dfrac{1}{5} + 3 \times \dfrac{2}{5} + 4 \times \dfrac{2}{5} = \dfrac{16}{5} .$

The possible combinations of sample values, together with the values of $\bar{x}$, are listed below.

Combination	Probability	$\bar{x}$
2,2	1/25	2
2,3	4/25	5/2
2,4	4/25	3
3,3	4/25	3
3,4	8/25	7/2
4,4	4/25	4

Note that the probabilities are calculated on the assumption that the selection is performed with replacement. Since there are a large number of discs, this will be a good approximation to a selection without replacement.

The sampling distribution of $\bar{X}$ is

$\bar{x}$	2	5/2	3	7/2	4
prob	$\frac{1}{25}$	$\frac{4}{25}$	$\frac{8}{25}$	$\frac{8}{25}$	$\frac{4}{25}$

Therefore

(a) $E(\bar{X}) = 2 \times \frac{1}{25} + \frac{5}{2} \times \frac{4}{25} + 3 \times \frac{8}{25} + \frac{7}{2} \times \frac{8}{25} + 4 \times \frac{4}{25} = \frac{16}{5} = \mu$

Thus $\bar{X}$ is an unbiased estimator for μ.

(b) $E(\frac{1}{\bar{X}}) = \frac{1}{2} \times \frac{1}{25} + \frac{2}{5} \times \frac{4}{25} + \frac{1}{3} \times \frac{8}{25} + \frac{2}{7} \times \frac{8}{25} + \frac{1}{4} \times \frac{4}{25}$

$\qquad\qquad = 0.322 \neq \frac{1}{\mu} = 0.3125.$

So $1/\bar{X}$ is not an unbiased estimator for $1/\mu$.

(c) $E(\bar{X}^2) = 4 \times \frac{1}{25} + \frac{25}{4} \times \frac{4}{25} + 9 \times \frac{8}{25} + \frac{49}{4} \times \frac{8}{25} + 16 \times \frac{4}{25}$

$\qquad\qquad = 10.52 \neq \mu^2 = 10.24.$

So $\bar{X}^2$ is not an unbiased estimator for μ^2.

(d) $E(a\bar{X}+b) = aE(\bar{X})+b = a\mu+b$ by (a).

Therefore $a\bar{X}+b$ is an unbiased estimator for $a\mu+b$.

6.   Let $X_1, X_2, \ldots, X_n$ be a random sample from the distribution of a random variable X with known mean μ and unknown variance σ^2. Show that

$$\frac{1}{n} \sum_{i=1}^{n} (X_i - \mu)^2$$

is an unbiased estimator for σ^2.

¶ $E(\frac{1}{n} \sum_{i=1}^{n} (X_i - \mu)^2) = \frac{1}{n} \sum_{i=1}^{n} E[(X_i - \mu)^2]$

But $E[(X_i - \mu)^2] = Var(X_i) = \sigma^2$.

Therefore $E(\frac{1}{n} \sum_{i=1}^{n} (X_i - \mu)^2) = \frac{1}{n} \times n\sigma^2 = \sigma^2$

as required.

7. An item is produced in two stages, the processing times for the two stages being T_1 and T_2 hours respectively. The production cost is £$(10T_1+30T_2)$. Processing times were recorded for 10 items selected at random, the results being as follows.

Stage 1	5.6	4.7	5.1	4.8	4.9	5.2	5.0	5.1	4.7	4.9
Stage 2	3.7	4.1	3.8	4.0	4.1	3.9	3.8	4.6	4.1	3.8

Find unbiased estimates for the mean and variance of the production cost of an item, assuming T_1 and T_2 to be independent.

¶ Using the sample mean and sample variance, we find unbiased estimates of the mean and variance of T_1 are 5 and $0.07\dot{3}$ respectively.

Similarly for T_2, the estimates are 3.99 and $0.067\dot{6}$.
Let the total cost be C = $10T_1+30T_2$.

$$E(C) = 10E(T_1)+30E(T_2)$$

and using the unbiased estimates above for $E(T_1)$ and $E(T_2)$, we see that $10 \times 5 + 30 \times 3.99 = 169.7$ is an unbiased estimate of the total cost.

Now Var(C) = 100 Var(T_1) + 900 Var(T_2),
as T_1 and T_2 are independent.

Therefore an unbiased estimate of the variance of the cost is

$$100 \times 0.07\dot{3} + 900 \times 0.067\dot{6} = 68.2\dot{3} .$$

8. A firm wishing to estimate the mean number of stoppages per day of a certain piece of machinery decides to make use of past records. These records are not, however, complete, and show only for each day whether there were either (i) no stoppages or (ii) at least one stoppage. Examination of these records shows that during a period covering 1000 working days, there were 96 days with no stoppages. Assuming that the number of stoppages in a

74

day is a Poisson random variable with mean λ, use this information to estimate λ.

¶ Let the number of stoppages in a day be X. Then X has probability function

$$p_x = \frac{e^{-\lambda} \lambda^x}{x!} , \quad x = 0,1,2,\ldots$$

and the probability of no stoppages is $p_o = e^{-\lambda}$.

Since the observed proportion of days with no stoppages is 96/1000, this is an estimate for $e^{-\lambda}$.

Taking logarithms, an estimate for λ is

$$-\log_e 96/1000 = 2.3434.$$

9. A firm produces items which are classified as either defective or perfect. From time to time the firm is required to take a random sample and estimate the proportion of defectives produced. A legal requirement is that the estimator used should have a variance not greater than 0.001. Show that this can always be achieved with a sample size of 250.

¶ Let p be the proportion of defective items. The variance of the sample proportion is given by

$$\frac{p(1-p)}{n}$$

where n is the sample size. Therefore we require that

$$\frac{p(1-p)}{n} \leq 0.001$$

or $n \geq 1000\, p(1-p)$ (1)

By differentiation we see that the maximum value of the right hand side occurs when $p = 1/2$ and then its value is 250. Thus if n is 250, condition (1) will always be satisfied and the variance will not exceed 0.0001.

10. A bag contains six balls numbered 1,2,3,4,5,6. Three of the balls are selected at random without replacement. Let

$$Z_1 = \frac{2X}{3} - 1$$

and $\quad Z_2 = 2Y - 1,$

where X,Y denote respectively the sum and mid-range of the numbers on the three selected balls. (The *mid-range* of a set of numbers is defined as the mean of the smallest and largest.) Derive the sampling distributions of X and Y and deduce that Z_1 and Z_2 are both unbiased estimators of the number of balls in the bag. Which is the more efficient estimator?

¶ There are $^6C_3$ = 20 possible combinations, each with probability 1/20. Simple enumeration of these leads to the following distributions for X and Y.

x	6	7	8	9	10	11	12	13	14	15
P_x	$\frac{1}{20}$	$\frac{1}{20}$	$\frac{2}{20}$	$\frac{3}{20}$	$\frac{3}{20}$	$\frac{3}{20}$	$\frac{3}{20}$	$\frac{2}{20}$	$\frac{1}{20}$	$\frac{1}{20}$

y	2	5/2	3	7/2	4	9/2	5
P_y	1/20	2/20	4/20	6/20	4/20	2/20	1/20

For example $P(X=9)$ = P (combination is 1,3,5 or 1,2,6 or 2,3,4)
$$= \frac{3}{20},$$

and $\quad P(Y=3)$ = P (combination is 1,2,5 or 1,3,5 or 1,4,5 or 2,3,4)
$$= 4/20.$$

Therefore $E(X) = 6 \times \frac{1}{20} + 7 \times \frac{1}{20} + \ldots + 15 \times \frac{1}{20} = 10.5$

and $\quad E(Y) = 2 \times \frac{1}{20} + \frac{5}{2} \times \frac{2}{20} + \ldots + 5 \times \frac{1}{20} = 3.5$.

It follows that
$$E(Z_1) = \frac{2}{3} E(X) - 1 = 6$$
$$\text{and} \quad E(Z_2) = 2E(Y) - 1 = 6$$

as required. To decide which is more efficient, we calculate their variances.

$$E(X^2) = 6^2 \times \frac{1}{20} + 7^2 \times \frac{1}{20} + \cdots + 15^2 \times \frac{1}{20} = 115.5$$

so that $Var(X) = 115.5 - 10.5^2 = 5.25$.

Therefore $Var(Z_1) = \frac{4}{9} Var(X) = 2.3\dot{3}$.

Similarly

$$E(Y^2) = 2^2 \times \frac{1}{20} + (\frac{5}{2})^2 \times \frac{2}{20} + \cdots + 5^2 \times \frac{1}{20} = 12.775$$

and $Var(Y) = 12.775 - 3.5^2 = 0.525$.

Therefore $Var(Z_2) = 4 Var(Y) = 2.1$.

Since $Var(Z_2) < Var(Z_1)$, Z_2 is more efficient.

11.   Show that if $X_1, X_2, \ldots, X_n$ is a random sample from a distribution having mean μ and variance σ^2, then

$$Y = \sum_{i=1}^{n} a_i X_i$$

is an unbiased estimator for μ provided $\sum_{i=1}^{n} a_i = 1$ and find an expression for $Var(Y)$.

In the case $n=4$, determine which of the following estimators are unbiased for μ:

(a) $Y_1 = (X_1 + X_2 + X_3 + X_4)/4$,

(b) $Y_2 = X_1 - X_2 + X_3 - X_4$,

(c) $Y_3 = (2X_1 + 3X_4)/5$,

(d) $Y_4 = (X_1 + X_3)/2$.

Which is the most efficient of those estimators which are unbiased?

¶
$$E(Y) = \sum_{i=1}^{n} E(a_i X_i)$$

$$= \sum_{i=1}^{n} a_i E(X_i) = \sum_{i=1}^{n} a_i \mu$$

$$= \mu \sum_{i=1}^{n} a_i.$$

Therefore Y is unbiased if $\sum_{i=1}^{n} a_i = 1$.

$$\text{Var}(Y) = \sum_{i=1}^{n} a_i^2 \, \text{Var}(X_i) = \sigma^2 \sum_{i=1}^{n} a_i^2.$$

Applying the criterion that $\sum_{i=1}^{n} a_i$ must be 1 for an unbiased estimator, we can see that Y_1, Y_3 and Y_4 are unbiased estimators. Using the formula just derived,

$$\text{Var}(Y_1) = \frac{\sigma^2}{4}, \qquad \text{Var}(Y_3) = \frac{13\sigma^2}{25}, \qquad \text{Var}(Y_4) = \frac{\sigma^2}{2}.$$

Therefore Y_1 is the most efficient of the unbiased estimators.

12. A symmetrical tetrahedral die, whose four faces are numbered 1,2,3 and 4, is tossed three times. Determine the distribution of (i) the mean score obtained, (ii) the mean of the smallest and largest scores obtained. Show that these two means are unbiased estimators for the expected score per throw and calculate the efficiency of the second relative to the first.

¶ Since there are 4 possible outcomes for each toss, there are $4^3 = 64$ possible results, each with probability 1/64. By enumerating these we can calculate the probability distributions of the mean score Y_1 and the mean Y_2 of the smallest and largest scores.

For example

$P(Y_1 = 1) = P$ (all scores are 1) $= 1/64$,

$P(Y_1 = 3) = P(3,3,3; 2,3,4; 3,2,4; 4,3,2; 4,2,3; 3,4,2; 2,4,3;$
$\qquad\qquad 1,4,4; 4,4,1; 4,1,4)$

$\qquad\quad = 10/64.$

We find that the distribution of Y_1 is

Y_1	1	4/3	5/3	2	7/3	8/3	3	10/3	11/3	4
prob	$\frac{1}{64}$	$\frac{3}{64}$	$\frac{6}{64}$	$\frac{10}{64}$	$\frac{12}{64}$	$\frac{12}{64}$	$\frac{10}{64}$	$\frac{6}{64}$	$\frac{3}{64}$	$\frac{1}{64}$

Similarly

$$P(Y_2=2) = P(1,1,3;1,3,1;3,1,1;1,3,3;3,1,3;3,3,1;$$
$$1,2,3;1,3,2;2,1,3;2,3,1;3,1,2;3,2,1;2,2,2)$$

$$= \frac{13}{64} ,$$

for example, and we find that Y_2 has the distribution

Y_2	1	3/2	2	5/2	3	7/2	4
prob	$\frac{1}{64}$	$\frac{6}{64}$	$\frac{13}{64}$	$\frac{24}{64}$	$\frac{13}{64}$	$\frac{6}{64}$	$\frac{1}{64}$

$$E(Y_1) = 1 \times \frac{1}{64} + \frac{4}{3} \times \frac{3}{64} + \ldots + 4 \times \frac{1}{64} = 5/2 ,$$

$$E(Y_2) = 1 \times \frac{1}{64} + \frac{3}{2} \times \frac{6}{64} + \ldots + 4 \times \frac{1}{64} = 5/2 .$$

Since the expected score μ per throw is given by

$$1 \times \frac{1}{4} + 2 \times \frac{1}{4} + 3 \times \frac{1}{4} + 4 \times \frac{1}{4} = 5/2 ,$$

Y_1 and Y_2 are unbiased estimators for μ.

$$E(Y_1^2) = 1^2 \times \frac{1}{64} + \left(\frac{4}{3}\right)^2 \times \frac{3}{64} + \ldots + 4^2 \times \frac{1}{64} = \frac{1280}{3 \times 64} = \frac{20}{3} ,$$

so that $\text{Var}(Y_1) = \frac{20}{3} - \left(\frac{5}{2}\right)^2 = 5/12$.

Similarly $E(Y_2^2) = 1^2 \times \frac{1}{64} + \left(\frac{3}{2}\right)^2 \times \frac{6}{64} + \ldots + 4^2 \times \frac{1}{64} = \frac{423}{64}$

so that $\text{Var}(Y_2) = \frac{423}{64} - \left(\frac{5}{2}\right)^2 = \frac{23}{64}$.

Hence the efficiency of Y_2 relative to Y_1 is

$$\frac{\text{Var}(Y_1)}{\text{Var}(Y_2)} = \frac{5}{12} \times \frac{64}{23} = \frac{80}{69} .$$

13. A coin when tossed has probability p of falling 'heads'. In
     order to estimate the probability θ of obtaining 2 heads in
     2 successive tosses the coin is tossed n times (n $\geqslant$ 2). If
     X heads are obtained, show that

$$\hat{\theta} = \frac{X(X-1)}{n(n-1)}$$

is an unbiased estimator for θ. Deduce an unbiased estimator
for the probability of obtaining 2 tails in 2 tosses of the
coin.

¶   The probability of obtaining 2 heads in 2 successive tosses
     is p^2. X is binomially distributed with parameters n and
     p. So

$$E(X) = np, \quad E(X^2) = Var(X) + (E(X))^2$$
$$= np(1-p) + n^2 p^2 .$$

Therefore

$$E(\hat{\theta}) = \frac{E(X^2)-E(X)}{n(n-1)} = \frac{np(1-p)+n^2 p^2 -np}{n(n-1)}$$

$$= p^2 \text{ as required.}$$

Since the number of tails obtained is n-X, an unbiased
estimate for the probability of obtaining 2 tails in
successive tosses is

$$\frac{(n-X)(n-X-1)}{n(n-1)} .$$

14. A physicist wants to estimate the volume v of a cuboid whose
     unequal edges are of lengths x, y and z. He can use either
     of the following two methods.

     (i)   Obtain a direct measurement V of the volume, using a
           procedure based on Archimedes' Principle. V can be
           regarded as a random variable having mean v and
           variance σ_1^2.

     (ii) Obtain measurements X, Y and Z of the unequal edges,
           and estimate the volume using

$$\hat{v} = XYZ$$

It may be assumed that X, Y and Z are independent random variables with respective means x, y and z and common variance σ_2^2.

Show that Method (ii) gives an unbiased estimate of the volume but that Method (i) is preferable to Method (ii) if

$$\sigma_1^2 < \sigma_2^6 + \sigma_2^4 (x^2+y^2+z^2) + \sigma_2^2 (x^2 y^2+x^2 z^2+y^2 z^2) .$$

¶ $E(\hat{v})$ = E(XYZ)

   = E(X)E(Y)E(Z)   (by independence)

   = xyz .

Thus $E(V) = E(\hat{v}) = v$ and both methods are unbiased.

$Var(\hat{v})$ = $E(\hat{v}^2) - (E(\hat{v}))^2$

   = $E(X^2 Y^2 Z^2) - v^2$

   = $E(X^2)E(Y^2)E(Z^2) - v^2$.

Now $E(X^2) = Var(X)+(E(X))^2 = \sigma_2^2 + x^2$

and similarly, $E(Y^2) = \sigma_2^2 + y^2$, $E(Z^2) = \sigma_2^2 + z^2$.

Thus

   $Var(\hat{v}) = (\sigma_2^2+x^2)(\sigma_2^2+y^2)(\sigma_2^2+z^2) - x^2 y^2 z^2$.

Thus Method (i) is preferable if $\sigma_1^2 < Var(\hat{v})$, that is if

$$\sigma_1^2 < (\sigma_2^2+x^2)(\sigma_2^2+y^2)(\sigma_2^2+z^2) - x^2 y^2 z^2 .$$

Expansion of the brackets leads to the required inequality.

15.   In the kinetic theory of gases a particle of mass m is assumed to have velocity V and kinetic energy $\frac{1}{2}mV^2$ where V is a random variable. If $\hat{\mu}$ is an unbiased estimator for $\mu=E(V)$, show that the bias of $\frac{1}{2}m\hat{\mu}^2$ as an estimator for the mean kinetic energy is given by

$$\frac{1}{2}m[Var(\hat{\mu}) - Var(V)] .$$

¶   The mean kinetic energy is

$$E(\tfrac{1}{2}mV^2) = \tfrac{1}{2}mE(V^2) \ .$$

$$
\begin{aligned}
E(\tfrac{1}{2}m\hat{\mu}^2) &= \tfrac{1}{2}m\ E(\hat{\mu}^2) \\
&= \tfrac{1}{2}m(Var(\hat{\mu})+[E(\hat{\mu})]^2) \\
&= \tfrac{1}{2}m(Var(\hat{\mu})+\mu^2) \text{ as } \hat{\mu} \text{ is unbiased.}
\end{aligned}
$$

The bias of $\tfrac{1}{2}m\hat{\mu}^2$ is

$$
\begin{aligned}
&E(\tfrac{1}{2}m\hat{\mu}^2) - E(\tfrac{1}{2}mV^2) \\
&= \tfrac{1}{2}m(Var(\hat{\mu})-\mu^2 - E(V^2)) \\
&= \tfrac{1}{2}m(Var(\hat{\mu})-\mu^2 - Var(V)+\mu^2) \text{ as } \mu = E(V) \\
&= \tfrac{1}{2}m(Var(\hat{\mu})-Var(V)).
\end{aligned}
$$

16.   The random variable X has a Poisson distribution with unknown mean λ, and it is required to estimate $\theta=\lambda^2$. If $X_1,X_2,\ldots,X_n$ is a random sample from the distribution of X, show that

$$\hat{\theta} = \frac{1}{n}\sum_{i=1}^{n}X_i^2 - \frac{1}{n}\sum_{i=1}^{n}X_i$$

is an unbiased estimator for λ^2.

¶   Since X has a Poisson distribution,

$$E(X_i) = Var(X_i) = \lambda,$$

and $E(X_i^2) = Var(X_i) +(E(X_i))^2 = \lambda+\lambda^2 \quad (i=1,2,\ldots,n) \ .$

So $E(\hat{\theta}) = \dfrac{1}{n}\sum_{i=1}^{n} E(X_i^2) - \dfrac{1}{n}\sum_{i=1}^{n}E(X_i)$

$$= \lambda+\lambda^2-\lambda = \lambda^2$$

as required.

17.   A library has an empty shelf 1.55 m long and has ordered 60 new books. The thicknesses, in centimetres, of 30 randomly selected books from current stock are as follows

        1.4, 3.2, 1.8, 2.0, 2.2, 1.7, 1.8, 2.5, 3.2, 1.4,
        1.4, 2.0, 2.3, 3.8, 1.8, 1.6, 2.5, 2.5, 2.5, 3.4,
        2.7, 2.6, 2.0, 1.7, 3.1, 5.0, 3.3, 3.1, 3.2, 2.9.

Estimate the probability that the new books will fit on the shelf. State any assumptions that you make.

¶   Let X_i be the thickness of the i-th book, i = 1,...,60. We assume that the X_i's are independent and identically distributed with mean μ and variance σ^2.

Let
$$T = \sum_{i=1}^{60} X_i$$

be the total thickness of the books.

We want to estimate p = P(T $\leq$ 155).

By the Central Limit Theorem, the distribution of T is approximately normally distributed with mean 60μ and variance $60\sigma^2$.

Thus $p \approx \Phi\left(\dfrac{155-60\mu}{\sigma\sqrt{60}}\right)$

As μ and σ are unknown, we replace them by estimates $\hat{\mu}$ and $\hat{\sigma}$ and estimate p using

$$\hat{p} = \Phi\left(\frac{155-60\hat{\mu}}{\hat{\sigma}\sqrt{60}}\right).$$

Using the sample mean and sample standard deviation as estimates, we find that

$$\hat{\mu} = 2.48\dot{6}$$
$$\hat{\sigma} = 0.82743 .$$

Therefore
$$\hat{p} = \Phi\left(\frac{155 - 60\times 2.48\dot{6}}{0.82743\sqrt{60}}\right)$$
$$= \Phi(0.90494)$$
$$= 0.81725.$$

18. In a cosmological study, a photograph of a section of the sky was taken. The photographic plate, of size 10 cm × 10 cm, is reproduced below with stars denoted by *.

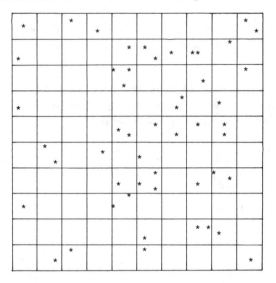

Estimate the mean number of stars per cm², and hence estimate the probability that a given centimetre square contains at least 1 star.

(Assume that the number of stars per unit area is Poisson distributed.)

¶   There are 51 stars shown on the plate. Since the area of this is 100 cm², the mean number of stars per cm² is estimated by 51/100 = 0.51.

The number of stars in a given centimetre square has a Poisson distribution with estimated mean 0.51.

Hence   P(at least 1 star) = 1−P(no stars)

$$= 1 - e^{-0.51}$$

$$= 0.3995.$$

Note that of the 100 squares, 37 contain at least one star. Thus an alternative estimate which does not make use of the

assumption that the number of stars per unit area has a
Poisson distribution is 37/100 = 0.37.

19. Circular discs, produced by a machine, have radii which are
    independent random variables, each with mean μ and variance
    σ^2.
    A random sample $R_1, R_2, \ldots, R_n$ of the radii of n discs is
    obtained. Show that $2\pi\bar{R}$ is an unbiased estimator for the
    mean circumference of a disc. Write down an expression for
    the mean area of a disc and find an unbiased estimator for it.

¶   The circumference of a disc is $2\pi R$, where R is the radius of
    the disc, and this has mean $2\pi\mu$.

$$E(2\pi\bar{R}) = 2\pi E(\bar{R}) = 2\pi E(R) = 2\pi\mu \text{ as required.}$$

Let A be the area of a disc.
Then $E(A) = \pi E(R^2)$
$\qquad\qquad = \pi(\text{Var}(R) + (E(R))^2)$
$\qquad\qquad = \pi(\sigma^2 + \mu^2)$.

Now $E(R_i^2) = E(R^2) = \sigma^2 + \mu^2$

and so $E(\frac{1}{n} \sum_{i=1}^{n} R_i^2) = \sigma^2 + \mu^2$.

Therefore $E(\frac{\pi}{n} \sum_{i=1}^{n} R_i^2) = \pi(\sigma^2 + \mu^2) = E(A)$

and $\frac{\pi}{n} \sum_{i=1}^{n} R_i^2$ is an unbiased estimator for the mean area.

20. A random variable X has probability density function

$$f(x) = kx^{\alpha-1}(1-x) \qquad \text{if } 0 \leqslant x \leqslant 1,$$
$$= 0 \qquad\qquad \text{otherwise,}$$

    where $\alpha > 0$ and k is a constant. Show that

    (i) $k = \alpha(\alpha+1)$,
    (ii) $E(X) = \frac{\alpha}{\alpha+2}$.

Use (ii) to obtain an estimator for α based on $\bar{X}$, the mean of a random sample of size n from the distribution of X.

¶   (i)   Since $\displaystyle\int_{-\infty}^{\infty} f(x)\ dx = 1$,

$$1 = \int_0^1 k\ x^{\alpha-1}\ (1-x)\ dx$$

$$= k \int_0^1 (x^{\alpha-1} - x^{\alpha})\ dx$$

$$= k \left[\frac{x^{\alpha}}{\alpha} - \frac{x^{\alpha+1}}{\alpha+1} \right]_0^1$$

$$= k\left(\frac{1}{\alpha} - \frac{1}{\alpha+1}\right) = \frac{k}{\alpha(\alpha+1)} \ .$$

Hence $k = \alpha(\alpha+1)$.

(ii) $\displaystyle E(X) = \int_0^1 x.kx^{\alpha-1}(1-x)\ dx$

$$= k \int_0^1 x^{\alpha} - x^{\alpha+1}\ dx$$

$$= \frac{k}{(\alpha+1)(\alpha+2)}$$

$$= \frac{\alpha}{\alpha+2} \text{ using the value of k found above.}$$

From (ii) $E(\bar{X}) = E(X) = \dfrac{\alpha}{\alpha+2}$.

Therefore $\bar{X}$ is an unbiased estimator for $\alpha/(\alpha+2)$.
A natural estimator for α is obtained by solving the equation

$$\bar{X} = \frac{\hat{\alpha}}{\hat{\alpha}+2}\ ,$$

leading to $\hat{\alpha} = \dfrac{2\bar{X}}{1-\bar{X}}$.

21.   The random variable X has probability density function

$$f(x) = \alpha(\alpha+1)x^{\alpha-1}(1-x) \quad \text{if } 0 \leqslant x \leqslant 1$$
$$= 0 \qquad\qquad\qquad\qquad \text{otherwise,}$$

where α is an unknown positive constant.

In order to estimate α, a random sample $X_1, X_2, \ldots, X_n$ is obtained from the distribution of X. Show that

$$\hat{\alpha} = \frac{1}{n} \sum_{i=1}^{n} Y_i$$

is an unbiased estimator for α, where $Y_i = X_i / (1 - X_i)$, $i = 1, 2, \ldots, n$.

¶   Let $Y = \dfrac{X}{1-X}$

Then $E(Y) = \displaystyle\int_0^1 \dfrac{x}{1-x} \cdot \alpha(\alpha+1) \, x^{\alpha-1} (1-x) \, dx$

$= \alpha(\alpha+1) \displaystyle\int_0^1 x^\alpha \, dx$

$= \alpha.$

Hence $E(Y_i) = \alpha$ for all i and so
$\quad\quad E(\hat{\alpha}) = \alpha.$

Thus $\hat{\alpha}$ is an unbiased estimator for α.

22.   The 30 fifth-formers in a boys school are timed over a
200 m sprint with the following results (measured in
minutes):

      0.74, 0.52, 0.63, 0.47, 0.56, 0.72, 0.92, 0.83, 0.64, 0.89
      0.38, 0.76, 0.64, 0.86, 0.68, 0.53, 0.62, 0.43, 0.61, 0.72
      0.81, 0.75, 0.76, 0.58, 0.91, 0.84, 0.55, 0.80, 0.71, 0.86

The sports master passes these times to the statistics teacher
who decided that it would be appropriate to assume that these
times constitute a random sample from the distribution with
probability density function

$$f(x) = \alpha(\alpha+1) x^{\alpha-1} (1-x) \quad \text{if } 0 \le x \le 1,$$
$$= 0 \quad\quad\quad\quad\quad\quad\quad\quad \text{otherwise,}$$

where α is an unknown parameter.

Use the methods of Exercises 20 and 21 to obtain two estimates of α. Construct a frequency table of the data using the intervals 0.30-0.39,...,0.90-0.99, and hence draw a relative frequency histogram. Draw the probability density curves corresponding to your two estimates of α and comment on your results.

¶ In the notation of Problems 20 and 21, we have two estimates for α, namely

$$\frac{2\bar{x}}{1-\bar{x}} \quad \text{and} \quad \frac{1}{30} \sum_{i=1}^{30} \frac{x_i}{1-x_i} \ .$$

We can calculate the average time taken from the data and we find that $\bar{x} = 0.690\overset{.}{6}$.

Hence one estimate of α is

$$\hat{\alpha}_1 = \frac{2 \times 0.690\overset{.}{6}}{1 - 0.690\overset{.}{6}} = 4.4655.$$

We can also calculate $x_i/(1-x_i)$ for each i and compute the second estimate; for example the first term is 0.74/0.26 i.e. 2.846.

We find that

$$\hat{\alpha}_2 = \frac{1}{30} \sum_{1}^{30} \frac{x_i}{1-x_i} = 3.3025 \ .$$

The frequency table is as follows

0.30-0.39	0.40-0.49	0.50-0.59	0.60-0.69	0.70-0.79	0.80-0.89	0.90-0.99
1	2	5	6	7	7	2

Below is shown a relative frequency histogram, together with the density functions

$$f_1(x) = \hat{\alpha}_1(\hat{\alpha}_1+1) \ x^{\hat{\alpha}_1-1} (1-x)$$

and

$$f_2(x) = \hat{\alpha}_2(\hat{\alpha}_2+1) \ x^{\hat{\alpha}_2-1} (1-x).$$

In the histogram, the heights are the relative frequency densities, that is the actual frequencies divided by the interval width, 0.1, and by the total sample size 30. Thus, for example, the height of the block corresponding to the class 0.6-0.69 is $\frac{6}{0.1 \times 30}$ = 2.

It is clear from the graph that the probability density function using $\hat{\alpha}_1$ is a much better fit to the histogram and this would appear to be the better estimate.

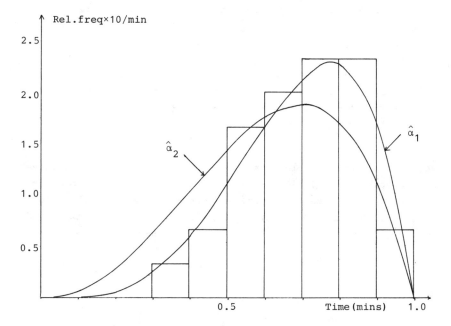

23. A sequence of n Bernoulli trials was carried out, each having probability p of success. A total of m successes was obtained. The probability of this event is

$$^n C_m \, p^m (1-p)^{n-m} \; .$$

Show that the value of p which maximises this probability is m/n.

¶   We find the value of p which maximises this probability by differentiating. Ignoring the term ^nC_m, which is constant, we obtain

$$mp^{m-1}(1-p)^{n-m} - (n-m)(1-p)^{n-m-1}p^m = 0$$

at a stationary point.
Thus

$$m(1-p) - (n-m)p = 0$$
$$\text{and } p = m/n.$$

The first derivative is clearly positive for p < m/n and negative for p > m/n and so this corresponds to a maximum.

This example illustrates the maximum likelihood method of estimation. We write down the probability of the actual outcome of an experiment in terms of the unknown parameter, θ say. We then choose as the estimate the value of θ which maximises this probability. So we maximise the probability of the event that has occurred.

24.   The random variable X takes the values 1,2,3 with respective probabilities θ, 2θ, $1-3\theta$ $(0 < \theta < 1/3)$. In order to estimate θ, n independent observations of X are taken. If the values 1,2,3 occur R_1, R_2, R_3 times respectively, show that the following estimators of θ are all unbiased:

$$\hat{\theta}_1 = \frac{R_1}{n},$$

$$\hat{\theta}_2 = \frac{R_2}{2n},$$

$$\hat{\theta}_3 = \frac{1}{3}\left[1 - \frac{R_3}{n}\right].$$

Show that, of the three estimators, $\hat{\theta}_3$ has the smallest variance for all permissible values of θ.

¶   Since each outcome is 1 with probability θ and not 1 with probability $1-\theta$, R_1 has a binomial distribution $B(n,\theta)$. Similarly, R_2 is $B(n,2\theta)$ and R_3 is $B(n,1-3\theta)$.

Therefore $E(R_1) = n\theta$, $E(R_2) = 2n\theta$, $E(R_3) = n(1-3\theta)$.

So $\quad E(\hat{\theta}_1) = \dfrac{1}{n} E(R_1) = \theta$,

$\quad\quad E(\hat{\theta}_2) = \dfrac{1}{2n} E(R_2) = \theta$

and $\quad E(\hat{\theta}_3) = \dfrac{1}{3} - \dfrac{1}{3n} E(R_3) = \theta$

and all are unbiased estimators for θ.

Now

$$\text{Var}(\hat{\theta}_1) = \dfrac{1}{n^2} \text{Var}(R_1) = \dfrac{1}{n^2} n\theta(1-\theta) = \dfrac{\theta(1-\theta)}{n} \,,$$

$$\text{Var}(\hat{\theta}_2) = \dfrac{1}{4n^2} \text{Var}(R_2) = \dfrac{1}{4n^2} n.2\theta.(1-2\theta) = \dfrac{\theta(1-2\theta)}{2n} \,,$$

$$\text{Var}(\hat{\theta}_3) = \dfrac{1}{9n^2} \text{Var}(R_3) = \dfrac{1}{9n^2} n.(1-3\theta).3\theta = \dfrac{\theta(1-3\theta)}{3n} \,.$$

So $\quad \dfrac{\text{Var}(\hat{\theta}_1)}{\text{Var}(\hat{\theta}_2)} = \dfrac{2(1-\theta)}{1-2\theta} > 1$,

and $\quad \dfrac{\text{Var}(\hat{\theta}_2)}{\text{Var}(\hat{\theta}_3)} = \dfrac{3(1-2\theta)}{2(1-3\theta)} = \dfrac{3-6\theta}{2-6\theta} > 1$.

Thus $\hat{\theta}_3$ has the smallest variance.

25. An amateur gardener wishes to estimate the proportion p
of marrow seeds that germinate when planted in seed compost.
He plants 12 seeds, and estimates p using

$$\hat{p}_1 = \dfrac{X}{12}\,,$$

where X denotes the number of seeds germinating. A friend,
who is a nurseryman, offers the following alternative
estimator based on past experience:

$$\hat{p}_2 = 0.8\,.$$

If the true value of p is 0.73, show that $\hat{p}_2$ has a smaller
mean square error than $\hat{p}_1$ and calculate the probability that
$\hat{p}_1$ actually gives a better estimate than $\hat{p}_2$.

Suppose now that the gardener decides to plant n seeds and estimates p using

$$\hat{p}_3 = \frac{X}{n} \ ,$$

where X has the same meaning as before. Find the smallest value of n for which $\hat{p}_3$ has a smaller mean square error than $\hat{p}_2$.

¶   X has a binomial distribution $B(12,p)$ and so $E(X) = 12p$, $Var(X) = 12p(1-p)$.

As $E(\hat{p}_1) = \frac{1}{12} E(X) = p$,

$\hat{p}_1$ is unbiased and

$$MSE(\hat{p}_1) = Var(\hat{p}_1) = \frac{1}{144} Var(X)$$
$$= \frac{p(1-p)}{12}$$

As the true value of p is 0.73,

$$MSE(\hat{p}_1) = \frac{0.73 \times 0.27}{12}$$
$$= 0.016425 \ .$$

Clearly $E(\hat{p}_2) = 0.8$, $Var(\hat{p}_2) = 0$

and $MSE(\hat{p}_2) = (bias(\hat{p}_2))^2$
$$= (0.8-0.73)^2$$
$$= 0.0049 < MSE(\hat{p}_1) \ .$$

$\hat{p}_1$ gives a better estimate if the difference between its estimate and the true value is less than 0.07, the error in $\hat{p}_2$. We therefore require

$$P(|\hat{p}_1 - 0.73| < 0.07) = P(0.66 < \hat{p}_1 < 0.80)$$
$$= P(0.66 < \frac{X}{12} < 0.80)$$
$$= P(7.92 < X < 9.6)$$

Since X is an integer-valued variable we require

$$P(8 \leq X \leq 9) = {}^{12}C_8 \; 0.73^8 \; 0.27^4 + {}^{12}C_9 \; 0.73^9 \; 0.27^3$$

$$= 0.46708,$$

as X has a binomial distribution B(12,0.73).

$\hat{p}_3$, like $\hat{p}_1$, is unbiased and

$$Var(\hat{p}_3) = \frac{0.73 \times 0.27}{n}$$

$$= MSE(\hat{p}_3)$$

For this to be less than that of $\hat{p}_2$,

$$\frac{0.73 \times 0.27}{n} < 0.0049$$

and   n > 40.22.

Thus the minimum value of n is 41.

26. The lifetime T of an electrical component has the probability density function

$$f(t) = \alpha^2 te^{-\alpha t} \qquad \text{if } t \geq 0,$$
$$= 0 \qquad \text{otherwise,}$$

where α is an unknown positive constant. Ten components were tested to destruction and the observed lifetimes, in hours, were

> 870.2, 502.9, 540.3, 62.5, 589.8,
> 351.4, 369.9, 83.0, 1248.5, 322.2.

Show that the expected value of T is twice the mode and hence find an unbiased estimate of the most likely value of T. What is the estimated standard error of the estimator?

¶ $E(T) = \displaystyle\int_0^\infty \alpha^2 \; t^2 \; e^{-\alpha t} \; dt$

$\qquad = [-\alpha t^2 \; e^{-\alpha t}]_0^\infty + 2\alpha \displaystyle\int_0^\infty t \; e^{-\alpha t} \; dt$

$\qquad = 2[-t \; e^{-\alpha t}]_0^\infty + 2 \displaystyle\int_0^\infty e^{-\alpha t} \; dt$

$$= 2[- \frac{1}{\alpha} e^{-\alpha t}]_0^\infty$$

$$= \frac{2}{\alpha} .$$

The mode is the value of t which maximises $\alpha^2 t e^{-\alpha t}$.
Differentiating, $\alpha^2 e^{-\alpha t} - \alpha^3 t e^{-\alpha t} = 0$
at a stationary point. The solution is

$$t = \frac{1}{\alpha}$$

and this clearly corresponds to a maximum.

Thus the mode is $\frac{1}{\alpha}$ and the expected value, $\frac{2}{\alpha}$, is twice
the mode.

The sample mean is $\bar{t}$ = 494.07 hrs and this estimates the
true mean, $\frac{2}{\alpha}$.

Hence $\qquad \frac{2}{\alpha} \approx$ 494.07

and $\qquad \alpha \approx \frac{2}{494.07}$ = 0.004048 .

The estimate of the mode will be half of that of the mean,
namely 247.035 hrs.

The variance of the sample mean is σ^2/n, where σ^2 is the
variance of the distribution. Now

$$E(T^2) = \int_0^\infty \alpha^2 t^3 e^{-\alpha t} dt$$

$$= [-\alpha t^3 e^{-\alpha t}]_0^\infty + 3 \int_0^\infty \alpha t^2 e^{-\alpha t} dt$$

$$= \frac{3}{\alpha} \int_0^\infty \alpha^2 t^2 e^{-\alpha t} dt$$

$$= \frac{6}{\alpha^2} \text{ using the result for } E(T).$$

Hence Var(T) $= \frac{6}{\alpha^2} - (\frac{2}{\alpha})^2 = \frac{2}{\alpha^2}$.

This is estimated by $\frac{2}{0.004048^2}$ = 122052.6 .

Hence the estimate of $\frac{\sigma^2}{n}$ is 12205.26, as n = 10, and the estimated standard error is $\sqrt{12205.26}$ = 110.477.

Since the mode is half the mean, its estimator is half that of the mean, and so its standard error is half that of the sample mean. The estimated standard error is thus

$$\frac{1}{2} \times 110.477 = 55.239 \text{ hours.}$$

27. The time that a customer has to wait for service in a restaurant has the probability density function

$$f(x) = \frac{3\theta^3}{(x+\theta)^4} \quad \text{if } x \geq 0,$$
$$= 0 \qquad \text{otherwise,}$$

where θ is an unknown positive constant. Let $X_1, X_2, \ldots X_n$ denote a random sample from this distribution. Show that

$$\hat{\theta} = \frac{2}{n} \sum_{i=1}^{n} X_i$$

is an unbiased estimator for θ. Find the standard error of $\hat{\theta}$ and deduce that $\hat{\theta}$ is a consistent estimator of θ.

¶ The mean of the distribution is

$$E(X) = \int_0^\infty \frac{3\theta^3 x}{(x+\theta)^4} \, dx$$

$$= 3\theta^3 \int_\theta^\infty \frac{y-\theta}{y^4} \, dy \qquad \text{where } y = x+\theta$$

$$= 3\theta^3 \left[-\frac{1}{2y^2} + \frac{\theta}{3y^3} \right]_\theta^\infty$$

$$= 3\theta^3 \left(\frac{1}{2\theta^2} - \frac{1}{3\theta^2} \right) = \theta/2.$$

Hence $\quad E(X_i) = \theta/2, \quad i = 1, 2, \ldots, n,$

and $\quad E(\hat{\theta}) = \theta.$

Thus $\hat{\theta}$ is an unbiased estimator for θ.

$$E(X^2) = \int_0^\infty \frac{3\theta^3 x^2}{(x+\theta)^4}\, dx = 3\theta^3 \int_\theta^\infty \frac{(y-\theta)^2}{y^4}\, dy$$

$$= 3\theta^3 \left[-\frac{1}{y} + \frac{\theta}{y^2} - \frac{\theta^2}{3y^3} \right]_\theta^\infty$$

$$= \theta^2 .$$

So $\quad \mathrm{Var}(X) = \theta^2 - \left(\frac{\theta}{2}\right)^2 = \frac{3\theta^2}{4}$.

Hence $\mathrm{Var}(\hat\theta) = 4\,\mathrm{Var}(\bar X) = \dfrac{3\theta^2}{n}$

and $\quad SE(\hat\theta) = \sqrt{\dfrac{3}{n}}\ \theta$.

Since $\hat\theta$ is unbiased and has a variance which tends to zero as n tends to infinity, $\hat\theta$ is consistent.

28. Electrical components of a certain type have life lengths which are exponentially distributed with mean μ. The n members of a random sample are tested simultaneously, their life lengths being $X_1, X_2, \ldots, X_n$. Let W be the time until the first component fails. Show that W has the probability density function

$$h(w) = \frac{n}{\mu}\, e^{-nw/\mu} \qquad \text{if } w \geq 0,$$

$$= 0 \qquad\qquad \text{otherwise,}$$

and deduce that nW is an unbiased estimator for μ.

Suppose that when 50 components are tested, the first failure occurs after 26.4 hours and that the average life length is 1342 hours. Two estimates of μ are 50×26.4 and 1342. Which would you prefer?

¶ $\quad W = \min(X_1, X_2, \ldots, X_n)$.

$P(W \geq w) = P(\text{each } X_i \geq w)$

$\qquad\qquad = (P(X_i \geq w))^n$ by independence.

Now $\quad P(X_i \geqslant w) = \displaystyle\int_w^\infty \frac{1}{\mu} e^{-\frac{x}{\mu}} dx$, as μ is the mean of X,

$$= [-e^{-x/\mu}]_w^\infty$$

$$= e^{-w/\mu}, \quad w \geqslant 0.$$

Hence $P(W \geqslant w) = e^{-nw/\mu}$.

The probability density function of W is therefore

$$- \frac{d}{dw} (e^{-nw/\mu}) = \frac{n}{\mu} e^{-nw/\mu}, \ w \geqslant 0.$$

This is an exponential distribution with mean μ/n.

Therefore $\quad E(nW) = n \times \dfrac{\mu}{n} = \mu$

and nW is an unbiased estimator for μ.

Since the sample mean gives an unbiased estimate of μ, 1342 is an unbiased estimate. Similarly, as 26.4 is the observed value of W, 50×26.4 = 1320 is another unbiased estimate.

Now $\quad \text{Var}(\bar{X}) = \dfrac{1}{50} \text{Var}(X) = \dfrac{\mu^2}{50}$

as the variance of an exponential distribution is the square of the mean.

Also $\quad \text{Var}(nW) = n^2 \, \text{Var}(W) = n^2 \cdot \dfrac{\mu^2}{n^2} = \mu^2 .$

Therefore nW has a much larger variance than $\bar{X}$ and so the estimate 1342, based on $\bar{X}$, is preferable.

29. A set of Christmas tree lights has 20 bulbs. The bulbs are connected in series so that the lights go out if one bulb fails. The lifetime T of a randomly selected bulb has probability density function

$$f(t) = \lambda e^{-\lambda t} \qquad \text{if } t \geqslant 0,$$
$$= 0 \qquad\qquad \text{otherwise.}$$

The times until failure, in days, of ten sets of lights of the above type were

10.8, 64.7, 66.4, 5.5, 14.6, 9.1, 14.3, 24.7, 58.5, 1.2.

Use these data to estimate λ.

¶ The time until failure of a set of lights is the time until
the first bulb fails. If the lifetimes of the bulbs are
$T_1, \ldots, T_{20}$ then the time until failure is

$$W = \min(T_1, \ldots, T_{20}).$$

Following the result of the previous exercise, W has an
exponential distribution with parameter 20λ.

The 10 sample values of W have a mean of 26.98 and this is
an estimate of $\frac{1}{20\lambda}$, the mean of W.

Therefore an estimate of λ is

$$\hat{\lambda} = \frac{1}{20 \times 26.98}$$

$$= 0.0018532.$$

30. A production process produces bags of sugar, each nominally
containing 1 kg. Past experience shows that the actual amount
contained, X, is a normally distributed random variable with
standard deviation 3 grams. When a bag is tested it is
rejected if it is found to contain less than 992 grams. An
estimate of the probability p that a randomly selected bag
is rejected is required. A random sample of 20 bags gave
a mean mass of 998.5 grams. Find an estimate for p.

¶ p = P(a bag is rejected)
= P(X < 992).

Now X has a normal distribution $N(\mu, 9)$, where μ is the mean.
Hence

$$p = \Phi\left(\frac{992 - \mu}{3}\right) \ .$$

Now we can estimate p by inserting an estimate of μ in this
equation, that is

$$\hat{p} = \Phi\left(\frac{992 - \hat{\mu}}{3}\right) \ .$$

The mean of 20 bags was 998.5 and this is $\hat{\mu}$.

Hence

$$\hat{p} = \Phi\left(\frac{992-998.5}{3}\right) = \Phi\left(-\frac{6.5}{3}\right)$$
$$= 1-\Phi(2.1\dot{6})$$
$$= 1-0.98487$$
$$= 0.01513.$$

31. Consider the integral

$$I = \int_0^1 g(x)\ dx$$

for some function $g(X)$. Let $U_1, U_2, \ldots, U_n$ be a random sample from a uniform distribution on $[0,1]$ and let

$$\hat{I} = \frac{1}{n} \sum_{i=1}^{n} g(U_i).$$

Show that $\hat{I}$ is an unbiased estimator for I.

Estimate

$$\int_0^1 e^{-\frac{1}{2}x^2}\ dx,$$

using a random sample of size 15. Compare your answer with the true value, calculated from tables of the normal distribution.

¶   For $i = 1, 2, \ldots, n$,

$$E(g(U_i)) = \int_0^1 g(u)\cdot1\,du$$
$$= I$$

as U_i has probability density function

$$g(u) = 1, \qquad 0 \leqslant u \leqslant 1,$$
$$= 0 \qquad \text{otherwise.}$$

Thus $E(\hat{I}) = \frac{1}{n} \times nI = I$, and $\hat{I}$ is an unbiased estimator for I.

Consider $\quad I = \int_0^1 e^{-\frac{1}{2}x^2}\ dx.$

Now $\dfrac{I}{\sqrt{2\pi}} = \dfrac{1}{\sqrt{2\pi}} \displaystyle\int_0^1 e^{-\frac{1}{2}x^2}\ dx = \Phi(1) - \Phi(0)$
$$= 0.34134$$

and so $\qquad\qquad\qquad I = 0.8556.$

Using the set of random digits given in Table 11, we obtain the following 15 values $u_1,\ldots,u_{15}$, taking the 6-th column.

0.32750, 0.84788, 0.22119, 0.31757, 0.63380, 0.99643, 0.96744,
0.16851, 0.81859, 0.28427, 0.95136, 0.32329, 0.74296, 0.66153, 0.28452.

The corresponding values of $g(u_i) = e^{-\frac{1}{2}u_i^2}$ are

0.94778, 0.69806, 0.97583, 0.95082, 0.81803, 0.60870, 0.62627,
0.98590, 0.71531, 0.96040, 0.63601, 0.94908, 0.75882, 0.80347, 0.96033.

The average of these is 0.82632 and this is the value of $\hat{I}$. The agreement is fairly close and within the limits of sampling error. It is possible to derive more efficient methods, which lead to more accurate estimates, but this is the basis of most methods of estimation of definite integrals.

32. $\hat{\theta}_1$ and $\hat{\theta}_2$ are independent unbiased estimators for an unknown parameter θ, with respective variances of σ_1^2 and σ_2^2. Show that

$$\hat{\theta}_3 = \lambda\hat{\theta}_1 + (1-\lambda)\,\hat{\theta}_2$$

is also unbiased for all values of λ. Calculate the variance of $\hat{\theta}_3$ and show that the value of λ which minimises it is

$$\lambda = \frac{\sigma_2^2}{\sigma_1^2 + \sigma_2^2}\ .$$

(i)   Let $\bar{X}_1$ and $\bar{X}_2$ be the means of two independent random samples of sizes n_1 and n_2 from the distributions $N(\mu,\sigma_1^2)$ and $N(\mu,\sigma_2^2)$ respectively, where the values of σ_1^2 and σ_2^2 are known. Find the value of λ which minimises the variance of the estimator

$$\hat{\mu} = \lambda\bar{X}_1 + (1-\lambda)\bar{X}_2.$$

(ii) Let S_1 and S_2 be the standard deviations of two independent random samples of sizes n_1 and n_2 from the distributions $N(\mu_1,\sigma^2)$ and $N(\mu_2,\sigma^2)$ respectively. Find the value of λ which minimises the variance of the estimator

$$\sigma^2 = \lambda S_1^2 + (1-\lambda)S_2^2\ .$$

(It may be assumed that if S^2 is the variance of a random sample of size n from the distribution $N(\mu,\sigma^2)$ then

$$\mathrm{Var}(S^2) = \frac{2\sigma^4}{n-1}\ .)$$

¶ $E(\hat{\theta}_3) = \lambda E(\hat{\theta}_1) + (1-\lambda)E(\hat{\theta}_2)$

$\qquad = \lambda\theta + (1-\lambda)\theta$

$\qquad = \theta$

and $\hat{\theta}_3$ is unbiased for θ.

$Var(\hat{\theta}_3) = \lambda^2 Var(\hat{\theta}_1) + (1-\lambda)^2 Var(\hat{\theta}_3)$

$\qquad = \lambda^2\sigma_1^2 + (1-\lambda)^2\sigma_2^2.$

Differentiating, we see that at a stationary point

$\qquad 2\lambda\sigma_1^2 - 2(1-\lambda)\sigma_2^2 = 0$

and $\qquad\qquad\qquad \lambda = \dfrac{\sigma_2^2}{\sigma_1^2+\sigma_2^2}$.

Differentiating again, we obtain $2\sigma_1^2 + 2\sigma_2^2 > 0$ so that this is indeed the minimising value of λ.

(i) $\bar{X}_1$ and $\bar{X}_2$ are both unbiased estimators for μ, with variances $\dfrac{\sigma_1^2}{n_1}$ and $\dfrac{\sigma_2^2}{n_2}$ respectively.

The value of λ which minimises the variance of $\hat{\mu}$ is thus

$$\frac{\sigma_2^2/n_2}{\sigma_1^2/n_1+\sigma_2^2/n_2} = \frac{n_1\sigma_2^2}{n_2\sigma_1^2+n_1\sigma_2^2}$$

(ii) S_1^2 and S_2^2 are unbiased estimators of σ^2, with variances $\dfrac{2\sigma^4}{n_1-1}$ and $\dfrac{2\sigma^4}{n_2-1}$ respectively. The minimising value of λ is therefore

$$\frac{2\sigma^4/(n_2-1)}{2\sigma^4/(n_1-1)+2\sigma^4/(n_2-1)} = \frac{n_1-1}{n_1+n_2-2}$$

33. A cell contains spherical grains which are of equal but unknown diameter d. A section of the cell is observed under a microscope and is found to contain circular sections of n grains. It may be assumed that the diameters $X_1, X_2, \ldots, X_n$ of these sections constitute a random sample from the uniform distribution defined on the interval $[0,d]$. If

$$Z = \max(X_1, X_2, \ldots, X_n),$$

find the value of k such that

$$Y = kZ$$

is an unbiased estimator for d. Show further that Y over-estimates d with approximate probability $1-e^{-1}$ for large n.

¶ $P(Z \leq z)$ $= $ $P(\max (X_i) \leq z)$

                 $= $ $P(X_i \leq z$ for $i = 1,\ldots,n)$

                 $= $ $P(X_1 \leq z)P(X_2 \leq z)\ldots P(X_n \leq z)$ by independence

                 $= $ $(P(X \leq z))^n,$

where X has a uniform distribution on $[0,d]$.

Now $P(X \leq z) = z/d$

and $P(Z \leq z) = (z/d)^n.$ (1)

Differentiating, we find that Z has probability density function

$$g(z) = \frac{nz^{n-1}}{d^n}, \qquad 0 \leq z \leq d.$$

So $E(Z) = \displaystyle\int_0^d \frac{nz^n}{d^n} \, dz$

                   $= \dfrac{nd}{n+1}.$

Thus $E(Y) = kE(Z) = \dfrac{kn}{n+1} \cdot d$

and so if $k = \dfrac{n+1}{n}$, then Y is an unbiased estimator for d.

$$P(Y > d) = P(\tfrac{n+1}{n} Z > d)$$

$$= P(Z > \tfrac{n}{n+1} d)$$

$$= 1-P(Z \leq \tfrac{nd}{n+1})$$

$$= 1 - (\tfrac{n}{n+1})^n \qquad \text{by (1)}.$$

Now $(1 + \tfrac{1}{n})^n \approx e$ and so $(\tfrac{n}{n+1})^n \approx e^{-1}.$

Hence Y overestimates with probability approximately $1-e^{-1}.$

34.   If an event A occurs with probability p, then the 'odds against A' are defined by the ratio $(1-p)/p$. In order to estimate the odds against scoring a six with a biased die, a gambler decides to carry on throwing it until he obtains a fixed number s of

sixes. In the process he obtains X scores which are not sixes. Find the probability function of X and show that X/s is an unbiased estimator for the odds against scoring a six.

(Hint:

$$\sum_{x=0}^{\infty} {}^{n+x}C_x a^x = (1-a)^{-(n+1)} .)$$

¶ For X to have the value x, there must be x 'not sixes' in the first x+s-1 throws, followed by a six.

If p is the probability of scoring a six, then the probability of this is

$${}^{x+s-1}C_x (1-p)^x p^{s-1} .p$$

Hence $\quad P(X=x) = {}^{x+s-1}C_x p^s (1-p)^x .$

Then $\quad E(X) = \displaystyle\sum_{x=0}^{\infty} x.{}^{x+s-1}C_x p^s (1-p)^x$

$$= p^s \sum_{x=1}^{\infty} x \frac{(x+s-1)!}{(s-1)!x!} (1-p)^x$$

$$= p^s \sum_{x=1}^{\infty} \frac{(x+s-1)!}{(s-1)!(x-1)!} (1-p)^x$$

Let y = x-1. Then

$$E(X) = (1-p)s \; p^s \sum_{y=0}^{\infty} {}^{y+s}C_y (1-p)^y$$

$$= (1-p)s \; p^s (1-(1-p))^{-s-1}$$

$$= s \frac{(1-p)}{p} .$$

Therefore $E(\frac{X}{s}) = \dfrac{1-p}{p}$ as required.

35. The probability that an event A occurs at any given trial is constant and equal to p. Four independent trials are carried out and the random variables X_1, X_2, X_3 are defined as follows:

$\quad X_i = 1 \quad$ if A occurs on both the ith and (i+1)th trials,
$\qquad = 0 \quad$ otherwise. $\qquad$ (i = 1,2,3).

Show that

$$Y = \frac{X_1 + X_2 + X_3}{3}$$

is an unbiased estimator for p^2 and find its standard error.

¶ Clearly $P(X_i = 1) = P$ (A occurs on successive trials)

$$= p^2$$

and so $E(X_i) = 1.p^2 + 0.(1-p^2) = p^2$.

Hence $E(Y) = \frac{1}{3}(p^2 + p^2 + p^2) = p^2$

and Y is unbiased for p^2.

Using the result of Miscellaneous Problem 39(i), Chapter 5,

$$\text{Var}(Y) = \frac{1}{9}(\text{Var}(X_1) + \text{Var}(X_2) + \text{Var}(X_3) + 2\ \text{Cov}(X_1, X_2)$$

$$+ 2\ \text{Cov}(X_1, X_3) + 2\ \text{Cov}(X_2, X_3)).$$

Now $E(X_i^2) = 1^2 \times p^2 = p^2$

so that $\text{Var}(X_i) = p^2 - p^4 = p^2(1-p^2)$ $(i=1,2,3)$.

Also $\text{Cov}(X_1, X_3) = 0$,

since X_1 depends on the first two trials only and X_3 on the third and fourth trials only.

Furthermore $\text{Cov}(X_1, X_2) = E(X_1 X_2) - E(X_1)E(X_2)$

$$E(X_1\ X_2) = 1.P(X_1 = 1,\ X_2 = 1)$$

$$= P(\text{A occurs at trials 1, 2 and 3})$$

$$= p^3$$

so that $\text{Cov}(X_1, X_2) = p^3 - p^4 = p^3(1-p)$.

Similarly $\text{Cov}(X_2, X_3) = p^3(1-p)$.

Therefore $\text{Var}(Y) = \frac{1}{9}(3p^2(1-p^2) + 4p^3(1-p))$

$$= \frac{1}{9} p^2(1-p)(3(1+p) + 4p)$$

$$= \frac{1}{9} p^2(1-p)(3+7p)$$

and the standard error is

$$\frac{1}{3} p\sqrt{(1-p)(3+7p)}.$$

36. A bag contains n balls numbered 1,2,...,n, where n is unknown. In order to estimate n, two balls are selected at random with replacement. If the numbers on the two balls are X_1 and X_2, show that X_1+X_2-1 is an unbiased estimator for n and find an expression for its variance.

Let $Z = \max(X_1, X_2)$. Show that Z has the probability function

$$p_z = \frac{2z-1}{n^2} \ , \ z = 1,2,...,n.$$

Also show that if n is large, 3Z/2 is approximately unbiased for estimating n, with variance approximately $n^2/8$.

Which estimator is preferable for large n?

¶ For i = 1,2

$$P(X_i = x) = \frac{1}{n}, \ x = 1,2,...,n.$$

So
$$E(X_i) = \sum_{x=1}^{n} \frac{x}{n}$$
$$= \frac{1}{n} \cdot \frac{n}{2}(n+1) = (n+1)/2 \ .$$

Therefore $E(X_1+X_2-1) = n+1-1 = n$ as required.

$$E(X_1^2) = \sum_{x=1}^{n} \frac{x^2}{n} = \frac{1}{n} \cdot \frac{n}{6}(n+1)(2n+1)$$
$$= \frac{(n+1)(2n+1)}{6} \ .$$

Thus
$$Var(X_1) = \frac{(n+1)(2n+1)}{6} - \left(\frac{n+1}{2}\right)^2$$
$$= \frac{n+1}{12}(4n+2 - 3n-3)$$
$$= \frac{n^2-1}{12} \ .$$

Therefore $Var(X_1+X_2-1) = Var(X_1)+Var(X_2)$
$$= \frac{n^2-1}{6} \ .$$

Consider now $Z = \max(X_1, X_2)$ and let z be an integer between 1 and n.

$$P(Z \leq z) = P(X_1 \leq z, X_2 \leq z)$$
$$= P(X_1 \leq z) \, P(X_2 \leq z)$$
$$= \left(\frac{z}{n}\right)^2,$$

since $P(X_1 \leq z) = P(X_2 \leq z) = z/n$.

Therefore $P(Z=z) = P(Z \leq z) - P(Z \leq z-1)$

$$= \left(\frac{z}{n}\right)^2 - \left(\frac{z-1}{n}\right)^2$$

$$= \frac{2z-1}{n^2} .$$

Now $E(Z) = \sum_{z=1}^{n} z \, \frac{(2z-1)}{n^2}$

$$= \frac{2}{n^2} \sum_{1}^{n} z^2 - \frac{1}{n^2} \sum_{1}^{n} z$$

$$= \frac{2}{n^2} \cdot \frac{n}{6} (n+1)(2n+1) - \frac{1}{n^2} \, \frac{n}{2} (n+1)$$

$$= \frac{(n+1)(2n+1)}{3n} - \frac{n+1}{2n}$$

$$= \frac{n+1}{6n} (4n-1).$$

Thus $E\left(\frac{3}{2} Z\right) = \frac{n+1}{4n} (4n-1) = \frac{n}{4} \left(1 + \frac{1}{n}\right)\left(4 - \frac{1}{n}\right) \approx n$ for large n.

$$E(Z^2) = \sum_{z=1}^{n} z^2 \, \frac{(2z-1)}{n^2}$$

$$= \frac{2}{n^2} \sum_{1}^{n} z^3 - \frac{1}{n^2} \sum_{1}^{n} z^2$$

$$= \frac{2}{n^2} \frac{n^2}{4} (n+1)^2 - \frac{1}{n^2} \cdot \frac{n}{6} (n+1)(2n+1)$$

$$= \frac{(n+1)}{6n} (3n(n+1)-(2n+1))$$

$$= \frac{(n+1)(3n^2+n-1)}{6n} .$$

Therefore $E\left(\left[\frac{3}{2} Z\right]^2\right) = \frac{3(n+1)}{8n} (3n^2+n-1)$

and $Var\left(\frac{3Z}{2}\right) = \frac{3(n+1)}{8n} (3n^2+n-1) - \left(E\left(\frac{3}{2}Z\right)\right)^2.$

If n is large we can obtain an approximate expression by considering only the highest powers of n.

Thus $\mathrm{Var}(\frac{3Z}{2}) \approx \frac{9n^2}{8} - n^2 = \frac{n^2}{8}$.

For large n,

$$\frac{\mathrm{Var}(3Z/2)}{\mathrm{Var}(X_1 + X_2 - 1)} \approx \frac{n^2/8}{(n^2-1)/6} \approx \frac{3}{4} < 1$$

and $\frac{3}{2} Z$ is preferable to $X_1 + X_2 - 1$.

37. A city has n taxis numbered $1, 2, \ldots, n$. A boy spots ten taxis with the following numbers

$$25, \ 93, \ 305, \ 201, \ 94, \ 127, \ 3, \ 252, \ 169, \ 21.$$

What is the probability of observing these particular taxis assuming that they are a random sample with replacement from the population of the city's taxis? Estimate n by finding the value which maximises this probability.

¶   Let X be the number of a taxi observed by the boy. Then

$$P(X=x) = \frac{1}{n}, \quad x = 1, 2, \ldots, n$$
$$= 0 \quad \text{otherwise.}$$

So the probability of any set of 10 numbers being observed is $(\frac{1}{n})^{10}$, provided all the numbers lie between 1 and n.

So the probability of his sample is

$\qquad (\frac{1}{n})^{10}$ if $n \geq$ all observed numbers,

$\qquad 0$ otherwise

i.e. $\qquad (\frac{1}{n})^{10}$ if $n \geq 305$,

$\qquad 0$ if $n < 305$.

This probability is maximised by making n as small as possible, subject to the constraint that $n \geq 305$.

Therefore it is maximised by n = 305 and this is the estimate of n.

This will be a biased estimate; it can never over-estimate n and may well under-estimate it.

Problem 33 deals with the continuous analogue of this and there we had to multiply the maximum sample value by $\frac{n+1}{n}$ to obtain an unbiased estimate. In the discrete case this will lead to an approximately unbiased estimate (see Problem 36 for the case n = 2).

38. Let $X_1, X_2, \ldots, X_n$ be a random sample from a uniform distribution on $[0, \theta]$ and consider the three unbiased estimators for θ

$$\hat{\theta}_1 = 2\bar{X}, \quad \hat{\theta}_2 = \frac{(n+1)Z}{n}, \quad \hat{\theta}_3 = (n+1)W,$$

where Z and W denote the sample maximum and sample minimum respectively. For i = 1,2,3, find the probability that $\hat{\theta}_i$ gives an estimate of θ within 10% of the true value if (a) n = 10, (b) n = 25.

¶ The uniform distribution on $[0, \theta]$ has mean $\theta/2$ and variance $\theta^2/12$.

Therefore

$$E(2\bar{X}) = 2.\theta/2 = \theta,$$
$$\text{Var}(2\bar{X}) = 4 \text{Var}(\bar{X}) = \frac{4}{n} \cdot \frac{\theta^2}{12} = \frac{\theta^2}{3n} \cdot$$

Now Z has probability density function

$$g(z) = \frac{nz^{n-1}}{\theta^n}, \quad 0 \leq z \leq \theta \quad \text{(see page 213, Volume 2)}$$

and W has probability density function

$$h(w) = \frac{n}{\theta^n} (\theta-w)^{n-1}, \quad 0 \leq w \leq \theta$$

(see also Example 7.7, Volume 2).

We require the probability that $\hat{\theta}_i$ lies within 10% of θ, that is

$$P(|\hat{\theta}_i - \theta| < \frac{\theta}{10}) = P(0.9\theta \leq \hat{\theta}_i \leq 1.1\theta).$$

<u>i=1</u>   We do not know the probability density function of $\hat{\theta}_1$ but we can use the Central Limit Theorem to find an approximation to the required probability.

By the Central Limit Theorem, $\bar{X}$ is approximately $N(\frac{\theta}{2}, \frac{\theta^2}{12n})$ and so $2\bar{X}$ is approximately $N(\theta, \frac{\theta^2}{3n})$.

Therefore

$$P(0.9\theta \leq 2\bar{X} \leq 1.1\theta) \approx \Phi(\frac{1.1\theta-\theta}{\theta/\sqrt{3n}}) - \Phi(\frac{0.9\theta-\theta}{\theta/\sqrt{3n}})$$

$$= 2\Phi(\frac{\sqrt{3n}}{10}) - 1.$$

(a)   If n = 10, this is 0.41611.

(b)   If n = 25, it is 0.61352.

<u>i=2</u> $P(0.9\theta \leq \frac{n+1}{n} Z \leq 1.1\theta) = P(\frac{0.9n}{n+1} \theta \leq Z \leq \frac{1.1n}{n+1} \theta)$

Now Z has cumulative distribution function

$$F(z) = (\frac{z}{\theta})^n \quad \text{if } 0 \leq z \leq \theta,$$

$$= 1 \quad \text{if } z > \theta.$$

Hence the probability is

$$(\frac{1.1n}{n+1})^n - (\frac{0.9n}{n+1})^n \quad \text{provided } \frac{1.1n\theta}{n+1} \leq \theta$$

and $1 - (\frac{0.9n}{n+1})^n \quad \text{if} \quad \frac{1.1n\theta}{n+1} > \theta.$

(a)   n = 10. The probability is $1 - (\frac{9}{11})^{10} = 0.86557$

(b)   n = 25. The probability is

$$1 - (\frac{0.9 \times 25}{26})^{25} \quad \text{since } \frac{1.1 \times 25}{26} \theta > \theta$$

$$= 0.97397 .$$

<u>i=3</u> $P(0.9\theta \leq (n+1) W \leq 1.1\theta) = P(W \geq \frac{0.9\theta}{n+1}) - P(W \geq \frac{1.1\theta}{n+1}).$

Now $P(W \geq w) = (\frac{\theta-w}{\theta})^n$

Hence $P(0.9\theta \leq (n+1) W \leq 1.1\theta) = (1 - \frac{0.9}{n+1})^n - (1 - \frac{1.1}{n+1})^n.$

(a)   n = 10. The probability is 0.07720.

(b)   n = 25. The probability is 0.07513.

The results are summarised below

	$\hat{\theta}_1$	$\hat{\theta}_2$	$\hat{\theta}_3$
n = 10	0.41611	0.86557	0.07720
n = 25	0.61352	0.97307	0.07513

If the calculations are repeated for n = 100, we obtain

n = 100	0.91674	0.99999	0.07406

It is clear that $\hat{\theta}_2$ is the best and $\hat{\theta}_3$ the worst.
As $n \to \infty$, the first two probabilities $\to 1$, though $\hat{\theta}_1 \to 1$
much more slowly than $\hat{\theta}_2$.   The third probability tends to

$$e^{-0.9} - e^{-1.1} = 0.0737.$$

39. The random variable X has a Poisson distribution with mean λ.
Show that, if n is a positive integer,

$$E(e^{-X/n}) = e^{-\lambda(1 - e^{-1/n})}.$$

Use this result to show that, if $X_1, X_2, \ldots, X_n$ is a random
sample from the distribution of X, then

$$E(e^{-\bar{X}}) = e^{-n\lambda(1 - e^{-1/n})}.$$

Deduce that $e^{-\bar{X}}$ is a biased estimator for $e^{-\lambda}$, even though $\bar{X}$
is an unbiased estimator for λ.

¶   X has probability function

$$p_x = \frac{e^{-\lambda}\lambda^x}{x!} \quad , \quad x = 0, 1, 2, \ldots$$

So $$E(e^{-X/n}) = \sum_{x=0}^{\infty} e^{-x/n} \cdot \frac{e^{-\lambda}\lambda^x}{x!}$$

$$= e^{-\lambda} \sum_{x=0}^{\infty} \frac{(\lambda e^{-1/n})^x}{x!}$$

$$= e^{-\lambda} \cdot e^{\lambda e^{-1/n}}$$

$$= e^{-\lambda(1 - e^{-1/n})}.$$

If $X_1, X_2, \ldots, X_n$ is a random sample from the distribution of X,

$$E(e^{-\bar{X}}) = E(e^{-(X_1 + \ldots + X_n)/n})$$

$$= E(e^{-X_1/n}) \, E(e^{-X_2/n}) \ldots E(e^{-X_n/n}) \text{ by independence}$$

$$= e^{-n\lambda(1-e^{-1/n})} \text{ by the above result.}$$

If $e^{-\bar{X}}$ were unbiased for $e^{-\lambda}$, then $E(e^{-\bar{X}})$ would be $e^{-\lambda}$.

However, $e^{-n\lambda(1-e^{-1/n})} \neq e^{-\lambda}$.

For example, if we expand $e^{-1/n}$ as $1 + (-\frac{1}{n}) + \frac{1}{2}(-\frac{1}{n})^2 + \ldots,$

$$e^{-n\lambda(1-e^{-1/n})} \approx e^{-n\lambda(1/n - 1/2n^2)}$$

$$= e^{-\lambda} \cdot e^{\lambda/2n}$$

As $n \to \infty$ this $\to e^{-\lambda}$ but for small n

$$e^{-n\lambda(1-e^{-1/n})} \neq e^{-\lambda}.$$

40. The random variable X is binomially distributed with
parameters n (known) and p (unknown). In order to estimate
p, the following estimators are proposed:

$$\hat{p}_1 = \frac{X}{n},$$

$$\hat{p}_3 = \frac{X+1}{n+2}.$$

Show that, given n, $\hat{p}_3$ has the smaller mean square error
provided that p lies in the interval $(\frac{1}{2} - d_n, \frac{1}{2} + d_n)$, where

$$d_n = \frac{\sqrt{(n+1)(2n+1)}}{2(n+1)}.$$

Evaluate this interval for n = 1,2,3,4 and show that for
large n it approximates to (0.146, 0.854).

¶ Since X has a binomial distribution $B(n,p)$,

$$E(X) = np, \quad Var(X) = npq \quad \text{where } q = 1-p.$$

Therefore $E(\hat{p}_1) = p$, $Var(\hat{p}_1) = \frac{pq}{n}$.

Also $MSE(\hat{p}_1) = Var(\hat{p}_1)$ (as $\hat{p}_1$ is unbiased)

$$= \frac{pq}{n} \ .$$

Now $\quad E(\hat{p}_3) = \frac{np+1}{n+2}$

and $\quad bias(\hat{p}_3) = \frac{np+1}{n+2} - p = \frac{1-2p}{n+2} \ .$

$$Var(\hat{p}_3) = \frac{Var(X)}{(n+2)^2} = \frac{npq}{(n+2)^2}$$

and so $\quad MSE(\hat{p}_3) = \frac{npq}{(n+2)^2} + \frac{(1-2p)^2}{(n+2)^2}$

Thus $\quad MSE(\hat{p}_3) < MSE(\hat{p}_1)$ if

$$\frac{npq+(1-2p)^2}{(n+2)^2} < \frac{pq}{n}$$

i.e. if $n^2pq + n(1-2p)^2 < pq(n+2)^2$

$$n(1-2p)^2 < (4n+4)pq$$

$$n-4pn+4p^2n < 4np-4np^2+4p-4p^2$$

$$p^2(8n+4)-p(8n+4)+n < 0.$$

This is satisfied if p lies between the two roots of the quadratic equation

$$p^2(8n+4)-p(8n+4)+n = 0.$$

These are given by

$$\frac{8n+4 \pm \sqrt{(8n+4)^2-4n(8n+4)}}{2(8n+4)}$$

$$= \frac{1}{2} \pm \frac{\sqrt{32n^2+48n+16}}{8(2n+1)}$$

$$= \frac{1}{2} \pm \frac{\sqrt{2n^2+3n+1}}{2(2n+1)}$$

$$= \frac{1}{2} \pm \frac{\sqrt{(2n+1)(n+1)}}{2(2n+1)} \ .$$

Thus $MSE(\hat{p}_3) < MSE(\hat{p}_1)$ if p lies in the interval $(\frac{1}{2} - d_n, \frac{1}{2} + d_n)$ where

$$d_n = \frac{\sqrt{(2n+1)(n+1)}}{2(2n+1)}$$

For n = 1,2,3,4 the interval endpoints are shown below.

n		
1	0.09175	0.90825
2	0.11270	0.88730
3	0.12204	0.87796
4	0.12732	0.87268

Now
$$d_n = \frac{1}{2}\sqrt{\frac{n+1}{2n+1}} \to \frac{1}{2\sqrt{2}} \quad \text{as } n \to \infty.$$

Hence the interval tends to

$$\frac{1}{2} \pm \frac{1}{2\sqrt{2}}$$

i.e. (0.146, 0.854).

8

Confidence Intervals

Exercises 8.1 Means of Normal Distributions of Known Variance

1. The random sample
    2.982, 1.934, 4.028, 3.502, 0.732, 4.695, 3.082, 2.975, 5.206
    was obtained from a $N(\mu,1)$ distribution. Calculate the three
    confidence intervals for μ whose confidence levels are respect-
    ively 60%, 95% and 99%.

¶   If $\bar{x}$ is the value of the mean of a random sample of size n from
    a $N(\mu,\sigma^2)$ distribution (σ^2 known) the interval

    $$[\bar{x} - z_\gamma \frac{\sigma}{\sqrt{n}} , \quad \bar{x} + z_\gamma \frac{\sigma}{\sqrt{n}}],$$

    where $\gamma = 1 - \frac{1}{2}\alpha$ and $\Phi(z_\gamma) = \gamma$, is a confidence interval for μ
    with confidence level $100(1-\alpha)\%$.

    Here $n = 9$, $\sigma = 1$, $\bar{x} = 3.237\dot{3}$.

    For a 60% interval, $\gamma = 0.8$ and $z_\gamma = 0.8416$ so that the interval
    is

    $$[3.237\dot{3} - \frac{0.8416}{3} , \quad 3.237\dot{3} + \frac{0.8416}{3}]$$

    i.e. $[2.957, 3.518]$.

    Similarly for a 95% interval, $z_\gamma = 1.96$ and the interval is

    $$[2.584, 3.891],$$

    while for a 99% interval, $z_\gamma = 2.5758$ and the interval is

    $$[2.379, 4.096].$$

2. The amount of coffee dispensed by a vending machine is normally
    distributed with standard deviation 1.2 cl. The mean amount
    dispensed can be adjusted using a control inside the machine.
    With the control on a particular setting, it is found that 25

successive deliveries gave a total of 520 cl of coffee. Calculate a confidence interval for the mean amount of coffee dispensed per delivery at a level of (i) 80%, (ii) 90%, (iii) 99.8%.

¶   In the usual notation, the interval

$$[\bar{x} - z_\gamma \frac{\sigma}{\sqrt{n}} , \quad \bar{x} + z_\gamma \frac{\sigma}{\sqrt{n}}]$$

is a $100(1-\alpha)\%$ confidence interval for the mean.
Here $\sigma = 1.2$, $n = 25$, $\bar{x} = 520/25 = 20.8$.
For an 80% interval, $z_\gamma = z_{0.9} = 1.2816$ and the interval is

$$[20.8 - 1.2816 \times \frac{1.2}{5} , \quad 20.8 + 1.2816 \times \frac{1.2}{5}]$$

i.e.   [20.49, 21.11].

For a 90% interval $z_\gamma = z_{0.95} = 1.6449$ and the interval is

[20.41, 21.19]

while for a 99.8% interval, $z_\gamma = z_{0.999} = 3.09$ and the interval is

[20.06, 21.54].

3.   A random sample of size n is obtained from a $N(\mu,1)$ distribution. Find the width of the 95% confidence interval for μ when

(i) $n = 9$,   (ii) $n = 16$,   (iii) $n = 100$.

¶   In the usual notation, the width of the 95% (symmetric) confidence interval is

$$\frac{2}{\sqrt{n}} z_{0.975} = \frac{3.92}{\sqrt{n}}$$

If $n = 9$,   the width is 1.307.
If $n = 16$,   the width is 0.980.
If $n = 100$,   the width is 0.392.

4.   A random sample from a $N(\mu,16)$ distribution was used to obtain the 99% confidence interval [27.7533, 30.1327] for μ. Deduce the value of (a) the sample mean, (b) the size of the sample.

¶   The 99% symmetric confidence interval is

$$[\bar{x} - 2.5758 \frac{\sigma}{\sqrt{n}} , \quad \bar{x} + 2.5758 \frac{\sigma}{\sqrt{n}}].$$

Here $\sigma = 4$ and so the interval is

$$[\bar{x} - \frac{10.3032}{\sqrt{n}}, \quad \bar{x} + \frac{10.3032}{\sqrt{n}}].$$

Assuming that the quoted confidence interval is symmetric, this is [27.7533, 30.1327] and $\bar{x}$ is the average of the endpoints, i.e. [27.7533 + 30.1327]/2 = 28.943.

Therefore $\dfrac{10.3032}{\sqrt{n}} = 28.943 - 27.7533 = 1.1897$,

so that $\sqrt{n} = \dfrac{10.3032}{1.1897}$, and $n = 75$.

5. A certain method for measuring the pH values of chemical solutions gives measurements which are normally distributed with mean equal to the true value and standard deviation 0.04. What is the smallest number of independent measurements that must be made on a given solution in order to obtain a 95% confidence interval for the pH value whose width is less than (i) 0.04, (ii) 0.02, (iii) 0.01?

¶ The narrowest 95% confidence interval is

$$[\bar{x} - 1.96 \times \frac{0.04}{\sqrt{n}}, \quad \bar{x} + 1.96 \times \frac{0.04}{\sqrt{n}}].$$

Its width is

$$\frac{2 \times 1.96 \times 0.04}{\sqrt{n}} = \frac{0.1568}{\sqrt{n}}.$$

(i) If this is to be less than 0.04, we require

$$\frac{0.1568}{\sqrt{n}} < 0.04,$$

i.e. $n > (\frac{0.1568}{0.04})^2 = 15.3664$.

Therefore the smallest number of measurements is 16.

(ii) Now $n > (\frac{0.1568}{0.02})^2 = 61.4656$

and the required number is 62.

(iii)Now $n > (\frac{0.1568}{0.01})^2 = 245.8624$

and the required number is 246.

6. In an experiment, 100 observations were taken from a normal distribution with variance 16. The experimenter quoted [1.545, 2.861] as the confidence interval for μ. What level of confidence was used?

¶   The $100(1-\alpha)\%$ symmetric confidence interval is

$$[\bar{x} - z_\gamma \times \frac{4}{10} \, , \; \bar{x} + z_\gamma \times \frac{4}{10}] \qquad (\gamma = 1 - \tfrac{1}{2}\alpha)$$

and its width is $0.8z_\gamma$. The width of the quoted confidence interval is 1.316. Therefore, assuming that the quoted interval is symmetric,

$$0.8z_\gamma = 1.316,$$
$$z_\gamma = 1.645,$$
$$\gamma = 0.95$$

and $100(1-\alpha) = 90,$

i.e. the confidence level is 90%.

7.   The reaction time to a certain stimulus is normally distributed among rats with unknown mean μ and unknown variance σ^2. One hundred rats were selected at random and subjected to the stimulus. The sample mean and sample standard deviation of their reaction times were found to be 0.113 and 0.015 seconds respectively. Replacing σ by its estimate 0.015, calculate an approximate 95% confidence interval for μ.

¶   If σ were known then the 95% confidence interval for μ would be

$$[0.113 - 1.96 \times \frac{\sigma}{10} \, , \; 0.113 + 1.96 \times \frac{\sigma}{10}].$$

As the sample size is large, σ can be replaced by the sample standard deviation to obtain an interval whose confidence level is approximately 95%. This interval is

$$[0.113 - 1.96 \times \frac{0.015}{10} \, , \; 0.113 + 1.96 \times \frac{0.015}{10}]$$

i.e. $[0.1101, 0.1159].$

8.   In an investigation of the effect of an additive on the viscosity of an oil, the mean of 5 independent measurements of its viscosity without the additive was 6.87 units whereas the mean of 6 independent measurements of its viscosity with the additive was 7.41 units. Assuming that in both cases the measurements are normally distributed with mean equal to the true value and standard deviation 0.5, find (i) a 90% confidence interval, (ii) a 99% confidence interval for the difference in viscosities with and without the additive. Comment on your results.

¶   In the usual notation, a $100(1-\alpha)$% confidence interval for the difference of means is

$$[\bar{x} - \bar{y} - z_\gamma \sqrt{\frac{\sigma_x^2}{m} + \frac{\sigma_y^2}{n}}, \quad \bar{x} - \bar{y} + z_\gamma \sqrt{\frac{\sigma_x^2}{m} + \frac{\sigma_y^2}{n}}]$$

Here

$$\sigma_x = \sigma_y = 0.5, \ \bar{x} = 7.41, \ \bar{y} = 6.87, \ m = 5, \ n = 6.$$

The interval is

$$[7.41-6.87 - z_\gamma \sqrt{\frac{0.5^2}{5} + \frac{0.5^2}{6}}, \quad 7.41-6.87 + z_\gamma \sqrt{\frac{0.5^2}{5} + \frac{0.6^2}{6}}]$$

i.e. $[0.54 - 0.302765 \, z_\gamma, \ 0.54 + 0.302765 \, z_\gamma]$

For a 90% confidence level, $z_\gamma = 1.6449$ and the interval is

$$[0.042, \ 1.038].$$

For a 99% confidence level, $z_\gamma = 2.5758$ and the interval is

$$[-0.240, \ 1.320].$$

We are 90% confident that the true value of $\mu_x - \mu_y$ is between 0.042 and 1.038 and hence that it is positive. We are thus 90% confident that the mean viscosity is greater with the additive. We cannot say the same at the 99% level of confidence, however, since the interval contains some positive values and some negative ones.

The conclusion that we draw depends on the level of confidence that we wish to have in it. At the 90% level we conclude that the additive increases the mean viscosity but at the 99% level we cannot conclude this.

9.   Suppose that the numbers of hours spent during an evening watching television by children and by adults are both normally distributed with standard deviation 0.8 hours. Two random samples, one consisting of n children and one consisting of n adults, are to be obtained. What is the smallest value of n which ensures that the width of the 95% confidence interval for the difference in mean viewing times does not exceed (i) 30 minutes, (ii) 15 minutes?

¶   The 95% confidence interval for the difference in mean viewing times is

$$[\bar{x} - \bar{y} - 1.96 \sqrt{\frac{0.8^2}{n} + \frac{0.8^2}{n}} , \ \bar{x} - \bar{y} + 1.96 \sqrt{\frac{0.8^2}{n} + \frac{0.8^2}{n}}]$$

where $\bar{x}$, $\bar{y}$ are the respective sample means of the hours spent by the adults and the children. The width of the interval is therefore

$$3.92 \times 0.8 \sqrt{\frac{2}{n}} \text{ hours,}$$

i.e. $\qquad \dfrac{266.098}{\sqrt{n}}$ minutes.

If the width is to be at most 30 minutes,

$$\frac{266.098}{\sqrt{n}} \le 30$$

so that $\qquad\qquad n \ge 78.67$

and n must be at least 70.

If the width is to be at most 15,

$$\frac{266.098}{\sqrt{n}} \le 15$$

so that $\qquad\qquad n \ge 314.7$

and n must be at least 315.

10. Let μ_a denote the mean volume dispensed by chemist A when he attempts to dispense exactly 1 ml of a chemical. Let μ_b denote the corresponding mean volume dispensed by chemist B. The sample mean and sample standard deviation of the volumes dispensed in 100 attempts by A were 1.005 ml and 0.015 ml respectively. The corresponding figures for 70 attempts by B were 0.998 and 0.012. Assuming that the volumes dispensed are independent and normally distributed, calculate approximate 99% confidence intervals for μ_a, μ_b and $\mu_a - \mu_b$. Comment on your results.

¶ Let σ_a and σ_b denote the respective standard deviations of the volumes dispensed by A and B. If σ_a were known then a 99% confidence interval for μ_a would be

$$[1.005 - 2.5758 \times \frac{\sigma_a}{10}, \ 1.005 + 2.5758 \times \frac{\sigma_a}{10}].$$

The sample size is 100 which is large enough for σ_a to be replaced by the sample standard deviation 0.015. The resulting approximate 99% confidence interval for μ_a is

$$[1.0011, 1.0089].$$

Similarly for μ_b, replacing σ_b by 0.012 in

$$[0.998-2.5758 \times \frac{\sigma_b}{\sqrt{70}}, \; 0.998+2.5758 \times \frac{\sigma_b}{\sqrt{70}}],$$

we obtain

$$[0.9943, 1.0017].$$

For $\mu_a-\mu_b$, replacing σ_a by 0.015 and σ_b by 0.012 in

$$[1.005-0.998-2.5758 \sqrt{\frac{\sigma_a^2}{100} + \frac{\sigma_b^2}{70}}, \; 1.005-0.998+2.5758 \sqrt{\frac{\sigma_a^2}{100} + \frac{\sigma_b^2}{70}}],$$

we obtain

$$[0.0017, 0.0123].$$

As the confidence interval for μ_a contains values greater than 1 only, we conclude that chemist A dispenses more than 1 ml on average. As the confidence interval for μ_b contains the value 1, chemist B may not be biased in either direction. The confidence interval for $\mu_a-\mu_b$ contains positive values only and we conclude that chemist A dispenses more than chemist B on average. Note that this conclusion cannot be reached by comparing the confidence intervals for μ_a and μ_b.

Exercises 8.2 Confidence Intervals using the Central Limit Theorem

1. One hundred fibres were selected at random from a large bundle of fibres. The breaking strength of each one was measured. The mean and standard deviation of the measurements were 10.57 and 0.215 Newtons respectively. Calculate an approximate 95% confidence interval for the mean breaking strength of the fibres in the bundle.

    A second random sample of one hundred fibres was taken after the bundle had been washed with a chemical. The mean and standard deviation of the breaking strengths of these fibres were 11.12 and 0.207 Newtons. Calculate an approximate 95% confidence interval for the change in the mean breaking strength of the fibres.

¶ The sample size is large. So if σ, the standard deviation of the measurements, were known then, by the Central Limit Theorem, an approximate 95% confidence interval for the mean breaking strength would be

$$[10.57 - 1.96\frac{\sigma}{\sqrt{100}} \quad , \quad 10.57 + 1.96 \frac{\sigma}{\sqrt{100}}].$$

As σ is unknown but the sample size is large, we can replace σ by its estimate 0.215 to obtain the approximate 95% confidence interval

$$[10.528, 10.612].$$

Similarly for an approximate 95% confidence interval for the change in mean breaking strength, we appeal to the Central Limit Theorem and replace the unknown standard deviations by their estimates to obtain

$$[11.12-10.57-1.96 \sqrt{\frac{0.215^2}{100} + \frac{0.207^2}{100}} ,$$
$$11.12-10.57+1.96 \sqrt{\frac{0.215^2}{100} + \frac{0.207^2}{100}}]$$

i.e. $[0.492, 0.608]$.

2. A group of 150 patients was divided into two equal subgroups A and B. Patients in subgroup A were given a tranquiliser of one type while patients in subgroup B were given a tranquiliser of a different type. The sample mean and sample standard deviation of the number of hours of sleep for patients in subgroup A were 7.25 hours and 0.85 hours respectively. The corresponding figures for subgroup B were 7.45 hours and 0.70 hours. Find an approximate 90% confidence interval for the difference in the mean hours of sleep produced by the two types of tranquiliser among patients of the type participating in the trial. What assumptions need to be made in order to solve this problem?

¶ In using the formula for the confidence interval for the difference of means we assume that we have two independent random samples. This will be so if the 150 patients constitute a random sample from some large population and the patients are assigned to their subgroups at random. Assuming that the sample sizes are large enough to justify the use of the Central Limit Theorem and the replacement of the unknown standard deviations by their estimates, an approximate 90% confidence interval for the difference in the mean hours of sleep is

$$[7.25-7.45-1.645 \sqrt{\frac{0.85^2}{75} + \frac{0.70^2}{75}} ,$$
$$7.25-7.45+1.645 \sqrt{\frac{0.85^2}{75} + \frac{0.70^2}{75}}]$$

i.e. $[-0.409, 0.009]$.

3.   An opinion poll reveals that 750 out of a random sample of 1800 citizens are in favour of a proposal to build a new concert hall. Calculate an approximate 99% confidence interval for the proportion of citizens who support the proposal.

¶   The 99% confidence interval is given approximately by

$$[\hat{p}-2.576 \sqrt{\frac{\hat{p}(1-\hat{p})}{n}}, \quad \hat{p}+2.576 \sqrt{\frac{\hat{p}(1-\hat{p})}{n}}],$$

where $\hat{p}$ is the observed proportion in favour. Here $\hat{p} = 750/1800$ and we obtain

$$[\frac{750}{1800} - 2.576 \sqrt{\frac{750 \times 1050}{1800^3}} , \frac{750}{1800} + 2.576 \sqrt{\frac{750 \times 1050}{1800^3}}]$$

i.e. $[0.387, 0.447]$.

4.   At the end of a severe winter a certain insurance company found that of 972 policy holders living in a large city who had insured their homes with the company, 357 had suffered more than £500-worth of snow and frost damage. Calculate an approximate 95% confidence interval for the proportion of all home-owners in the city who suffered more than £500-worth of damage. State any assumptions that you make.

¶   Assuming that although the 972 homeowners are all insured with the same company they constitute a random sample from the population of all homeowners in the city, the 95% interval is given approximately by

$$[\hat{p} - 1.96 \sqrt{\frac{\hat{p}(1-\hat{p})}{n}} , \quad \hat{p} + 1.96 \sqrt{\frac{\hat{p}(1-\hat{p})}{n}}],$$

where n = 972 and $\hat{p}$ = 357/972. The interval is therefore

[0.337, 0.398].

5. In a study of the smoking habits of people in a certain country it was found that 450 of a random sample of 1000 people were smokers. A second random sample of size 1000 was obtained one year later, after an anti-smoking campaign had taken place. This sample contained 400 smokers. Let p_1 and p_2 denote the true proportions of smokers in the country before and after the anti-smoking campaign. Calculate 95% and 99% confidence intervals for p_2-p_1 and comment on your result.

¶ A 100(1-α)% confidence interval for p_2-p_1 is given by

$$[\hat{p}_2-\hat{p}_1 - z_\gamma \sqrt{\frac{\hat{p}_1(1-\hat{p}_1)}{n_1} + \frac{\hat{p}_2(1-\hat{p}_2)}{n_2}} ,$$

$$\hat{p}_2-\hat{p}_1 + z_\gamma \sqrt{\frac{\hat{p}_1(1-\hat{p}_1)}{n_1} + \frac{\hat{p}_2(1-\hat{p}_2)}{n_2}}]$$

where $\gamma = 1-\alpha/2$.

Here $\hat{p}_1$ = 0.45, $\hat{p}_2$ = 0.40 and $n_1 = n_2 = 1000$.

For a 95% interval, z_γ = 1.96, and the interval is

$$[0.40-0.45-1.96 \sqrt{\frac{0.4\times0.6+0.45\times0.55}{1000}} ,$$

$$0.40-0.45+1.96 \sqrt{\frac{0.4\times0.6+0.45\times0.55}{1000}}]$$

i.e. [-0.093, -0.007].

For a 99% interval, z_γ = 2.576. We find that the interval is [-0.107, 0.007].

As the 95% interval contains negative values only, it suggests that p_2-p_1 is less than 0 and that the campaign has had a real effect. This is not true of the 99% interval, however. There is therefore some evidence that the campaign was effective; whether we accept the evidence or not depends on the degree of confidence we wish to have in our decision.

6. Among random samples of 100 washing machines of make A and 180
    washing machines of make B there were 45 and 108 machines of
    makes A and B respectively which developed faults during their
    first year of use. Calculate a 99% confidence interval for
    $p_b - p_a$, where p_a and p_b are the respective probabilities that
    machines of makes A and B develop faults during the year.
    Comment on the claim that any apparent difference in reliabi-
    lity between makes can be attributed to sampling error.

    Suppose instead that the samples consist of 200 machines of
    make A and 360 machines of make B and that 90 out of 200 and
    216 out of 360 develop faults during the year. Recalculate
    the 99% confidence interval for $p_b - p_a$ and comment on your
    result.

¶   An approximate 99% confidence interval is given by

$$[\hat{p}_b - \hat{p}_a - 2.576\theta, \ \hat{p}_b - \hat{p}_a + 2.576\theta]$$

where $\quad \theta = \sqrt{\dfrac{\hat{p}_a(1-\hat{p}_a)}{n_a} + \dfrac{\hat{p}_b(1-\hat{p}_b)}{n_b}}$.

Here $\hat{p}_a = 45/100 = 0.45$, $\hat{p}_b = 108/180 = 0.6$, $n_a = 100$,
$n_b = 180$. Thus $\theta = 0.0617$ and the interval is

$\quad$ [-0.009, 0.309].

Since the interval contains both positive and negative values,
we cannot conclude that $p_b > p_a$ at this level of confidence.

With the larger samples, $\hat{p}_a$ and $\hat{p}_b$ have the same values as
before but now the interval is

$\quad$ [0.038, 0.262]

and we can conclude that, with this degree of confidence,
$p_b > p_a$ since the interval contains positive values only.

7. In a certain parliamentary constituency there are only two
    candidates, A and B. Let p_a and p_b denote the probabilities
    that a randomly selected voter supports A and B respectively.
    Of a random sample of 200 voters, 90 said that they would
    vote for candidate A. If all voters support either A or B,
    calculate an approximate 80% confidence interval for $p_a - p_b$.

¶ Since all voters support either A or B, $p_b = 1-p_a$ and so $p_a-p_b = 2p_a-1$. We find a confidence interval for p_a and then multiply each endpoint by 2 and subtract 1.

For p_a the 90% interval is

$$[\hat{p} - 1.645\sqrt{\frac{\hat{p}(1-\hat{p})}{n}} , \quad \hat{p} + 1.645\sqrt{\frac{\hat{p}(1-\hat{p})}{n}}]$$

i.e. $[0.45 - 1.645\sqrt{\frac{0.45 \times 0.55}{200}} , \quad 0.45 + 1.645\sqrt{\frac{0.45 \times 0.55}{200}}]$

or $[0.392, 0.508]$.

That for p_a-p_b is therefore

$$[2 \times 0.392-1, \; 2 \times 0.508-1]$$

i.e. $[-0.216, 0.016]$.

8. The number of emissions per minute from a radioactive source is Poisson distributed with unknown mean μ. In order to estimate μ, the number of emissions during each of 60 one minute intervals was counted. Given that a total of 5000 emissions was recorded, calculate a 95% confidence interval for μ.

¶ Let $\bar{x}$ be the observed sample mean. A 95% confidence interval for μ is given approximately by

$$[\bar{x} - 1.96\sqrt{\frac{\bar{x}}{n}} , \quad \bar{x} + 1.96\sqrt{\frac{\bar{x}}{n}}]$$

i.e. $[\frac{5000}{60} - 1.96\sqrt{\frac{5000}{60^2}} , \quad \frac{5000}{60} + 1.96\sqrt{\frac{5000}{60^2}}]$

or $[81.02, 85.64]$.

A more accurate interval is given by

$$[\bar{x} + \frac{1.96^2}{2n} -1.96\theta, \; \bar{x} + \frac{1.96^2}{2n} + 1.96\theta],$$

where $\theta = \sqrt{\frac{\bar{x}}{n} + \frac{1.96^2}{4n^2}}$.

Evaluating this we obtain $[81.06, 85.68]$.

9. The number of errors made by a typist on a page is Poisson distributed with unknown mean λ. Evaluate an approximate 90% confidence interval for λ given the following numbers of errors on 20 pages:

   2, 3, 0, 1, 2, 4, 3, 1, 2, 3, 4, 0, 2, 1, 0, 5, 0, 1, 1, 1.

   (It may be assumed that numbers of errors on different pages are independent.)

¶ As in the previous question an approximate interval is

$$[\bar{x} - 1.645\sqrt{\tfrac{\bar{x}}{n}}, \quad \bar{x} + 1.645\sqrt{\tfrac{\bar{x}}{n}}].$$

Here $n = 20$ and $\bar{x} = 36/20 = 1.8$. The interval is therefore $[1.31, 2.29]$.

In this case the more accurate version is $[1.37, 2.37]$, obtained by replacing the 1.96 of Exercise 8 by 1.645 since the level of confidence is 90%. There is a greater difference than before between the intervals; this arises because the sample size is quite small here.

10. $X_1, X_2, \ldots, X_n$ is a random sample from an exponential distribution with mean θ. Use the Central Limit Theorem to show that, when n is large,

$$P(\theta(1 - 1.96/\sqrt{n}) \leq \bar{X} \leq \theta(1 + 1.96/\sqrt{n})) \approx 0.95$$

and deduce that

$$[\bar{X}/(1 + 1.96/\sqrt{n}), \; \bar{X}/(1 - 1.96/\sqrt{n})]$$

is an approximate 95% confidence interval for θ. Evaluate this interval, given that $n = 100$ and $\bar{X} = 4.2$.

¶ Each X_i has mean θ and variance θ^2, since X_i has an exponential distribution. Therefore $\bar{X}$ is approximately normally distributed with mean θ and variance θ^2/n. Hence

$$P\left(-1.96 \leq \frac{\bar{X}-\theta}{\theta/\sqrt{n}} \leq 1.96\right) \approx 0.95.$$

Now
$$\frac{\bar{X}-\theta}{\theta/\sqrt{n}} \leq 1.96 \iff \bar{X}-\theta \leq 1.96\,\frac{\theta}{\sqrt{n}}$$
$$\iff \theta \geq \frac{\bar{X}}{1+1.96/\sqrt{n}} \; .$$

Similarly $\quad \dfrac{\bar{X}-\theta}{\theta/\sqrt{n}} \geqslant -1.96 \iff \theta \leqslant \dfrac{\bar{X}}{1-1.96/\sqrt{n}}$.

Therefore

$$P(\dfrac{\bar{X}}{1+1.96/\sqrt{n}} \leqslant \theta \leqslant \dfrac{\bar{X}}{1-1.96/\sqrt{n}}) \approx 0.95$$

and so

$$[\bar{X}/(1+1.96/\sqrt{n}), \ \bar{X}/(1-1.96/\sqrt{n})]$$

is an approximate 95% confidence interval for θ.

If n = 100 and $\bar{X}$ is 4.2, the interval is

$$[3.512, \ 5.224].$$

Exercises 8.3 Means of Normal Distributions in Small Samples

1. The heights of n randomly selected seven year old children were measured. The sample mean and sample standard deviation were found to be 121 cm and 5 cm respectively. Assuming that height is normally distributed, calculate the following confidence intervals for the mean height of seven year old children:
    (i)   90% with n = 16,
    (ii)   99% with n = 16,
    (iii)   95% with n = 16, 25, 100, 225, 400.

¶   The $100(1-\alpha)$% confidence interval is, in the usual notation,

$$[\bar{x} - t_\gamma(n-1)\dfrac{s}{\sqrt{n}} \ , \ \bar{x} + t_\gamma(n-1)\dfrac{s}{\sqrt{n}}],$$

where $\gamma = 1-\alpha/2$. Here $\bar{x} = 121$ and s = 5.

(i)   Using Table 3, $t_{0.95}(15) = 1.753$ and the interval is
$$[121-1.753 \times \tfrac{5}{4}, \quad 121+1.753 \times \tfrac{5}{4}],$$

i.e.   [118.81, 123.19]

(ii) $t_{0.995}(15) = 2.947$ and the interval is
        [117.32, 124.68]

(iii)   We obtain the following table

n	$t_{0.975}(n-1)$	Confidence Limits	
16	2.131	118.34	123.66
25	2.064	118.94	123.06
100	1.984	120.01	121.99
225	1.96	120.35	121.65
400	1.96	120.51	121.49

For the last two values of n the value of 1.96 was used as we cannot obtain the correct value from Table 3. The values tend to 1.96 as n tends to infinity and so this is a reasonable method. It is equivalent to assuming that 5 is the true standard deviation and using the normal distribution to obtain a confidence interval.

2. Use the t distribution to calculate a 95% confidence interval for the mean reaction time of rats using the information given in Question 7, Exercises 8.1. Compare this interval with the approximate one given there.

¶ In this case $\bar{x}$ = 0.113, s = 0.015 and n = 100. The 95% confidence interval is therefore

$$[0.113-1.984 \times \frac{0.015}{10}, \quad 0.113+1.984 \times \frac{0.015}{10}]$$

as $t_{0.975}(99)$ = 1.984. The interval is therefore

$$[0.1100, 0.1160].$$

Because of the large sample size, this differs only slightly from the approximate interval [0.1101, 0.1159] obtained in Question 7, Exercises 8.1.

3. In six independent attempts, a boy completed a Rubik cube in 145.3, 156.3, 153.7, 155.0, 149.6 and 162.1 seconds. Find a 90% confidence interval for the expected time it takes him to complete the cube. State any assumptions that you make.

¶ In the usual notation

$$\sum x_i = 922, \quad \sum x_i^2 = 141847.04.$$

Hence $\bar{x}$ = 153.6$\dot{6}$, s = 5.7684. Since $t_{0.95}(5)$ = 2.015, the interval is

$$[153.6\dot{6}-2.015 \times \frac{5.7684}{\sqrt{6}} \ , \ 153.6\dot{6}+2.015 \times \frac{5.7684}{\sqrt{6}}]$$

i.e.   [148.92, 158.41]

We have assumed that the times have a common normal distribution, implying that there is no tendency for his performance to improve with successive attempts.

4. A random variable is known to be normally distributed, but its mean μ and variance σ^2 are unknown. A 95% confidence interval for μ based on 9 observations was found to be [22.4, 25.6]. Calculate unbiased estimates of μ and σ^2.

¶   As $t_{0.975}(8) = 2.306$, the interval is

$$[\bar{x} - 2.306 \times \frac{s}{3} \ , \ \bar{x} + 2.306 \times \frac{s}{3}].$$

The midpoint is $\bar{x}$ and therefore

$$\bar{x} = \frac{22.4 + 25.6}{2} = 24.0.$$

This is an unbiased estimate of μ.
Also

$$\frac{2.306s}{3} = \frac{25.6-22.4}{2} = 1.6$$

Hence $s = 2.0815$

so that $s^2 = 4.333.$

This is an unbiased estimate of σ^2.

5. The wavelength of radiation from a certain source is 1.372 microns. The following ten independent measurements of the wavelength were obtained using a measuring device,

1.359, 1.368, 1.360, 1.374, 1.375, 1.372, 1.362, 1.372, 1.363, 1.371.

Assuming that the measurements are normally distributed, calculate 95% confidence limits for the mean error in measurements obtained with this device and comment on your result.

¶   In the usual notation,

$$\sum x_i = 13.676, \qquad \sum x_i^2 = 18.703628.$$

These lead to

$$\bar{x} = 1.3676, \quad s = 0.00606.$$

Thus a 95% confidence interval for the mean is

$$[1.3676 - 2.262 \times \frac{0.00606}{\sqrt{10}}, \quad 1.3676 + 2.262 \times \frac{0.00606}{\sqrt{10}}]$$

i.e. [1.3633, 1.3719].

A 95% confidence interval for the mean error is obtained by subtracting the true wavelength of 1.372 from each endpoint. This gives

$$[-0.0087, -0.0001].$$

As this contains negative values only, we conclude that the device tends to underestimate the true value.

6. Sixteen students in a laboratory each made a determination of μ, the coefficient of thermal expansion of nickel. The sum and sum of squares of the sixteen determinations are 204.96×10^{-6} and $2625.5701 \times 10^{-12}$ respectively. By making certain assumptions, which should be stated, obtain a 90% confidence interval for μ.

¶ We shall assume that the observations are independent of each other and that they form a random sample from a normal distribution.

Since $\sum x_i = 204.96 \times 10^{-6}$, $\sum x_i^2 = 2625.5701 \times 10^{-12}$ we find that

$$\bar{x} = 12.81 \times 10^{-6}, \quad s = 0.04655 \times 10^{-6}.$$

Since $t_{0.95}(15) = 1.753$, a 90% confidence interval is

$$[12.81 \times 10^{-6} - 1.753 \times \frac{0.04655 \times 10^{-6}}{\sqrt{16}},$$

$$12.81 \times 10^{-6} + 1.753 \times \frac{0.04655 \times 10^{-6}}{\sqrt{16}}]$$

i.e. $[12.790 \times 10^{-6}, 12.830 \times 10^{-6}]$.

7. Two independent determinations of a 95% confidence interval for the unknown mean μ of a normal population whose standard deviation is also unknown, yielded the following results (using Student's t distribution):

(i)   [58.2, 63.1] based on a sample of 8 observations,

(ii)   [59.3, 62.0] based on a sample of 12 observations.

If the two sets of results are combined, find

(a)   an unbiased estimate of μ,

(b)   a 95% confidence interval for μ.

¶   The $100(1-\alpha)$% confidence interval for μ is

$$[\bar{x} - t_\gamma(n-1)\frac{s}{\sqrt{n}} \, , \quad \bar{x} + t_\gamma(n-1)\frac{s}{\sqrt{n}}] \, ,$$

where $\gamma = 1-\alpha/2$.

Let $\bar{x}_1, s_1$ and $\bar{x}_2, s_2$ denote respectively the mean and standard deviation of the first and second samples.

Now $\bar{x}_1 = \dfrac{58.2+63.1}{2} = 60.65$

and $\bar{x}_2 = \dfrac{59.3+62.0}{2} = 60.65$.

Therefore the mean of the combined sample is 60.65 and this is an unbiased estimate of μ.

Using the fact that the half-width of the interval is given by $t_\gamma(n-1)s/\sqrt{n}$, we have

$$2.45 = 2.365 \times \frac{s_1}{\sqrt{8}}$$

and $$1.35 = 2.201 \times \frac{s_2}{\sqrt{12}}$$

Therefore $s_1 = 2.93008, s_2 = 2.12473$

so that the sum of squares for the first sample is

$$8\bar{x}_1^2 + 7s_1^2 = 29487.478$$

and the sum of squares for the second sample is

$$12\bar{x}_2^2 + 11s_2^2 = 44190.729.$$

Thus the total sum of squares is 73678.207 and the variance of the combined sample is

$$\frac{1}{19}(73678.207-20\times60.65^2) = 5.7767.$$

Therefore, as $t_{0.975}(19) = 2.093$, a 95% confidence interval for μ based on the combined sample is:

$$[60.65-2.093 \times \sqrt{\frac{5.7767}{20}} , \quad 60.65+2.093 \times \sqrt{\frac{5.7767}{20}}]$$

i.e. $\quad$ [59.53, 61.77].

8. In an experiment on the capacitance of electrolytic cells, nine cells were selected at random. Five were filled with 1 ml of electrolyte and four were filled with 1.2 ml of electrolyte. The measured capacitances of the cells containing 1 ml of electrolyte were 250.55, 260.11, 248.90, 251.00, 253.72. The measured capacitances of the other four cells were

$$258.37, \quad 265.82, \quad 270.16, \quad 260.35.$$

Let μ_1 and μ_2 denote the mean capacitances of cells containing 1 ml and 1.2 ml of electrolyte respectively. Calculate a 95% confidence interval for $\mu_2-\mu_1$. State any assumptions that you make.

¶ Using x to denote measurements on 1 ml of electrolyte and y for those on 1.2 ml, we find that

$$\sum x_i = 1264.28, \qquad \sum x_i^2 = 319758.563,$$

$$\sum y_i = 1054.7, \qquad \sum y_i^2 = 278183.8774,$$

leading to $\quad \bar{x} = 252.856, \qquad s_x^2 = 19.4448,$

$$\bar{y} = 263.675, \qquad s_y^2 = 28.6183.$$

The 95% confidence limits for $\mu_2-\mu_1$ are

$$\bar{y} - \bar{x} \pm t_{0.975}(7)\sqrt{\frac{4s_x^2 + 3s_y^2}{7} \left(\frac{1}{5} + \frac{1}{4}\right)}$$

and, since $t_{0.975}(7) = 2.365$, we obtain the interval

$$[3.148, \quad 18.490].$$

We have assumed that the two samples are independent random samples from normal distributions with the same variance. The values of s_x and s_y are fairly similar so the assumption of equal variances is not unreasonable.

9. In five independent attempts, a girl completed a Rubik cube in 135.4, 152.1, 146.7, 143.5 and 146.0 seconds. In five further attempts, made two weeks later, she completed the cube in 133.1, 126.9, 129.0, 139.6 and 144.0 seconds. Find a 90% confidence interval for the change in the mean time taken to complete the cube. State your assumptions.

¶ Using x to refer to the early attempts and y to refer to the later ones, we find from the data that

$$\sum x_i = 723.7, \quad \sum x_i^2 = 104896.71,$$

$$\sum y_i = 672.6, \quad \sum y_i^2 = 90684.38.$$

This gives $\bar{x} = 144.74$, $s_x^2 = 37.093$,

$\bar{y} = 134.52$, $s_y^2 = 51.557$.

Confidence limits for the change in mean time are

$$\bar{y} - \bar{x} \pm t_{0.95}(8) \sqrt{\frac{4s_x^2 + 4s_y^2}{8}} \, (\tfrac{1}{5} + \tfrac{1}{5}),$$

leading to the interval $[-18.05, -2.39]$.

As it contains only negative values, this suggests that there is a real decrease in the mean time taken to complete the cube. We have assumed that the two samples are independent random samples from normal distributions of equal variance.

10. In an experiment to study the effect of a certain concentration of insulin on blood glucose levels in rats, each member of a random sample of 10 rats was treated with insulin. The blood glucose level of each rat was measured both before and after treatment. The results, in suitable units, were as follows.

Rat	1	2	3	4	5	6	7	8	9	10
Level before	2.30	2.01	1.92	1.89	2.15	1.93	2.32	1.98	2.21	1.78
Level after	1.98	1.85	2.10	1.78	1.93	1.93	1.85	1.67	1.72	1.90

Let μ_1 and μ_2 denote respectively the mean blood glucose levels of a randomly selected rat before and after treatment with insulin. By considering the differences of the measurements on each rat and assuming that they are normally distributed, find a 95% confidence interval for $\mu_1-\mu_2$.

¶ Let $d_1, d_2, \ldots, d_{10}$ denote the differences in levels before and after treatment. Their values are

0.32, 0.16, -0.18, 0.11, 0.22, 0.00, 0.47, 0.31, 0.49, -0.12.

Then $\quad \sum_1^{10} d_i = 1.78, \qquad \sum_1^{10} d_i^2 = 0.7924$

so that $\quad \bar{d} = 0.178, \qquad s_d = 0.2299.$

A 95% confidence interval for the mean difference $\mu_1-\mu_2$ is

$$[\bar{d} - t_{0.975}(9) \frac{s_d}{\sqrt{10}} , \quad \bar{d} + t_{0.975}(9) \frac{s_d}{\sqrt{10}}]$$

i.e. $[0.178-2.262 \times \frac{0.2299}{\sqrt{10}}, \quad 0.178+2.262 \times \frac{0.2299}{\sqrt{10}}]$

or $\quad [0.014, 0.342].$

Note that the two samples are not independent. Thus the standard method of finding a confidence interval for $\mu_1-\mu_2$, as used in Question 9 for example, would be inappropriate.

Miscellaneous Problems

1. The nominal weight of each loaf of bread sold in a supermarket is 800 grams. Twenty-five loaves are selected at random and weighed. The sample mean and sample standard deviation are 798 grams and 3.5 grams respectively. Assuming that the weights of loaves are normally distributed, calculate a 99% confidence interval for the mean weight of loaves sold in the supermarket.

¶ A 99% confidence interval is given by

$$[\bar{x}-t_{0.995}(24) \frac{s}{\sqrt{25}} , \quad \bar{x}+t_{0.995}(24) \frac{s}{\sqrt{25}}],$$

where $\bar{x}$ and s are respectively the sample mean and sample standard deviation. As $\bar{x}$ = 798 and s = 3.5, the interval is

$$[798-2.797 \times \frac{3.5}{5} \; , \quad 798+2.797 \times \frac{3.5}{5}] ,$$

i.e.   [796.04, 799.96].

Since this interval does not contain 800, we conclude that the mean weight is less than the nominal weight.

2.   An instrument maker claims that a certain pipette will dispense 1 ml of fluid. The pipette was used ten times and the amounts dispensed were measured accurately. The results (in ml) were 0.9992, 1.0255, 0.9766, 1.0022, 1.0052, 1.0066, 1.0124, 1.0079, 1.0019, 0.9889. Calculate a 95% confidence interval for the mean volume dispensed by the pipette and comment on your result. What assumptions have you made?

¶   From the data we find that

$$\bar{x} = 1.00264 \quad \text{and} \quad s = 0.01311.$$

As $t_{0.975}(9)$ = 2.262, a 95% confidence interval is

$$[1.00264 - 2.262 \times \frac{0.01311}{\sqrt{10}} \; , \; 1.00264 + 2.262 \times \frac{0.01311}{\sqrt{10}}]$$

i.e.   [0.9933, 1.0120].

As the interval contains unity, there is no reason to doubt that the pipette dispenses 1 ml on average.

We have assumed that the results constitute a random sample from a normal distribution.

3.   The heights (in metres) of 10 fifteen year old boys were as follows:

1.59, 1.67, 1.55, 1.63, 1.69, 1.58, 1.66, 1.62, 1.64, 1.61.

Assuming that heights are normally distributed, find a 99% confidence interval for the mean height of fifteen year old boys.

If you were told that the true mean height of boys of this age was 1.67 m, what would you conclude?

¶   The mean of the heights is 1.624 and the standard deviation is
0.04326. A 99% confidence interval for the mean height is therefore

$$[1.624-3.250 \times \frac{0.04326}{\sqrt{10}} \; , \; \; 1.624+3.250 \times \frac{0.04326}{\sqrt{10}}]$$

i.e.   [1.580, 1.668],

as $t_{0.995}(9) = 3.250$.

If we were told that the true mean height was 1.67 m then,
discounting the possibility that this information is false,
we would conclude that either our sample is not a random
sample from the population of all fifteen year old boys or
that we have such a sample but an event with probability
0.01 has occurred, namely that the 99% confidence interval
does not contain the true mean height.

4.   The volume of wine poured into a 70 cl bottle by an automatic
filler at a bottling plant is known to be normally distributed.
A Weights and Measures inspector obtains 10 bottles and measures
the volume of wine contained in each bottle. He finds that

$$\sum_{i=1}^{10} x_i = 680, \qquad \sum_{i=1}^{10} x_i^2 = 46260,$$

where x_i denotes the volume (in cl) in the ith bottle. Calculate
a 95% confidence interval for the mean volume of wine delivered
by the filler if
(i)   the volume delivered has a standard deviation of 1.2 cl,
(ii)   the standard deviation is unknown.
State any assumption that you make.

(i)   Assuming that the inspector obtains a random sample,
       a 95% interval for the mean volume delivered is given by

$$[\bar{x} - 1.96 \frac{\sigma}{\sqrt{10}} \; , \; \; \bar{x} + 1.96 \frac{\sigma}{\sqrt{10}}]$$

where σ is the standard deviation. Here $\bar{x} = 68$ and
$\sigma = 1.2$. Thus the interval is

$$[68-1.96 \times \frac{1.2}{\sqrt{10}} \; , \; \; 68+1.96 \times \frac{1.2}{\sqrt{10}}]$$

i.e.   [67.256, 68.744].

(ii)   If the standard deviation is unknown, the confidence interval becomes

$$[\bar{x}-t_{0.975}(9)\,\frac{s}{\sqrt{10}}\,,\quad \bar{x}+t_{0.975}(9)\,\frac{s}{\sqrt{10}}].$$

Now

$$s = \sqrt{\frac{10}{9}}\,(4626-68^2) = 1.4907,$$

$$t_{0.975}(9) = 2.262$$

and we find that the interval is [66.934, 69.066].

5.   A farmer weighs 30 of his beetroot and finds that

$$\sum_{i=1}^{30} x_i = 3060,\qquad \sum_{i=1}^{30} (x_i-\bar{x})^2 = 31080,$$

where $x_1,x_2,\ldots,x_{30}$ denote the weights in grams. The variance of the weights of last year's crop was 1400. Assuming that this is also the variance of this year's crop and that the weights are normally distributed, calculate a 95% confidence interval for the mean weight of a beetroot.

What interval would be obtained if no assumption were made about the variance?

¶   Assuming that the variance of this year's crop is 1400, a 95% confidence interval for the mean weight is

$$[102-1.96\sqrt{\frac{1400}{30}}\,,\quad 102+1.96\sqrt{\frac{1400}{30}}]$$

as $\bar{x}$ = 3060/30 = 102. This is [88.611, 115.389].

If no assumption is made about the variance, we estimate it by

$$s^2 = \frac{1}{29}\sum_{1}^{30}(x_i-\bar{x})^2 = 1071.72$$

As $t_{0.975}(29) = 2.045$, the interval is

$$[102-2.045\sqrt{\frac{1071.72}{30}}\,,\quad 102+2.045\sqrt{\frac{1071.72}{30}}]$$

i.e.   [89.777, 114.223].

6.   Use a table of random numbers to obtain five random samples of size two from a normal distribution with mean 3 and variance ½ as in Question 9, Exercises 6.5. Hence construct five 90%

confidence intervals for the mean of this distribution as if the mean and variance were unknown. Plot these intervals as in Figure 8.1 of Volume 2.

¶   To obtain the sample values we use the result that if $U_1, U_2, \ldots, U_n$ are independent random variables which are uniformly distributed on $[0,1]$, then

$$Z = (\bar{U}-0.5)\sqrt{12n}$$

has a distribution which is approximately $N(0,1)$, and so $\mu+\sigma Z=Y$ is approximately $N(\mu,\sigma^2)$. Taking the random digits from Table 11 in blocks of 5, each block giving a single U_i, we obtain from the first six blocks in the first row a value for $\bar{U}$ of 0.39115, a value of Z of -0.92365 and a value for Y of 2.34688.

Using the next nine rows, we obtain the following values of Y:

3.76984, 2.91000, 3.17461, 3.46051, 3.73622,
3.82875, 1.99775, 3.60727, 3.37805.

Given a random sample of size 2, a 90% confidence interval for the mean is

$$[\bar{x}-12.706 \times \frac{s}{\sqrt{2}} , \quad \bar{x}+12.706 \times \frac{s}{\sqrt{2}}].$$

Taking the ten sample values in pairs, we obtain the five confidence intervals $[-5.982, 12.098]$, $[1.361, 4.723]$, $[1.847, 5.350]$, $[-8.719, 14.546]$, $[2.036, 4.949]$.

These are shown in the figure. We note that the true mean, 3, is contained in each interval.

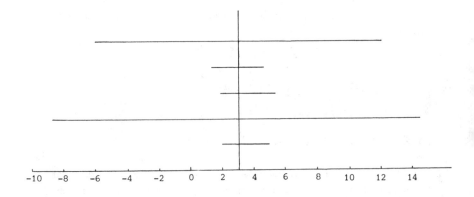

7. Is it true to say that a $100(1-\alpha)\%$ confidence interval for the mean of a normal distribution based on n observations is necessarily of smaller width if the variance is known than if the variance is unknown? Justify your answer.

¶ If the variance is known, then the half-width of the interval is $z_\gamma \sigma/\sqrt{n}$, where $\gamma = 1-\alpha/2$, while if the variance is unknown, it is $t_\gamma(n-1)s/\sqrt{n}$. While $t_\gamma(n-1) > z_\gamma$ for all n, s may be smaller than σ and so the interval can be wider when the variance is known than when it is unknown. (This is illustrated in Problem 5 above.)

8. Show that
$$\sum_{i=1}^{n}(x_i-c)^2 = \sum_{i=1}^{n}(x_i-\bar{x})^2 + n(c-\bar{x})^2,$$
where $\bar{x} = \sum_{i=1}^{n} x_i/n$.

A random sample of size 20 from the normal distribution $N(\mu,\sigma^2)$ yielded results $x_1,x_2,\ldots,x_{20}$ such that
$$\sum_{i=1}^{20} x_i = 6320, \qquad \sum_{i=1}^{20}(x_i-300)^2 = 212000.$$

(i) Find unbiased estimates of μ and σ^2.

(ii) Determine a 95% confidence interval for μ.

¶ $\sum(x_i-x)^2 = \sum[(x_i-\bar{x})+(\bar{x}-c)]^2$

$\qquad = \sum(x_i-\bar{x})^2 + 2(\bar{x}-c)\sum(x_i-\bar{x}) + n(\bar{x}-c)^2$

Now $\sum(x_i-\bar{x}) = \sum x_i-n\bar{x} = 0$, by definition.

Hence $\sum(x_i-c)^2 = \sum(x_i-\bar{x})^2 + n(c-\bar{x})^2$.

(i) From the data, $\bar{x} = 6320/20 = 316$.

Hence $\sum(x_i-\bar{x})^2 = \sum(x_i-300)^2 - 20(300-316)^2$

$\qquad\qquad = 212000-5120$

$\qquad\qquad = 206880$

and $\frac{1}{19}\sum(x_i-\bar{x})^2 = 10888.4$.

Therefore 316 and 10888.4 are unbiased estimates of μ and σ^2.

(ii) A 95% confidence interval for μ is given by

$$[316-2.093\sqrt{\frac{10888.4}{20}} \;,\quad 316+2.093\sqrt{\frac{10888.4}{20}}],$$

as $t_{0.975}(19) = 2.093$.

The interval is therefore [267.16, 364.84].

9. The following is a summary of data collected in an investigation of the earnings of two professions A and B.

Profession A

Sample size = 60, $\quad \sum_{i=1}^{60} x_i = 9060, \quad \sum_{i=1}^{60} x_i^2 = 1431485,$

where x_i is the income of the ith member of the sample in £100 units.

Profession B

Sample size = 80, $\quad \sum_{j=1}^{80} y_j = 13280, \quad \sum_{i=1}^{80} y_j^2 = 2246271,$

where y_j is the income of the jth member of the sample in £100 units.

Find (a) unbiased estimates of μ_A, μ_B, σ_A^2 and σ_B^2, the population means and variances,

     (b) an approximate 95% confidence interval for $\mu_B - \mu_A$.

¶ We find from the data that, in the obvious notation,

$$\bar{x} = 151, \quad s_x^2 = 1075,$$
$$\bar{y} = 166, \quad s_y^2 = 529.$$

These are unbiased estimates for $\mu_A, \sigma_A^2, \mu_B, \sigma_B^2$ respectively.

Assuming that the sample sizes are sufficiently large to justify the use of the Central Limit Theorem, and replacing the unknown variances by their estimates, we obtain the confidence limits

$$166-151 \pm 1.96\sqrt{\frac{1075}{60} + \frac{529}{80}} \;,$$

giving a confidence interval of [5.29, 24.71].

10. The sample mean and sample standard deviation of the masses of 20 pebbles picked at random from beach A are 132.5 and 20.61 grams respectively. The corresponding figures for 18 pebbles picked at random from beach B are 147.2 and 23.53. Use Student's t distribution to obtain a 95% confidence interval for the difference in the mean mass of pebbles from the two beaches. State your assumptions.

¶ We assume that the two samples are random samples from normal distributions of equal variance. Then, in the obvious notation, 95% confidence limits are given by

$$\bar{x}_B - \bar{x}_A \pm t_{0.975}(36) \sqrt{\frac{19s_A^2 + 17s_B^2}{36} \left(\frac{1}{20} + \frac{1}{18}\right)}$$

As $t_{0.975}(36) = 2.028$, these are

$$147.2 - 132.5 \pm 2.028 \sqrt{\frac{19 \times 20.61^2 + 17 \times 23.53^2}{36} \left(\frac{1}{20} + \frac{1}{18}\right)},$$

giving the confidence interval [0.18, 29.22].

11. Two classes were taught a subject by two different methods. At the end of term they were given the same examination and the marks were as follows.

   Class A
   47, 88, 55, 53, 58, 60, 68, 62, 53, 33,
   62, 33, 32, 49, 49, 54, 43, 49, 57, 54.

   Class B
   55, 51, 34, 44, 66, 75, 54, 82, 68, 51,
   55, 62, 45, 52, 59, 57, 69, 39, 47, 48.

Use Student's t distribution to obtain a 99% confidence interval for $\mu_B - \mu_A$, the difference in the mean marks obtained with the two teaching methods. Comment on your result.

¶ In the obvious notation,

$$\bar{x}_A = 52.95, \quad s_A^2 = 164.892,$$
$$\bar{x}_B = 55.65, \quad s_B^2 = 144.661.$$

The 95% confidence limits are

$$55.65 - 52.95 \pm 2.712 \sqrt{\frac{19 \times 164.892 + 19 \times 144.661}{38} \left(\frac{1}{20} + \frac{1}{20}\right)},$$

as $t_{0.995}(38) = 2.712$.

The 99% confidence interval is therefore $[-7.97, 13.37]$.

Although class B attained the higher mean mark, the confidence interval for $\mu_B - \mu_A$ contains zero and so it cannot be concluded that one teaching method is more effective than the other in general.

12. A psychologist believes that there is a tendency for the reaction time to a certain stimulus to increase after the age of nineteen. To investigate the question he measured the reaction times of 9 people when they were nineteen and when they were twenty-one. For each person and on each occasion the figure recorded was the mean of the results of 10 identical and independent tests. The results (in seconds) are shown below.

Subject	1	2	3	4	5	6	7	8	9
Age 19	0.275	0.321	0.267	0.305	0.350	0.302	0.293	0.259	0.268
Age 21	0.290	0.345	0.278	0.301	0.371	0.320	0.296	0.271	0.282

Calculate a 99% confidence interval for the difference in mean reaction times at the ages of nineteen and twenty-one and comment on whether or not the results support the psychologist's belief. State your assumptions.

¶ As this is a paired comparison we consider the differences between the two reaction times for each subject. These differences are

$-0.015, -0.024, -0.011, 0.004, -0.021, -0.018, -0.003, -0,012, -0.014$

The mean difference is $-0.012\dot{6}$, and the standard deviation is 0.008718.

A 99% confidence interval for the differences in the mean reaction times is therefore

$$[-0.012\dot{6} - 3.355 \times \frac{0.008718}{\sqrt{9}} \; , \; -0.012\dot{6} + 3.355 \times \frac{0.008718}{\sqrt{9}}]$$

i.e. $[-0.0224, -0.0029]$,

as $t_{0.995}(8) = 3.355$.

Since this interval contains negative values only, the experimental results support the psychologist's belief.

We assume that the differences are independent and identically distributed normal random variables.

13. A multinational company decided to instruct its many overweight executives to go jogging each lunchtime. The company measured the weights of 10 executives before they started their jogging programme and again two months later. The weights before and after are shown below.

Before (kg)   92.5 97.2 94.6 95.4 98.6 87.2 95.6 89.4 91.5 93.2
After (kg)   88.7 95.2 89.4 94.2 94.5 84.6 87.8 85.9 88.2 85.7

Assuming that changes in weight are normally distributed, obtain a 95% confidence interval for the mean decrease in weight of executives participating in the programme.

¶ As this is a paired comparison we take differences and consider the changes in weight. The decreases are

    3.8, 2.0, 5.2, 1.2, 4.1, 2.6, 7.8, 3.5, 3.3, 7.5.

The mean of these is 4.1 and the standard deviation is 2.176. A 95% confidence interval for the mean decrease is

$$[4.1-2.262 \times \frac{2.176}{\sqrt{10}} , \quad 4.1+2.262 \times \frac{2.176}{\sqrt{10}}]$$

i.e.   [2.543, 5.657],

as $t_{0.975}(9) = 2.262$.

14. A certain calculation involves the addition of 10000 numbers. Each number is subject to a rounding error which is uniformly distributed over the interval $(-5\times10^{-6}, 5\times10^{-6})$. Assuming that the errors are independent, find 99.9% confidence limits for the true value of the sum given that its computed value is exactly 10000.

¶ Let μ denote the true value of the sum and let X_i denote the error in the ith number.
Then

$$Y = \sum_{i=1}^{10000} X_i$$

is the total error and $\mu+Y$ is the computed value. As each X_i has zero expectation, Y has zero expectation and the computed value has mean μ.

Now
$$\text{Var}(X_i) = \frac{(5 \times 10^{-6} - (-5 \times 10^{-6}))^2}{12} = \frac{10^{-10}}{12}$$

and $\text{Var}(Y) = \frac{10^{-6}}{12}$.

Therefore, by the Central Limit Theorem, the computed value has the distribution $N(\mu, \frac{10^{-6}}{12})$ and 99.9% confidence limits for μ are

$$10000 \pm 3.29 \times \sqrt{\frac{10^{-6}}{12}}$$

i.e. 10000 ± 0.00095.

15. Two independent random variables X,Y are normally distributed with known, common variance σ^2 but unknown means μ_x, μ_y respectively. Two random samples are obtained, one from the distribution of X and one from the distribution of Y, and it is desired to find a 95% confidence interval for $\mu_x - \mu_y$. Given that the combined sample size is 100, prove that the width is minimised when both sample sizes are equal to 50.

¶ Let n be the sample size from the distribution of X, so that 100-n is that from the distribution of Y.

The half-width of the interval for $\mu_x - \mu_y$ is

$$1.96 \sqrt{\frac{\sigma^2}{n} + \frac{\sigma^2}{100-n}}$$

and is minimised if

$$\frac{1}{n} + \frac{1}{100-n} = \frac{100}{n(100-n)}$$

is minimised, that is if n(100-n) is maximised.

Now $n(100-n) = 2500-(50-n)^2$

and this is maximised if n = 50.

16. (a) Let $X_1, X_2, \ldots, X_{16}$ be a random sample from a normal distribution with unknown mean μ and unknown variance σ^2. Show that

$$[\bar{X} - 0.6505S, \infty)$$

is a 99% confidence interval for μ.

(b) A company develops a new type of fibre and claims that the mean breaking strength exceeds 50 Newtons. The breaking strength of 16 randomly selected fibres are as follows:

48.73, 52.79, 51.05, 51.31, 50.65, 51.23, 52.01, 50.52,

49.43, 50.59, 50.60, 50.37, 49.29, 49.70, 51.82, 52.10.

Assuming that the breaking strengths of the fibres are normally distributed, examine the company's claim using a 99% confidence interval of the form considered in (a).

¶ (a) From the definition of Student's t-distribution, we know that

$$T = \frac{\bar{X}-\mu}{S/\sqrt{n}}$$

has a Student's t-distribution with n-1 degrees of freedom. Therefore

$$T = \frac{4(\bar{X}-\mu)}{S}$$

has a t-distribution with 15 degrees of freedom.

Now from Table 3,

$$P(T \leq 2.602) = 0.99.$$

Hence $0.99 = P(T \leq 2.602)$

$$= P(\bar{X}-\mu \leq 0.6505S)$$

$$= P(\mu \geq \bar{X} - 0.6505S)$$

Hence $[\bar{X} - 0.6505S, \infty)$ is a 99% confidence interval for μ. This is called a *one-sided* confidence interval.

(b) From the data we find that

$$\bar{x} = 50.762, \ s = 1.1154.$$

Thus the interval of the type in (a) is given by

$$[50.762-0.6505 \times 1.1154, \infty) = [50.036, \infty).$$

The company's claim seems to be well founded. We are 99% certain that the mean breaking strength is at least 50.036. Because we are interested in whether the mean is at least a certain value, this type of confidence interval is a natural one to consider here.

17. In a flag-day appeal, members of the public are asked to buy a flag to wear in their buttonhole. The price of a flag is either ten pence or fifty pence, depending on the buyer's generosity. At the end of the day 20000 flags have been sold and the proceeds are returned to the secretary in a large

number of collection boxes. He is asked for a quick estimate of
the total proceeds, and he opens one of the boxes. He finds that
it contains 71 ten pence pieces and 29 fifty pence pieces. Find
a 95% confidence interval for the total proceeds.
He opens a second box and finds that this contains 80 ten pence
pieces and 32 fifty pence pieces. Find a new 95% confidence
interval for the total proceeds, using all the available information.

¶ An approximate 95% confidence interval for p, the proportion of
50 pence pieces in the whole collection, is

$$[0.29 - 1.96 \sqrt{\frac{0.29 \times 0.71}{100}} \; , \; 0.29 + 1.96 \sqrt{\frac{0.29 \times 0.71}{100}}]$$

i.e. $[0.20106, 0.37894]$.
The total proceeds, in pounds, are

$$200(50p + 10(1-p)) = 2000(1+4p).$$

Therefore an approximate 95% confidence interval for the total
proceeds is

$$[2000(1 + 4 \times 0.20106), \; 2000(1 + 4 \times 0.37894)] = [3608.50, 5031.50].$$

After the second sample the observed proportion of 50 pence
pieces is $61/212$ and a new 95% confidence interval for p is

$$[\frac{61}{212} - 1.96 \sqrt{\frac{61 \times 151}{212^3}} \; , \; \frac{61}{212} + 1.96 \sqrt{\frac{61 \times 151}{212^3}}]$$

i.e. $[0.22680, 0.34868]$.
This leads to the confidence interval $[3814.40, 4789.44]$ for
the total proceeds.

18. A sociologist wishes to estimate the proportion of wives in a
city who are happy with their marriage. To overcome the diffi-
culty that a wife, if asked directly, may say that her marriage
is happy even when it is not, the following procedure is
adopted. Each member of a random sample of 500 married women
is asked to toss a fair coin but not to disclose the result.
If the coin lands 'heads', the question to be answered is
'Does your family own a car?' If it lands 'tails', the
question to be answered is 'Is your marriage a happy one?'
In either case the response is to be either 'Yes' or 'No'.
The respondent knows that the sociologist has no means of
knowing which question has been answered. Suppose that of
the 500 responses, 350 are 'Yes' and 150 are 'No'. Assuming

that every response is truthful and given that 75% of families own a car, estimate the proportion of wives who are happy with their marriage and obtain an approximate 90% confidence interval for this proportion.

¶ Let p denote the proportion of wives who are happy with their marriage, and let r be the probability that a response is 'Yes'.

$$r = P(\text{response is yes})$$
$$= P(\text{response is yes}|\text{heads})P(\text{heads})$$
$$+ P(\text{response is yes}|\text{tails})P(\text{tails})$$
$$= \frac{3}{4} \times \frac{1}{2} + p \times \frac{1}{2}.$$

Hence $p = 2r - 0.75$.

Now $\hat{r} = 350/500 = 0.7$

and so $\hat{p} = 1.4 - 0.75 = 0.65$.

A 90% confidence interval for r is given approximately by

$$[\hat{r} - 1.645\sqrt{\frac{\hat{r}(1-\hat{r})}{500}} , \quad \hat{r} + 1.645\sqrt{\frac{\hat{r}(1-\hat{r})}{500}}]$$

i.e. $[0.7 - 1.645\sqrt{\frac{0.21}{500}} , \quad 0.7 + 1.645\sqrt{\frac{0.21}{500}}]$

or $[0.6663, 0.7337]$.

Hence an approximate 90% confidence interval for p is

$$[2 \times 0.6663 - 0.75, 2 \times 0.7337 - 0.75]$$

i.e. $[0.5826, 0.7174]$.

Note that we cannot estimate p directly as we do not know the proportion of answers 'yes' to the relevant question.

19. Let [a,b] be a 100(1-α)% confidence interval for a parameter θ. Write down the corresponding probability statement and deduce that

(i) [f(a),f(b)] is a 100(1-α)% confidence interval for f(θ) if f is a strictly increasing function of θ,

(ii) [f(b),f(a)] is a 100(1-α)% confidence interval for f(θ) if f is a strictly decreasing function of θ.

¶ Let A,B denote the statistics whose observed values are a,b respectively. Then $P(A \leq \theta \leq B) = 1-\alpha$.

(i)   Suppose that f is a strictly increasing function.
Then $A \leqslant \theta \leqslant B \Leftrightarrow f(A) \leqslant f(\theta) \leqslant f(B)$
and so
$$P(f(A) \leqslant f(\theta) \leqslant f(B)) = 1-\alpha.$$
Hence   [f(a),f(b)] is a 100(1-α)% confidence interval
for f(θ).

(ii)   Suppose that f is a strictly decreasing function of θ.
Then $A \leqslant \theta \leqslant B \Leftrightarrow f(A) \geqslant f(\theta) \geqslant f(B)$
and $P(A \leqslant \theta \leqslant B) = P(f(B) \leqslant f(\theta) \leqslant f(A)) = 1-\alpha.$

Therefore [f(b),f(a)] is a 100(1-α)% confidence interval
for f(θ).

20.   Suppose that X has a Poisson distribution with mean θ. A random
sample of size 100 is taken from the distribution of X. Given
that the sample mean is 6.1, obtain an approximate 90% confidence
interval for θ. Find also an approximate 90% confidence interval
for $e^{-\theta}$, the probability that X takes the value zero.

¶   A 90% confidence interval for θ is given approximately by

$$[\bar{x} - 1.645 \sqrt{\tfrac{\bar{x}}{n}} , \quad \bar{x} + 1.645 \sqrt{\tfrac{\bar{x}}{n}}]$$

This follows from the fact that, by the Central Limit Theorem,
$\bar{X}$ has approximately a $N(\theta,\theta/n)$ distribution.

Here the interval is

$$[6.1-1.645 \sqrt{\tfrac{6.1}{100}} , \quad 6.1+1.645 \sqrt{\tfrac{6.1}{100}}]$$

i.e. [5.694, 6.506].

Using the result of Problem 19, a 90% confidence interval
for $e^{-\theta}$ is given approximately by

$$[e^{-6.506}, e^{-5.694}] = [0.0015, 0.0034].$$

21.   A random variable X has the distribution N(μ,100). A random
sample of size 100 from this distribution has a mean of 40.5.
Obtain a 95% confidence interval for $\theta = P(X \leqslant 30)$.

¶ $P(X \leq 30) = \Phi(\frac{30-\mu}{10})$

and this is a decreasing function of μ.

Now a 95% confidence interval for μ is given by

$$[\bar{x} - 1.96\frac{\sigma}{\sqrt{n}} , \bar{x} + 1.96\frac{\sigma}{\sqrt{n}}]$$

i.e. $[40.5-1.96, 40.5+1.96]$

or $[38.54, 42.46].$

Therefore, by the result of Problem 19, a 95% confidence interval for $P(X \leq 30)$ is

$$[\Phi(\frac{30-42.46}{10}) , \Phi(\frac{30-38.54}{10})]$$

i.e. $[\Phi(-1.246), \Phi(-0.854)]$

or $[0.1064, 0.1966].$

22. It is desired to estimate the mean number of stoppages per day of a certain piece of machinery. Assuming that the numbers of stoppages on different days are independent, and given that there were 96 days out of 1000 without a stoppage, calculate an approximate 95% confidence interval for the probability p that there is no stoppage on a given day. Assuming that the number of stoppages in a day has a Poisson distribution with mean λ, convert this interval to a 95% confidence interval for λ.

¶   The number of days without a stoppage has a Binomial distribution B(1000,p). Hence a 95% confidence interval for p is given approximately by

$$[\hat{p}-1.96 \sqrt{\frac{\hat{p}(1-\hat{p})}{n}} , \hat{p}+1.96 \sqrt{\frac{\hat{p}(1-\hat{p})}{n}}].$$

Here $\hat{p} = 96/1000$, so that the interval is

        $[0.0777, 0.1143].$

If the number of stoppages in a day has a Poisson distribution with mean λ, the probability of no stoppages on a given day is $e^{-\lambda}$.

Therefore

$$\lambda = -\log_e p$$

and a 95% confidence interval for λ is

$$[-\log_e 0.1143, \ -\log_e 0.0777] = [2.169, \ 2.555],$$

using the result of Problem 19.

23. A warehouse has 200 shelves, each 150 cm high, on which to store a consignment of 20,000 sheets of a certain grade of chipboard whose nominal thickness is 1.5 cm. The actual thickness of a randomly selected sheet is normally distributed with fixed, but unknown, mean μ and standard deviation 0.1 cm. The consignment is divided into 200 shelf-lots of 100 sheets. Write down an expression for the probability that a given shelf-lot fits the shelf. Hence find an approximate 95% confidence interval for μ, given that of the 200 shelf-lots, 80 do not fit into their shelves.

¶ Let Y_i be the thickness of the i-th shelf-lot, i=1,...,200. As the thickness of a randomly selected sheet is $N(\mu, 0.01)$, Y_i is $N(100\mu, 1)$. The probability that a given shelf-lot fits the shelf is therefore

$$P(Y_i \leq 150) = \Phi(150 - 100\mu) = p, \text{ say.}$$

The observed proportion of shelf-lots that fit their shelves is $\hat{p} = 120/200 = 0.6$. Hence a 95% confidence interval for p is approximately

$$[0.6 - 1.96 \sqrt{\frac{0.4 \times 0.6}{200}}, \quad 0.6 + 1.96 \sqrt{\frac{0.4 \times 0.6}{200}}]$$

i.e. [0.5321, 0.6679].

Now $\quad 150 - 100\mu = \Phi^{-1}(p)$

and $\quad\quad \mu = 1.5 - \Phi^{-1}(p)/100.$

This is a decreasing function of p and, by the result of Problem 19, a 95% confidence interval for μ is given by

$$[1.5 - \Phi^{-1}(0.6679)/100, \ 1.5 - \Phi^{-1}(0.5321)/100].$$

From Table 2,

$$\Phi^{-1}(0.6679) \approx 0.4341, \ \Phi^{-1}(0.5321) \approx 0.0806.$$

and the confidence interval for μ is [1.496, 1.499].

24. The numbers of neutrinos detected each day by a counting device
are independent random variables with a common Poisson distribution. The frequency distribution of numbers of neutrinos for
1000 successive days is shown below.

number per day	0	1	2	3	4	5	6	7	8
frequency	130	277	264	175	98	33	16	6	1

Find an approximate 95% confidence interval for the mean of the
distribution. Find also an approximate 95% confidence interval
for the expected proportion of days during which no neutrinos
are detected using (a) the confidence interval already obtained
for the mean, (b) the observed proportion of days when no
neutrinos are detected. Offer an explanation of why the
interval obtained in (b) is wider than the one obtained in (a).

¶ The observed sample mean is found to be 2.033.
Hence an approximate 95% confidence interval is

$$[2.033-1.96\sqrt{\frac{2.033}{1000}} , \quad 2.033+1.96\sqrt{\frac{2.033}{1000}}]$$

i.e. [1.945, 2.121]

The probability p that no neutrino is detected on a given day
is $e^{-\lambda}$, where λ is the mean of the Poisson distribution. Using
the result of Problem 19, a confidence interval for p is therefore

$$[e^{-2.121}, e^{-1.945}] = [0.1199, 0.1430].$$

An alternative method is to use the fact that the number of
days with no detections has a binomial distribution. If $\hat{p}$ is
the observed proportion of such days, then a confidence interval
for p is

$$[\hat{p}-1.96\sqrt{\frac{\hat{p}(1-\hat{p})}{1000}} , \quad p+1.96\sqrt{\frac{\hat{p}(1-\hat{p})}{100}}].$$

Here $\hat{p} = 0.130$ and the interval is [0.1092, 0.1508].

This second interval is wider than the first, as it is based
on only a small part of the available information, namely the
number of days with no detections. The first method makes
fuller use of the data and so we would expect it to be narrower.

25. In an experiment, a beam of charged particles is aimed at a detector. A thin metal foil which deflects a proportion of these particles was placed between the source and the detector. The probability that a particular charged particle is detected is p, independently of all others. In one particular experiment 10^4 particles were fired at the detector and 5000 were detected. Obtain an approximate 95% confidence interval for p. In a second experiment two thin metal foils were positioned between the source and the detector in such a way that the probability of a particular particle being detected is p^2. In this experiment only 2500 of 10^4 particles were detected. Use the data from this experiment to obtain a 95% confidence interval for p.

¶ The observed proportion detected is 0.5 and a confidence interval for p is

$$[0.5 - 1.96 \sqrt{\frac{0.5 \times 0.5}{10000}} , \ 0.5 + 1.96 \sqrt{\frac{0.5 \times 0.5}{10000}}]$$

i.e. [0.4902, 0.5098].

If $r = p^2$, a 95% confidence interval for r is

$$[0.25 - 1.96 \sqrt{\frac{0.25 \times 0.75}{10000}}, \ 0.25 + 1.96 \sqrt{\frac{0.25 \times 0.75}{10000}}]$$

as a quarter of the particles were detected. This interval is

[0.2415, 0.2585].

As this is an interval for p^2, an interval for p is

$[\sqrt{0.2415}, \ \sqrt{0.2585}] = [0.4914, 0.5084]$.

26. Let f be a function such that $0 \leqslant f(x) \leqslant 1$ for $0 \leqslant x \leqslant 1$ and let p denote the probability that a point chosen at random in the unit square $\{(x,y): 0 \leqslant x \leqslant 1, 0 \leqslant y \leqslant 1\}$ will fall below the graph of f. Suppose that n points are chosen at random in the square and let $\hat{p}$ denote the proportion which fall below the graph of f. Show that $\hat{p}$ is an unbiased estimator of the definite integral

$$\int_0^1 f(x) \ dx$$

and write down an approximate 90% confidence interval for the value of this integral.

Use a table of random numbers to choose a random sample of
30 points from the square and hence obtain an approximate
90% confidence interval for

$$\int_0^1 \frac{e^{-\frac{1}{2}x^2}}{\sqrt{2\pi}} \; dx.$$

Can you think of a simple modification of the method which
will make it more efficient?

¶ As the area of the square is unity, the area below the graph
of f is equal to p

i.e. $\qquad p = \int_0^1 f(x) \; dx$

We know that $\hat{p}$ is an unbiased estimate of p and so $\hat{p}$ is an
unbiased estimator of the definite integral. Furthermore,
an approximate 90% confidence interval is given by

$$[\hat{p}-1.645 \; \sqrt{\tfrac{\hat{p}(1-\hat{p})}{n}} \; , \quad \hat{p}+1.645 \; \sqrt{\tfrac{\hat{p}(1-\hat{p})}{n}} \;].$$

We choose pairs of random numbers between 0 and 1 by using
Table 11, starting with the first row. The first two blocks
of digits are 43980 and 25863. Thus the first randomly
selected point is $(x_1, y_1) = (0.43980, 0.25863)$. We find that

$$\frac{1}{\sqrt{2\pi}} e^{-\frac{1}{2}x_1^2} = 0.36217 > y_1 = 0.25863.$$

So the first point lies below the curve.

The next point is $(x_2, y_2) = (0.26439, 0.96848)$ and, since

$$\frac{1}{\sqrt{2\pi}} e^{-\frac{1}{2}x_2^2} = 0.38524 < y_2 = 0.96848,$$

it lies above the curve.

If we do this for 30 points in all we obtain the following
sequence of results, where a denotes 'above' and b denotes
'below',

$\qquad$ babbabaabaabbaaabaaaaaabaaaaba.

Thus $\hat{p}$ = 10/30 and an approximate 90% confidence interval
is

$$[\tfrac{1}{3} - 1.645 \sqrt{\tfrac{1}{3} \times \tfrac{2}{3} \times \tfrac{1}{30}} \; , \; \tfrac{1}{3} + 1.645 \sqrt{\tfrac{1}{3} \times \tfrac{2}{3} \times \tfrac{1}{30}}]$$

i.e. $\quad [0.19175, 0.47491].$

The true value is $\Phi(1)-\Phi(0) = 0.3413$ which is in this interval.
The method is inefficient because the proportion of the points
that lie above the curve is unnecessarily high. The maximum
value of $e^{-\frac{1}{2}x^2}/\sqrt{2\pi}$ is $1/\sqrt{2\pi}$. We can therefore modify the method
by choosing points at random in the rectangle $\{(x,y) : 0 \leq x \leq 1,$
$0 \leq y \leq 1/\sqrt{2\pi}\}$. The proportion $\hat{a}$ of points that fall below the
curve estimates the proportion a of the rectangle occupied by
the area below the curve. Thus $\hat{a}/\sqrt{2\pi}$ will be an unbiased
estimate of the integral and 90% confidence limits are

$$\frac{\hat{a}}{\sqrt{2\pi}} \pm 1.645 \sqrt{\frac{\hat{a}(1-\hat{a})}{2\pi n}}$$

Using the same sequence of random digits as before, we find
that $\hat{a} = 27/30$. So the estimate of the integral is 0.35905
and the 90% confidence interval is [0.3231, 0.3950]. This
interval is shorter than the previous one, reflecting the
greater efficiency of the modified procedure.

27. Let $\hat{p}$ denote the proportion of successful trials in a sequence
of n independent Bernoulli trials with success probability p.
For large values of n the probability that $\hat{p}$ satisfies the
inequality

$$|\hat{p}-p| \leq 1.96 \sqrt{\frac{p(1-p)}{n}}$$

is approximately 0.95. By solving a certain quadratic equation,
show that 95% confidence limits for p are given approximately by

$$\frac{1}{1+1.96^2/n}(\hat{p} + \frac{1.96^2}{2n} \pm 1.96 \sqrt{\frac{\hat{p}(1-\hat{p})}{n} + \frac{1.96^2}{4n^2}}).$$

Evaluate these limits when (i) n=40 and $\hat{p}=0.5$, (ii) n=100 and
$\hat{p}=0.1$, (iii) n=400 and $\hat{p}=0.1$. Compare these limits with those
given by

$$\hat{p} \pm 1.96 \sqrt{\frac{\hat{p}(1-\hat{p})}{n}}.$$

¶ Since $\qquad P(|\hat{p}-p| \leq 1.96 \sqrt{\frac{p(1-p)}{n}}) \approx 0.95,$

$$P((\hat{p}-p)^2 \leq 1.96^2 \frac{p(1-p)}{n}) \approx 0.95.$$

Now

$$(\hat{p}-p)^2 \leq 1.96^2 \frac{p(1-p)}{n}$$

is equivalent to

$$p^2(1 + \frac{1.96^2}{n}) - 2p(\hat{p} + \frac{1.96^2}{2n}) + \hat{p}^2 \leq 0.$$

This is satisfied if p lies between the roots of the quadratic equation

$$p^2(1 + \frac{1.96^2}{n}) - 2p(\hat{p} + \frac{1.96^2}{2n}) + \hat{p}^2 = 0.$$

Using the formula for the roots of a quadratic equation and simplifying, we find that the roots are given by

$$\frac{1}{1+1.96^2/n}(\hat{p} + \frac{1.96^2}{2n} \pm 1.96 \sqrt{\frac{\hat{p}(1-\hat{p})}{n} + \frac{1.96^2}{4n^2}}) \tag{1}$$

These are the required confidence limits for p.

If the terms involving $1.96^2/n$ and $1.96^2/n^2$ are neglected these limits simplify to the well known expression

$$\hat{p} \pm 1.96 \sqrt{\frac{\hat{p}(1-\hat{p})}{n}} \tag{2}$$

This approximation works well provided n is large and $\hat{p}$ is not too close to O or 1.

(i)   When n=40 and $\hat{p}$=0.5, formula (1) gives the interval [0.3520, 0.6480] while formula (2) gives [0.3450, 0.6550].

(ii)   When n=100 and $\hat{p}$=0.1, (1) and (2) give the intervals [0.0552, 0.1744] and [0.0412, 0.1588].

(iii)   When n=400 and $\hat{p}$=0.1, (1) and (2) give the intervals [0.0743, 0.1333] and [0.0706, 0.1294].

28.   A random sample of 100 fragments of window glass is taken from a large population of such fragments. It is found that 10 of the 100 fragments had refractive indices of more than 1.52. Obtain approximate 95% confidence limits for p, the proportion of glass fragments in the population whose refractive indices exceed 1.52.

¶   This is the case n=100, $\hat{p}$=0.1 considered in Problem 27 and the required confidence interval is [0.0552, 0.1744].

29.   Let $\bar{X}$ denote the mean of a random sample of size n from a normal distribution with unknown mean μ and known variance σ^2. Show that, for $0 < \beta < \alpha < 1$,

$$[\bar{X} - z_{(1-\beta)}\sigma/\sqrt{n}, \ \bar{X} + z_{(1-\alpha+\beta)}\sigma/\sqrt{n}],$$

where $\Phi(z_p) = p \ (0 \leq p \leq 1)$, is a $100(1-\alpha)$% confidence interval for μ. Show, by differentiating the width of this interval with respect to β, that the shortest such interval is the symmetric one where $\beta=\frac{1}{2}\alpha$.

(Hint: Show first that

$$\frac{dz_p}{dp} = \frac{1}{\phi(z_p)}$$

where $\phi(x)$ denotes the standard normal probability density function.)

¶   Since $\bar{X}$ has the normal distribution $N(\mu,\sigma^2/n)$,

$$
\begin{aligned}
P(-z_{1-\alpha+\beta} \le \frac{\bar{X}-\mu}{\sigma/\sqrt{n}} \le z_{1-\beta}) &= \Phi(z_{1-\beta})-\Phi(-z_{1-\alpha+\beta}) \\
&= \Phi(z_{1-\beta})-1+\Phi(z_{1-\alpha+\beta}) \\
&= 1-\beta-1+1-\alpha+\beta \\
&= 1-\alpha.
\end{aligned}
$$

Now

$$-z_{1-\alpha+\beta} \le \frac{\bar{X}-\mu}{\sigma/\sqrt{n}} \le z_{1-\beta} \iff \bar{X}-z_{1-\beta}\frac{\sigma}{\sqrt{n}} \le \mu \le \bar{X}+z_{1-\alpha+\beta}\frac{\sigma}{\sqrt{n}}$$

and so

$$P(\bar{X}-z_{1-\beta}\frac{\sigma}{\sqrt{n}} \le \mu \le \bar{X}+z_{1-\alpha+\beta}\frac{\sigma}{\sqrt{n}}) = 1-\alpha.$$

Hence

$$[\bar{X}-z_{1-\beta}\frac{\sigma}{\sqrt{n}} \; , \; \bar{X}+z_{1-\alpha+\beta}\frac{\sigma}{\sqrt{n}}]$$

is a $100(1-\alpha)\%$ confidence interval for μ.

The width of the interval is

$$(z_{1-\alpha+\beta} + z_{1-\beta})\frac{\sigma}{\sqrt{n}}$$

and is minimised by minimising

$$f(\beta) = z_{1-\alpha+\beta} + z_{1-\beta}.$$

Now z_p is defined by the equation

$$p = \Phi(z_p) = \int_{-\infty}^{z_p} \phi(x)\, dx \quad \text{where } \phi(x) = \frac{1}{\sqrt{2\pi}}e^{-\frac{1}{2}x^2}.$$

Differentiating both sides with respect to p,

$$1 = \phi(z_p)\frac{dz_p}{dp}$$

so that

$$\frac{dz_p}{dp} = \frac{1}{\phi(z_p)}.$$

Now

$$\frac{df(\beta)}{d\beta} = \frac{d}{d\beta}(z_{1-\alpha+\beta}) + \frac{d}{d\beta}(z_{1-\beta})$$

$$= \frac{1}{\phi(z_{1-\alpha+\beta})} - \frac{1}{\phi(z_{1-\beta})} .$$

Therefore, at a minimum,

$$\phi(z_{1-\alpha+\beta}) = \phi(z_{1-\beta})$$

so that $z_{1-\alpha+\beta} = \pm z_{1-\beta}$.

Now if $z_{1-\alpha+\beta} = -z_{1-\beta}$, then

$$1-\alpha+\beta = 1-(1-\beta) = \beta$$

which is impossible as $\alpha < 1$.

Thus $z_{1-\alpha+\beta} = z_{1-\beta}$

so that $1-\alpha+\beta = 1-\beta$

i.e. $\beta = \frac{1}{2}\alpha$.

The shortest interval is therefore

$$[\bar{X} - z_{1-\alpha/2} \frac{\sigma}{\sqrt{n}} , \bar{X} + z_{1-\alpha/2} \frac{\sigma}{\sqrt{n}}] ,$$

as was to be shown.

30. Two independent random samples of sizes n_1 and n_2 are obtained from two normal distributions which have a common mean μ but different known variances σ_1^2 and σ_2^2 respectively. It is desired to construct a 95% confidence interval for μ based on the estimator

$$\hat{\mu} = \lambda \bar{X}_1 + (1-\lambda)\bar{X}_2 ,$$

where $\bar{X}_1$ and $\bar{X}_2$ are the respective sample means and λ is a constant. What choice of λ will produce the shortest confidence interval for μ? What is this interval?

¶ The distribution of $\hat{\mu}$ is $N(\mu, f(\lambda))$ where

$$f(\lambda) = \lambda^2 \frac{\sigma_1^2}{n_1} + (1-\lambda)^2 \frac{\sigma_2^2}{n_2} .$$

For a given value of λ, the shortest 95% confidence interval for μ is the symmetric interval

$$[\hat{\mu}-1.96\ \sqrt{f(\lambda)},\ \hat{\mu}+1.96\ \sqrt{f(\lambda)}\,].$$

Its width is minimised when $f(\lambda)$ is minimised. The equation

$$\frac{df(\lambda)}{d\lambda} = 2\lambda\ \frac{\sigma_1^2}{n_1} - 2(1-\lambda)\ \frac{\sigma_2^2}{n_2} = 0$$

gives

$$\lambda = \frac{\sigma_2^2/n_2}{\sigma_1^2/n_1 + \sigma_2^2/n_2}\ .$$

As the second derivative is positive, this value of λ minimises $f(\lambda)$ and we find that the minimum value is

$$\frac{\sigma_1^2\sigma_2^2}{n_2\sigma_1^2 + n_1\sigma_2^2}\ .$$

It follows that the shortest interval is

$$[\hat{\mu}-1.96\ \frac{\sigma_1\sigma_2}{\sqrt{n_2\sigma_1^2 + n_1\sigma_2^2}}\ ,\ \hat{\mu}+1.96\ \frac{\sigma_1\sigma_2}{\sqrt{n_2\sigma_1^2 + n_1\sigma_2^2}}\,]\ .$$

31. The percentage content of cobalt in a high quality magnet steel was estimated by one method of measurement to be 23.4 whereas a second independent method gave an estimate of 24.2. Both methods yield estimates which are normally distributed with their means equal to the true value but the variances of these two distributions are known to be 1.5 and 3.0 respectively. Find the shortest 95% confidence interval for the true percentage content.

¶ Let a measurement obtained by the first method be denoted by X and one obtained by the second by Y. Let μ be the true percentage content. Then X is $N(\mu, 1.5)$ and Y is $N(\mu, 3.0)$.

Consider $\qquad \hat{\mu} = \lambda X + (1-\lambda)Y.$

The result of Problem 30 shows that the shortest confidence interval for μ, based on $\hat{\mu}$, is found by taking λ to be

$$\frac{3.0}{1.5+3.0} = \frac{2}{3}\ ,$$

as the sample sizes are both 1.

Thus $\hat{\mu} = \frac{2}{3} \times 23.4 + \frac{1}{3} \times 24.2 = 23.\dot{6}$

and the interval is

$$[23.\dot{6} - 1.96 \sqrt{\frac{1.5 \times 3}{1.5 + 3}} \quad , \quad 23.\dot{6} + 1.96 \sqrt{\frac{1.5 \times 3}{1.5 + 3}}]$$

i.e.   [21.707, 25.627].

32. The random variable X has a binomial distribution B(n,p) and
     it is required to obtain a 90% confidence interval for p.
     One method is as follows. The upper confidence limit is
     obtained by finding the value of p for which the observed
     value of X is the 5th percentile of the distribution. The
     lower confidence limit is obtained by finding the value of
     p for which the observed value of X is the 95th percentile.
     Given that the observed value of X is zero, calculate a 90%
     confidence interval for p when (i) n=10, (ii) n=20,
     (iii) n=50, (iv) n=100.

¶   Denote the confidence interval by $[p_1, p_2]$. Let x be the
     observed value of X. Then p_2 is chosen so that

$$P(X \le x | X \text{ is } B(n,p_2)) = 0.05$$

and p_1 is chosen so that

$$P(X \le x | X \text{ is } B(n,p_1)) = 0.95.$$

If x = 0, these become

$$(1-p_2)^n = 0.05, \qquad (1-p_1)^n = 0.95$$

so that $p_2 = 1 - 0.05^{1/n}, \qquad p_1 = 1 - 0.95^{1/n}.$

For the specified values of n we obtain the following confidence
intervals.

(i)   n=10,   [0.0051, 0.2589],

(ii)   n=20,   [0.0026, 0.1391],

(iii) n=50,   [0.0010, 0.0582],

(iv)   n=100,   [0.0005, 0.0295].

This is a situation in which an interval based on the normal
approximation would be inaccurate. In fact the interval
with limits $\hat{p} \pm 1.645 \sqrt{\hat{p}(1-\hat{p})/n}$, has zero width.

33. Let $X_1, X_2, \ldots, X_n$ be a random sample from the uniform distribution on $[0, \theta]$ and let Z denote the sample maximum. Show that

$$[Z, \; Z(0.05)^{-1/n}]$$

is a 95% confidence interval for θ.

Obtain a random sample of size 10 from the uniform distribution on $[0, 6]$ and evaluate the above confidence interval. Carry out this exercise ten times in all and plot the results as in Figure 8.1 of Volume 2.

¶ Z has cumulative distribution function

$$G(z) = \left(\frac{z}{\theta}\right)^n, \qquad 0 \leq z \leq \theta.$$

Hence
$$P(a \leq Z \leq \theta) = G(\theta) - G(a)$$
$$= 1 - (a/\theta)^n.$$

Choose a so that
$$1 - (a/\theta)^n = 0.95.$$

Then
$$a = \theta(0.05)^{1/n}$$

and
$$0.95 = P(\theta(0.05)^{1/n} \leq Z \leq \theta)$$
$$= P(Z \leq \theta \leq Z(0.05)^{-1/n}).$$

Therefore $[Z, \; Z(0.05)^{-1/n}]$ is a 95% confidence interval for θ.

If Y is uniformly distributed on $[0, 1]$ then X=6Y is uniformly distributed on $[0, 6]$. We obtain a random sample from the distribution of Y in the usual way from Table 11 and so obtain a random sample from X by multiplying by 6.

Using the first row of Table 11, the sample maximum is $6 \times 0.96848 = 5.81088$ and the 95% confidence interval is therefore

$$[5.81088, \; 5.81088(0.05)^{-1/10}] = [5.81088, \; 7.84052].$$

Using the next nine rows of Table 11, the sample values of Z and the resulting confidence intervals are as follows.

Sample Maximum	Confidence Interval
5.9350	[5.9350, 8.0080]
5.1942	[5.1942, 7.0084]
5.3516	[5.3516, 7.2209]
5.2010	[5.2010, 7.0176]
5.9786	[5.9786, 8.0668]
5.8046	[5.8046, 7.8321]
3.4351	[3.4351, 4.6350]
4.9921	[4.9921, 6.7358]
5.8109	[5.8109, 7.8406]

Note that only one interval does not contain the upper limit of 6. All ten confidence intervals are plotted below.

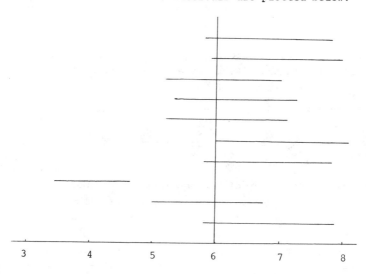

34. A large population whose mean is μ is divided into two sub-populations (or strata) A and B whose means and variances are respectively μ_a, σ_a^2 and μ_b, σ_b^2. Let p_a and p_b denote the respective probabilities that a randomly selected individual belongs to A and B. Suppose that random samples of sizes n_a and n_b are taken from A and B respectively and consider the weighted sample mean

$$\bar{X}_w = p_a \bar{X}_a + p_b \bar{X}_b,$$

where $\bar{X}_a$ and $\bar{X}_b$ are the means of the samples from A and B.

Assuming that the quantities p_a, p_b and σ_a^2, σ_b^2 are known, show that $\bar{X}_w$ is an unbiased estimator of μ and use the Central Limit Theorem to show that 95% confidence limits for μ are given approximately by

$$\bar{X}_w \pm 1.96 \sqrt{\frac{(p_a \sigma_a)^2}{n_a} + \frac{(p_b \sigma_b)^2}{n_b}} .$$

¶   We know that $E(\bar{X}_a) = \mu_a$, $E(\bar{X}_b) = \mu_b$.

Hence $E(\bar{X}_w) = p_a \mu_a + p_b \mu_b = \mu$

and $\bar{X}_w$ is an unbiased estimator for μ.

Also $Var(\bar{X}_w) = p_a^2 Var(\bar{X}_a) + p_b^2 Var(\bar{X}_b)$

$$= \frac{p_a^2 \sigma_a^2}{n_a} + \frac{p_b^2 \sigma_b^2}{n_b} .$$

By the Central Limit Theorem, $\bar{X}_a$ and $\bar{X}_b$ are approximately normally distributed. As $\bar{X}_w$ is a linear combination of $\bar{X}_a$ and $\bar{X}_b$, the same is true of $\bar{X}_w$.

Hence, by the standard argument, 95% confidence limits for μ are

$$\bar{X}_w \pm 1.96 \sqrt{\frac{(p_a \sigma_a)^2}{n_a} + \frac{(p_b \sigma_b)^2}{n_b}} .$$

35. When the concentration of hormone in a blood sample is measured the result is subject to error. Suppose that if the true concentration is μ and X is the measurement, then X is $N(\mu, \sigma^2)$ where $\sigma = k\mu$ and k is a known constant. Thus the standard deviation of X is directly proportional to μ and the coefficient of variation is equal to k. Let $\bar{X}$ denote the mean of n independent measurements of the concentration of hormone in the sample. Show that

$$[\frac{\bar{X}}{1+1.96k/\sqrt{n}} , \frac{\bar{X}}{1-1.96k/\sqrt{n}}]$$

is a 95% confidence interval for μ, provided that $\sqrt{n} > 1.96k$.

If the value of $\sigma = k\mu$ were known, then

$$[\bar{X} - 1.96\sigma/\sqrt{n}, \ \bar{X} + 1.96\sigma/\sqrt{n}]$$

would be a 95% confidence interval for μ. Replacing μ by $\bar{X}$ gives

$$[\bar{X}(1-1.96k/\sqrt{n}), \ \bar{X}(1+1.96k/\sqrt{n})] ,$$

which is an approximate 95% confidence interval for μ. Show that for large n the two confidence intervals are approximately equal.

¶ As X is $N(\mu, k^2\mu^2)$, $\bar{X}$ is $N(\mu, \dfrac{k^2\mu^2}{n})$.

Therefore $P(-1.96 \leq \dfrac{(\bar{X}-\mu)\sqrt{n}}{k\mu} \leq 1.96) = 0.95$

Now $-1.96 \leq \dfrac{(\bar{X}-\mu)\sqrt{n}}{k\mu} \leq 1.96 \iff -1.96k\mu \leq (\bar{X}-\mu)\sqrt{n} \leq 1.96k\mu$

$$\iff \mu(\sqrt{n}-1.96k) \leq \bar{X}\sqrt{n} \leq \mu(\sqrt{n}+1.96k)$$

$$\iff \frac{\bar{X}}{1+1.96k/\sqrt{n}} \leq \mu \leq \frac{\bar{X}}{1-1.96k/\sqrt{n}}$$

provided $1.96k/\sqrt{n} > 0$.

Hence

$$P(\frac{\bar{X}}{1+1.96k/\sqrt{n}} \leq \mu \leq \frac{\bar{X}}{1-1.96k/\sqrt{n}}) = 0.95$$

Thus

$$[\frac{\bar{X}}{1+1.96k/\sqrt{n}}, \frac{\bar{X}}{1-1.96k/\sqrt{n}}]$$

is a 95% confidence interval for μ.

If n is large, $\dfrac{1}{1-1.96k/\sqrt{n}} = (1-1.96\dfrac{k}{\sqrt{n}})^{-1}$

$$= 1+1.96\frac{k}{\sqrt{n}} + (1.96\frac{k}{\sqrt{n}})^2 + \ldots$$

$$\approx 1+1.96\frac{k}{\sqrt{n}}.$$

Similarly for large n,

$$\frac{1}{1+1.96\dfrac{k}{\sqrt{n}}} = (1+1.96\frac{k}{\sqrt{n}})^{-1} \approx 1-1.96\frac{k}{\sqrt{n}}.$$

Thus the interval is approximately

$$[\bar{X}(1-1.96k/\sqrt{n}), \bar{X}(1+1.96k/\sqrt{n})]$$

and the two intervals are approximately equal.

36. A gambler throws a fair die a large number of times. He is not prepared to say how many times he threw it, but he does say that he obtained 100 sixes. Use a suitable normal approximation to find a 95% confidence interval for the number of times he threw the die.

¶ Let n be the number of times that the die was thrown. We require a confidence interval for n. Let X_i be the number of sixes obtained with the i-th toss (i=1,...,n). The possible values of X_i are 0 and 1 and

$$Y = \sum_1^n X_i$$

has a binomial distribution $B(n,\frac{1}{6})$. Thus Y is approximately $N(n/6, 5n/36)$ and

$$P(-1.96 \le \frac{Y-n/6}{\sqrt{5n/36}} \le 1.96) \approx 0.95.$$

The event on the left hand side is equivalent to

$$\frac{(Y-n/6)^2}{5n/36} \le 1.96^2$$

i.e. $\frac{n^2}{36} - (\frac{Y}{3} + \frac{5 \times 1.96^2}{36})n + Y^2 \le 0.$

The roots of this quadratic function of n give approximate 95% confidence limits for n. Using the formula for the roots of a quadratic and simplifying, we obtain

$$6Y + \frac{5 \times 1.96^2}{2} \pm 18\sqrt{\frac{5 \times 1.96^2 Y}{54} + \frac{1.96^4 \times 25}{36^2}}$$

and these are the required limits.

Replacing Y by 100 we obtain the confidence interval

$$[501.8, 717.4]$$

As n is an integer we might prefer to quote the interval [501, 718].

9

Hypothesis Testing

Exercises 9.1 Introduction

1. A random sample is taken from the distribution of a random variable X. In each of the following cases, classify the hypothesis H as simple or composite.

   (i)   X is $N(\mu,1)$ and H: $\mu \neq 4$.

   (ii)   X is $B(10,p)$ and H: $p = \frac{1}{5}$.

   (iii)   X is $N(\mu,\sigma^2)$ and H: $\mu=0$, $\sigma=5$.

   (iv)   X has a Poisson distribution with mean λ and H: $\lambda=4$.

   (v)   X is $N(\mu,\sigma^2)$ and H: $\mu \neq 5$, $\sigma=2$.

   (vi)   X is $N(\mu,\sigma^2)$ and H: $\mu=-4$.

   (vii)   X is uniformly distributed on $[0,\theta]$ and H: $\theta=5$.

   (viii) X has an exponential distribution and H: $Var(X) = 1$.

   (ix)   H: X is normally distributed with mean 3.

   (x)   H: X has a Student's t distribution with 6 degrees of freedom.

¶ (i)   H is composite (the value of μ is not specified).

   (ii)   H is simple.

   (iii)   H is simple.

   (iv)   H is simple.

   (v)   H is composite (the value of μ is not specified).

   (vi)   H is composite (the value of σ^2 is not specified).

   (vii)   H is simple.

   (viii) H is simple (the density of X is $\lambda e^{-\lambda x}$ for $x \geqslant 0$, and if $Var(X) = 1$ it follows that $\lambda = 1$).

   (ix)   H is composite (the variance is not specified).

   (x)   H is simple.

2. Let $\bar{X}$ denote the mean of a random sample taken from the distribution of a random variable X whose mean is μ. The null hypothesis H_o: $\mu=4$ is to be tested against an alternative hypothesis H_1 using a critical region of one of the following forms:

$$C_1 = \{\bar{x}: \bar{x} > k_1\}, \quad C_2 = \{\bar{x}: \bar{x} < k_2\}, \quad C_3 = \{\bar{x}: \bar{x} < k_3 \text{ or } \bar{x} > k_4\}.$$

Which form is most appropriate in the following cases:
(i) H_1: $\mu \neq 4$, (ii) H_1: $\mu=2$, (iii) H_1: $\mu>4$, (iv) H_1: $\mu>6$ or $\mu<2$?

¶   (i) $C_3 = \{\bar{x}: \bar{x} < k_3 \text{ or } \bar{x} > k_4\}$, where $k_3 < 4$ and $k_4 > 4$, since extreme values support the alternative hypothesis.

(ii) $C_2 = \{\bar{x}: \bar{x} < k_2\}$, where $k_2 < 4$, since extreme values less than 4 support the alternative hypothesis.

(iii) $C_1 = \{\bar{x}: \bar{x} > k_1\}$, where $k_1 > 4$, since extreme values greater than 4 support the alternative hypothesis.

(iv) $C_3 = \{\bar{x}: \bar{x} < k_3 \text{ or } \bar{x} > k_4\}$, where $k_3 < 4$ and $k_4 > 4$, since extreme values support the alternative hypothesis.

3. Let Y be the number of heads obtained when a coin is tossed 10 times, and let p be the probability of obtaining a head. To choose between the hypotheses H_o: $p=0.5$ and H_1: $p=0.75$, a critical region of the form $C_k = \{y: y \geqslant k\}$ is used. Find the Type I and Type II error probabilities α and β for each integer value of k between 0 and 10 inclusive. Which critical region minimises $\alpha+\beta$?

¶   The Type I error probability α corresponding to the critical region C_k is given by

$$\begin{aligned}
\alpha &= P(\text{Reject } H_o | H_o \text{ true}) \\
&= P(Y \geqslant k | Y \text{ is } B(10,0.5)) \\
&= \sum_{i=k}^{10} {}^{10}C_i (0.5)^{10}.
\end{aligned}$$

The corresponding Type II error probability β is given by

$$\begin{aligned}
\beta &= P(\text{Accept } H_o | H_1 \text{ true}) \\
&= P(Y < k | Y \text{ is } B(10,0.75)) \\
&= \sum_{i=0}^{k-1} {}^{10}C_i (0.75)^i (0.25)^{10-i}.
\end{aligned}$$

The values of α and β can be calculated or obtained from binomial tables for all possible values of k, and are as follows.

k	α	β	α+β
0	1.00000	0.00000	1.00000
1	0.99902	0.00000	0.99902
2	0.98926	0.00003	0.98929
3	0.94531	0.00042	0.94573
4	0.82812	0.00351	0.83163
5	0.62305	0.01973	0.64278
6	0.37695	0.07813	0.45508
7	0.17187	0.22412	0.39599
8	0.05469	0.47441	0.52910
9	0.01074	0.75597	0.76671
10	0.00098	0.94369	0.94467

We see that k=7 minimises α+β.

4. The captain of a cricket team, about to play a series of five matches against another team, suspects that the opposing captain, who is a well known conjuror, is able to use unfair means to ensure that he always wins the toss. He decides to wait until the series is over and then, if he has lost all five tosses, to accuse the opposing captain of cheating. Let p denote the probability that the opposing captain wins the toss. If H_0: $p=\frac{1}{2}$ and H_1: $p=1$, describe in words the Type I and Type II errors and calculate their probabilities.

¶ Let H_0: $p=\frac{1}{2}$, i.e. the tossing is fair;
    H_1: $p=1$, i.e. the opposing captain cheats.
A Type I error occurs if H_0 is rejected when H_0 is true, i.e. the opposing captain is incorrectly accused of cheating.

A Type II error occurs if H_0 is accepted when H_1 is true, i.e. the tossing is said to be fair when in fact the opposing captain is cheating.

Let X denote the number of tosses won by the opposing captain. Then the critical region is given by
$$C = \{x: \ x=5\}.$$
With the usual notation,

$$\alpha = P(\text{Reject } H_o | H_o \text{ true})$$
$$= P(X=5 | X \text{ is } B(5,\tfrac{1}{2}))$$
$$= (\tfrac{1}{2})^5$$
$$= 1/32.$$

Also,

$$\beta = P(\text{Accept } H_o | H_1 \text{ true})$$
$$= P(X \leq 4 | X \text{ is } B(5,1))$$
$$= 0.$$

5. A seedsman sells two mixtures of tulip bulbs. Mixture A produces 50% red and 50% yellow flowers, while mixture B produces 75% red and 25% yellow flowers. He finds in a storeroom a large, unlabelled sack of tulip bulbs. In order to decide which mixture it contains he plants 100 bulbs and will conclude that the mixture is, in fact, B if the number of red flowers eventually produced exceeds a pre-selected integer m. Use binomial tables to find the Type I and Type II error probabilities α and β for m=62,63 and 64. Deduce the value of m which minimises $\alpha+\beta$. State carefully the assumptions you have made.

¶ Let X denote the number of red flowers obtained and define

$$H_o: X \text{ is } B(100, \tfrac{1}{2}), \text{ i.e. mixture A,}$$
$$H_1: X \text{ is } B(100, \tfrac{3}{4}), \text{ i.e. mixture B.}$$

The critical region is given by

$$C = \{x: x > m\}.$$

Now

$$\alpha = P(\text{Reject } H_o | H_o \text{ true})$$
$$= P(X > m | X \text{ is } B(100, \tfrac{1}{2}))$$
$$= 1 - P(X \leq m | X \text{ is } B(100, \tfrac{1}{2})).$$

Furthermore,

$$\beta = P(\text{Accept } H_o | H_1 \text{ true})$$
$$= P(X \leq m | X \text{ is } B(100, \tfrac{3}{4}))$$

To use binomial tables, we consider Y, the number of yellow flowers, which is $B(100, \tfrac{1}{4})$.

Now $\quad X+Y = 100.$

Thus, if $\quad X \leq m$

then

$$100-Y \leq m$$

or $Y \geq 100-m$.

Therefore

$$\beta = P(Y \geq 100-m \mid Y \text{ is } B(100,\tfrac{1}{4}))$$

$$= 1-P(Y \leq 100-m-1 \mid Y \text{ is } B(100,\tfrac{1}{4})).$$

We obtain the following values of α and β using binomial tables.

m	α	β	$\alpha+\beta$
62	0.00602	0.00275	0.00877
63	0.00332	0.00518	0.00850
64	0.00176	0.00941	0.01117

We see that m=63 minimises $\alpha+\beta$.

The assumptions made are

(i)   the bulbs are well mixed so that the number of 'reds'
      obtained can be taken to be binomially distributed,
(ii) all bulbs produce a single flower.

6. The random variable X has a normal distribution with standard
    deviation 3.5 but unknown mean μ. The hypothesis H_o: $\mu=3$ is
    to be tested against H_1: $\mu=4$ by taking a random sample of size
    50 from the distribution of X and rejecting H_o if the sample
    mean exceeds 3.4. Calculate the Type I and Type II error
    probabilities of this procedure.

¶   Under H_o, $\bar{X}$ is $N(3, 3.5^2/50)$.
    Under H_1, $\bar{X}$ is $N(4, 3.5^2/50)$.
    Then, with the usual notation,

$$\alpha = P(\text{Reject } H_o \mid H_o \text{ true})$$

$$= P(\bar{X} > 3.4 \mid \bar{X} \text{ is } N(3, 3.5^2/50))$$

$$= 1 - P(\bar{X} \leq 3.4 \mid \bar{X} \text{ is } N(3, 3.5^2/50))$$

$$= 1-\Phi\left[\frac{(3.4-3)\sqrt{50}}{3.5}\right]$$

$$= 1-\Phi(0.8081)$$

$$= 0.20952.$$

Also

$$\beta = P(\text{Accept } H_0 | H_1 \text{ true})$$
$$= P(\bar{X} \leq 3.4 | \bar{X} \text{ is } N(4, 3.5^2/50))$$
$$= \Phi\left[\frac{(3.4-4)\sqrt{50}}{3.5}\right]$$
$$= \Phi(-1.2122)$$
$$= 1-\Phi(1.2122)$$
$$= 1-0.88728$$
$$= 0.11272.$$

7. The internal diameter D of a randomly selected washer is $N(\mu, 0.0001)$. The hypothesis H_0: $\mu=10.00$ is to be tested against the hypothesis H_1: $\mu=10.01$ using the critical region $C=\{\bar{d}: \bar{d} \geq k\}$, where $\bar{d}$ is the mean of a random sample of n washer diameters. Find the smallest value of n for which both $\alpha \leq 0.05$ and $\beta \leq 0.10$.

¶ For the hypotheses given,

$$\alpha = P(\text{Reject } H_0 | H_0 \text{ true})$$
$$= P(\bar{D} \geq k | \bar{D} \text{ is } N(10.00, 0.0001/n))$$
$$= 1-\Phi(\frac{(k-10.00)\sqrt{n}}{0.01}).$$

Similarly,

$$\beta = P(\text{Accept } H_0 | H_1 \text{ true})$$
$$= P(\bar{D} < k | \bar{D} \text{ is } N(10.01, 0.0001/n))$$
$$= \Phi(\frac{(k-10.01)\sqrt{n}}{0.01}).$$

We therefore require to choose n and k so that

$$1-\Phi(\frac{(k-10.00)\sqrt{n}}{0.01}) \leq 0.05$$

and

$$\Phi(\frac{(k-10.01)\sqrt{n}}{0.01}) \leq 0.10.$$

It follows from these equations that

$$\Phi(\frac{(k-10.00)\sqrt{n}}{0.01}) \geq 0.95$$

or

$$\frac{(k-10.00)\sqrt{n}}{0.01} \geq 1.645. \tag{1}$$

Also,

$$\Phi(\frac{(10.01-k)\sqrt{n}}{0.01}) = 1-\Phi(\frac{(k-10.01)\sqrt{n}}{0.01})$$

$$\geq 0.90$$

so that

$$\frac{(10.01-k)\sqrt{n}}{0.01} \geq 1.282. \tag{2}$$

It follows from (1) and (2) that

$$(k-10.00)\sqrt{n} \geq 0.01645$$

and $(10.01-k)\sqrt{n} \geq 0.01282.$

Adding these inequalities, we obtain

$$0.01\sqrt{n} \geq 0.02927$$

or $n \geq 2.927^2 \approx 8.56.$

The smallest value of n satisfying this requirement is 9.

8. A random sample of size n is taken from a $N(\mu,\sigma^2)$ distribution. It is required to test the null hypothesis H_o: $\mu=\mu_o$ against the alternative hypothesis H_1: $\mu=\mu_1$, where $\mu_1 \geq \mu_o$, using a critical region of the form $C = \{\bar{x}:\bar{x} \geq k\}$. Show that

$$k = \frac{\mu_o + \mu_1}{2}$$

if the Type I and Type II error probabilities are to be equal.

¶ For the hypotheses given,

$$\alpha = P(\text{Reject } H_o | H_o \text{ true})$$
$$= P(\bar{X} \geq k | \bar{X} \text{ is } N(\mu_o, \sigma^2/n))$$
$$= 1 - \Phi\left(\frac{(k-\mu_o)\sqrt{n}}{\sigma}\right).$$

Similarly

$$\beta = P(\text{Accept } H_o | H_1 \text{ true})$$
$$= P(\bar{X} < k | \bar{X} \text{ is } N(\mu_1, \sigma^2/n))$$
$$= \Phi\left(\frac{(k-\mu_1)\sqrt{n}}{\sigma}\right)$$
$$= 1 - \Phi\left(\frac{(\mu_1-k)\sqrt{n}}{\sigma}\right).$$

If $\alpha=\beta$, it follows that

$$\Phi\left(\frac{(k-\mu_o)\sqrt{n}}{\sigma}\right) = \Phi\left(\frac{(\mu_1-k)\sqrt{n}}{\sigma}\right)$$

whence $\frac{(k-\mu_o)\sqrt{n}}{\sigma} = \frac{(\mu_1-k)\sqrt{n}}{\sigma}$

and $k = \frac{\mu_o + \mu_1}{2}.$

9. Let $X_1, X_2, \ldots, X_n$ be a random sample from a normal distribution
    with mean μ and standard deviation 2. The hypotheses
    $$H_o: \mu=2; \quad H_1: \mu=4$$
    are to be tested using a critical region of the form $C=\{\bar{x}: \bar{x}>k\}$.
    Find the value of k which minimises $\alpha+\beta$, the sum of the two
    error probabilities α and β. For this value of k, find the
    values of α and β in the cases $n=9,16,25,36$ and 49.

¶   For the hypotheses given,

$$\alpha = P(\text{Reject } H_o | H_o \text{ true})$$
$$= P(\bar{X} > k | \bar{X} \text{ is } N(2, \frac{4}{n}))$$
$$= 1-\Phi(\frac{(k-2)\sqrt{n}}{2}).$$

Similarly,

$$\beta = P(\text{Accept } H_o | H_1 \text{ true})$$
$$= P(\bar{X} \leq k | \bar{X} \text{ is } N(4, \frac{4}{n}))$$
$$= \Phi(\frac{(k-4)\sqrt{n}}{2}).$$

Thus
$$\alpha+\beta = 1-\Phi(\frac{(k-2)\sqrt{n}}{2}) + \Phi(\frac{(k-4)\sqrt{n}}{2}).$$

We require to choose k to minimise $\alpha+\beta$. Differentiating with
respect to k,

$$\frac{d}{dk}(\alpha+\beta) = -\frac{\sqrt{n}}{2}\phi(\frac{(k-2)\sqrt{n}}{2}) + \frac{\sqrt{n}}{2}\phi(\frac{(k-4)\sqrt{n}}{2})$$

where $\phi(x) = \Phi'(x)$.

Since $\Phi(x)$ is the standard normal distribution function, $\phi(x)$
is the standard normal probability density function given by

$$\phi(x) = \frac{1}{\sqrt{2\pi}} e^{-\frac{1}{2}x^2}.$$

Now $\alpha+\beta$ is minimised by putting

$$\frac{d}{dk}(\alpha+\beta) = 0$$

in which case

$$\phi(\frac{(k-2)\sqrt{n}}{2}) = \phi(\frac{(k-4)\sqrt{n}}{2})$$

i.e. $\dfrac{1}{\sqrt{2\pi}} e^{-\frac{1}{2}\cdot\frac{(k-2)^2 n}{4}} = \dfrac{1}{\sqrt{2\pi}} e^{-\frac{1}{2}\cdot\frac{(k-4)^2 n}{4}}$.

This requires either
$$(k-2) = (k-4)$$
which is impossible, or
$$(k-2) = -(k-4)$$
which gives
$$k = 3.$$

It can be verified that this gives a minimum for $\alpha+\beta$ by a further differentiation with respect to k.

With this value of k,
$$\alpha = 1-\Phi\left(\frac{\sqrt{n}}{2}\right)$$
and $$\beta = \Phi\left(-\frac{\sqrt{n}}{2}\right) = 1-\Phi\left(\frac{\sqrt{n}}{2}\right) = \alpha.$$

Evaluating this function for the given values of n, we obtain

n	α,β
9	0.06681
16	0.02275
25	0.00621
36	0.00135
49	0.00023

10. Let $X_1, X_2, \ldots, X_n$ be a random sample from the normal distribution $N(\mu, 16)$. The hypotheses
$$H_o: \mu=0; \quad H_1: \mu=4$$
are to be tested using a critical region of the form $C=\{\bar{x}: \bar{x}>k\}$. Let α and β denote the Type I and Type II error probabilities.

(a) Find α and β if n=25 and k=1.0.

(b) Find α and k if n=25 and β=0.05.

(c) Find n and k if α=0.05 and β=0.10.

(d) Find n and β if α=0.05 and k=0.75.

N.B. In (c) it is impossible to choose n to be an integer with α,β exactly equal to the values given. The value of n is to be chosen so that β is as close to 0.1 as possible. Similarly, in (d) the value of n is to be chosen so that α is as close to 0.05 as possible.

¶ For the hypotheses given,
$$\begin{aligned} \alpha &= P(\text{Reject } H_o | H_o \text{ true}) \\ &= P(\bar{X} > k | \bar{X} \text{ is } N(0, \frac{16}{n})) \\ &= 1-\Phi\left(\frac{k\sqrt{n}}{4}\right) \end{aligned}$$

and $\beta = P(\text{Accept } H_o | H_1 \text{ true})$
       $= P(\bar{X} \le k | \bar{X} \text{ is } N(4, \frac{16}{n}))$
       $= \Phi(\frac{(k-4)\sqrt{n}}{4})$
       $= 1 - \Phi(\frac{(4-k)\sqrt{n}}{4})$.

(a)   If n=25 and k=1.0 then

       $\alpha = 1 - \Phi(1.25)$
          $= 1 - 0.89435$
          $= 0.10565$

and $\beta = 1 - \Phi(3.75)$
          $= 1 - 0.99991$
          $= 0.00009$.

(b)   If n=25 and $\beta = 0.05$ then

       $0.05 = 1 - \Phi(\frac{5(4-k)}{4})$

       $\Phi(\frac{5(4-k)}{4}) = 0.95$

       $\frac{5(4-k)}{4} = 1.645$

whence $k = 2.684$.

It follows that
       $\alpha = 1 - \Phi(\frac{5 \times 2.684}{4})$
          $= 1 - \Phi(3.355)$
          $= 1 - 0.9996$
          $= 0.0004$.

(c)   If $\alpha = 0.05$ and $\beta = 0.10$ then

       $\Phi(\frac{k\sqrt{n}}{4}) = 1 - \alpha = 0.95$

so that
       $\frac{k\sqrt{n}}{4} = 1.645$

       or $k\sqrt{n} = 6.580$.   (1)

Also
       $\Phi(\frac{(4-k)\sqrt{n}}{4}) = 1 - \beta = 0.9$

so that
       $\frac{(4-k)\sqrt{n}}{4} = 1.282$

or $(4-k)\sqrt{n} = 5.128$.   (2)

Adding equations (1) and (2),

$$4\sqrt{n} = 11.708$$

or $n = 8.567$

This is not a permissible value for n, so we take n=8 or 9 since 8.567 is approximately midway between these values.

If we take n=8 then, to make α=0.05, we require

$$k\sqrt{n} = 6.580$$
$$k = \frac{6.580}{\sqrt{8}}$$
$$= 2.326.$$

In this case

$$\beta = 1-\Phi\left(\frac{(4-k)\sqrt{n}}{4}\right)$$
$$= 1-\Phi\left(\frac{(4-2.326)\sqrt{8}}{4}\right)$$
$$= 1-\Phi(1.1837)$$
$$= 1-0.8817$$
$$= 0.1183$$

If we take n=9 then, to make α=0.05, we require

$$k\sqrt{n} = 6.580$$
$$k = \frac{6.580}{\sqrt{9}}$$
$$= 2.193.$$

In this case,

$$\beta = 1-\Phi\left(\frac{(4-k)\sqrt{n}}{4}\right)$$
$$= 1-\Phi\left(\frac{(4-2.193)\sqrt{9}}{4}\right)$$
$$= 1-\Phi(1.3553)$$
$$= 1-0.91234$$
$$= 0.0877.$$

This second value of β is the closer to 0.1. So we take

n=9, k=2.193.

(d) If α=0.05 and k=0.75 then

$$0.05 = 1-\Phi\left(\frac{k\sqrt{n}}{4}\right)$$

or $\Phi\left(\frac{0.75\sqrt{n}}{4}\right) = 0.95$

$$\frac{0.75\sqrt{n}}{4} = 1.645$$

whence $\qquad$ n = 76.97.

It is clear without further investigation that we should take n=77.

It follows that

$$\beta = 1-\Phi\left(\frac{(4-k)\sqrt{n}}{4}\right)$$

$$= 1-\Phi\left(\frac{(4-0.75)\sqrt{77}}{4}\right)$$

$$= 1-\Phi(7.1297)$$

$$= 0.$$

11. The daily demand for a product has a Poisson distribution with mean λ, the demands on different days being statistically independent. It is desired to test the hypotheses H_0: $\lambda=0.7$, H_1: $\lambda=0.3$. The null hypothesis is to be accepted if in 20 days the number of days with no demand is less than 15. Calculate the Type I and Type II error probabilities.

¶ Let p denote the probability that the demand on a given day is zero.

Then
$$p = e^{-\lambda} = e^{-0.7} \text{ under } H_0,$$
$$= e^{-0.3} \text{ under } H_1.$$

If X denotes the number of days out of 20 with zero demand, it follows that

$$X \text{ is } B(20, e^{-0.7}) \text{ under } H_0,$$
$$X \text{ is } B(20, e^{-0.3}) \text{ under } H_1.$$

Thus

$$\alpha = P(\text{Reject } H_0 | H_0 \text{ true})$$
$$= P(X \geq 15 | X \text{ is } B(20, e^{-0.7}))$$
$$= 1-P(X \leq 14 | X \text{ is } B(20, 0.4966))$$
$$= 1-0.98028 \text{ (interpolating in binomial tables)}$$
$$= 0.01972.$$

Furthermore

$$\beta = P(\text{Accept } H_0 | H_1 \text{ true})$$
$$= P(X \leq 14 | X \text{ is } B(20, e^{-0.3}))$$
$$= P(X \leq 14 | X \text{ is } B(20, 0.7408)$$
$$= P(Y \geq 6 | Y \text{ is } B(20, 0.2592)$$

$= 1 - P(Y \le 5 | Y \text{ is } B(20, 0.2592))$

$= 1 - 0.58022$ (interpolating in binomial tables)

$= 0.41978$

12. A discrete random variable X has probability function $p(x)$. Consider the hypotheses

$$H_o: p(x) = p_o(x) = e^{-2}2^x/x!, \quad x=0,1,2,\ldots;$$

$$H_1: p(x) = p_1(x) = (\tfrac{1}{2})^{x+1}, \quad x=0,1,2,\ldots.$$

A single observation x is available and the hypotheses are to be tested using the critical region

$$C = \{x: \frac{p_1(x)}{p_o(x)} > 1\}.$$

Calculate the Type I and Type II error probabilities and comment on the choice of the critical region.

¶ x belongs to the given critical region if and only if x satisfies the inequality

$$p_1(x) > p_o(x).$$

Thus, with this choice of critical region, H_o is accepted if the observed value x is more likely to occur when H_o is true than if H_1 is true and H_o is rejected if x is more likely to occur when H_1 is true than if H_o is true.

To determine the values of x that satisfy the inequality we tabulate $p_o(x)$ and $p_1(x)$ below.

x	$p_o(x)$	$p_1(x)$
0	0.1353	0.5000
1	0.2707	0.2500
2	0.2707	0.1250
3	0.1804	0.0625
4	0.0902	0.0313
5	0.0361	0.0156
6	0.0120	0.0078
7	0.0034	0.0039
8	0.0009	0.0020

It is clear from this table that the critical region is

$$C = \{0, 7, 8, 9, \ldots\}.$$

Thus

$$\alpha = P(\text{Reject } H_0 | H_0 \text{ true})$$
$$= P(X = 0 \text{ or } X \geqslant 7 | H_0 \text{ true})$$
$$= 1 - P(1 \leqslant X \leqslant 6 | H_0 \text{ true})$$
$$= 1 - \sum_{x=1}^{6} e^{-2} \frac{2^x}{x!}$$
$$= 1 - (0.99547 - 0.13534) \quad \text{(using Poisson tables)}$$
$$= 0.13987.$$

Also

$$\beta = P(\text{Accept } H_0 | H_1 \text{ true})$$
$$= P(1 \leqslant X \leqslant 6 | H_1 \text{ true})$$
$$= \sum_{x=1}^{6} \left(\frac{1}{2}\right)^{x+1}$$
$$= \frac{63}{128}$$
$$\approx 0.49219.$$

Exercises 9.2 Significance Testing

1. The random variable X has a normal distribution with mean μ and unit variance. Given a random sample of size n, the hypotheses

$$H_0 : \mu = 2; \quad H_1 : \mu > 2$$

are to be tested using a critical region of the form

$$C = \{\bar{x} : \bar{x} > k\}.$$

If a result is significant at the 5% level, is it also significant at (a) the 10% level, (b) the 1% level?

¶ The significance level α is given by

$$\alpha = P(\text{Reject } H_0 | H_0 \text{ true})$$
$$= P(\bar{X} > k | \bar{X} \text{ is } N(2, 1/n))$$
$$= 1 - \Phi((k-2)\sqrt{n}).$$

Therefore the result is significant at level α if

$$\bar{x} > k = 2 + \frac{1}{\sqrt{n}} z_{1-\alpha}$$

where $\Phi(z_{1-\alpha}) = 1-\alpha$.

Since $z_{0.9} < z_{0.95} < z_{0.99}$, if the result is significant at the 5% level then it is certainly significant at the 10% level but not necessarily at the 1% level.

2. The lifetime T in days of an electrical component has an exponential distribution with probability density function

$$f(t) = \lambda e^{-\lambda t} \quad \text{if } t \geq 0,$$
$$= 0 \quad \text{otherwise.}$$

A single component was tested to destruction and its lifetime was 1056 hours. Test the hypothesis $H_0: \lambda=0.1$ against $H_1: \lambda<0.1$ at the 1% level of significance.

¶ Since the mean lifetime is $1/\lambda$ we take the critical region to be

$$C = \{t: t>t_0\},$$

where t_0 is a suitably chosen constant. The significance level α is given by

$$\alpha = P(T>t_0 \mid \lambda=0.1) = \int_{t_0}^{\infty} 0.1 \, e^{-0.1t} \, dt = e^{-0.1t_0}$$

so that $\qquad 0.1t_0 = -\log_e \alpha.$

Taking $\alpha = 0.01$, it follows that

$$t_0 = -10 \log_e 0.01 = 10 \log_e 100 = 46.05.$$

Since the observed lifetime is $1056/24 = 44$ days, the null hypothesis is not rejected at the 1% level of significance.

3. A firm which produces cardigans has found that when a particular machine is properly adjusted, 5% of the cardigans it produces are flawed. An inspection scheme requires 10 cardigans to be selected at random and examined for flaws. The machine is deemed to require adjustment if the number of substandard cardigans in the sample exceeds a specified integer k. If x denotes the percentage of flawed cardigans produced, what significance levels are possible for testing the null hypothesis $H_0: x=5$ against the alternative $H_1: x>5$?

¶ Let Y denote the number of substandard cardigans in the sample. The significance level α is given by

$$\alpha = P(\text{Reject } H_o | H_o \text{ true})$$
$$= P(Y > k | Y \text{ is } B(10,0.05))$$
$$= 1 - P(Y \leq k | Y \text{ is } B(10,0.05))$$

Using binomial tables, we obtain the following results:

k	α
0	0.40126
1	0.08614
2	0.01150
3	0.00103
4	0.00006
≥ 5	0

The values in the right hand column are the possible significance levels.

4. A leaf disease was reported to affect 25% of all beech trees. A botanist suspects that the incidence of the disease increases with the degree of atmospheric pollution and carries out a survey of beech trees in an urban area. Let p denote the probability that a randomly selected beech tree in the area is infected with the disease. Consider the hypotheses

$$H_o: p=0.25; \quad H_1: p>0.25.$$

If the botanist finds 31 infected beeches out of 100 examined, test these hypotheses using a significance level (a) as close to 10% as possible, (b) as close to 10% as possible but not exceeding 10%.

¶ Let X denote the number of infected beeches out of the 100 examined. Then a suitable critical region is

$$C = \{x: x \geq k\},$$

where k is an integer. The significance level α is given by

$$\alpha = P(\text{Reject } H_o | H_o \text{ true})$$
$$= P(X \geq k | X \text{ is } B(100,0.25))$$
$$= 1 - P(X \leq k-1 | X \text{ is } B(100,0.25)).$$

This is tabulated below for a number of values of k.

k	α
29	0.20754
30	0.14954
31	0.10379
32	0.06935

(a) With k=31, the significance level is as close to 10% as possible and H_o is rejected.

(b) With k=32, the significance level is as close as possible to 10% without exceeding it and H_o is not rejected.

5. The weekly sales of a certain type of video recorder in a shop have a Poisson distribution with mean λ, sales in different weeks being independent. The shop can make a profit from the recorders only if λ exceeds 1. The sales in 10 successive weeks were found to be

$$2,1,3,0,2,1,1,0,2,4.$$

Assuming that a sum of independent Poisson random variables also has a Poisson distribution, test the hypotheses

$$H_o: \lambda=1; \quad H_1: \lambda>1$$

using a significance level as close to 5% as possible.

¶ Let X denote the total number of sales in the 10 successive weeks. Then X has a Poisson distribution with mean 10λ and a suitable critical region is

$$C = \{x: x \geq k\}.$$

The significance level α is given by

$$\begin{aligned}
\alpha &= P(\text{Reject } H_o | H_o \text{ true}) \\
&= P(X \geq k \mid \lambda = 1) \\
&= 1-P(X \leq k-1 \mid \lambda = 1)
\end{aligned}$$

Using Poisson tables we find that $\alpha = 0.08346$ when $k = 15$ and $\alpha = 0.04874$ when $k = 16$. The critical region with significance level closest to 5% is therefore

$$C = \{x: x \geq 16\}.$$

From the sales data we see that the total number of sales in the 10 weeks was 16 and we therefore reject H_o in favour of H_1.

Exercises 9.3 Means of Normal Distributions of Known Variance

1. The weekly takings, in pounds, of a grocery shop before modernisation were normally distributed with mean 1243 and standard deviation 105. The takings in nine weeks after the modernisation had been completed were

      1263, 1306, 1178, 1175, 1309, 1263, 1418, 1387, 1339.

   Using a 10% significance level and assuming that the standard deviation is unchanged, carry out a test to decide if the mean weekly takings have increased.

¶ Let X denote the weekly takings after modernisation. We assume that X is $N(\mu, 105^2)$, and we take

$$H_0: \mu = 1243; \quad H_1: \mu > 1243.$$

The appropriate critical region of significance level 10% is

$$C = \{z: z > z_{0.90} = 1.282\}$$

where

$$z = \frac{\bar{x} - 1243}{105/\sqrt{9}}.$$

We find from the data that

$$\bar{x} = \frac{1263 + 1306 + \ldots + 1339}{9} = 1293.11.$$

Thus

$$z = 1.43.$$

This value is significant at the 10% level so that we conclude at this level that the mean weekly takings have increased.

2. A nautical chart shows the mean depth of the sea bed in a certain area of ocean to be 1515 fathoms. A survey vessel made 25 measurements in the area and the mean measured depth was 1546 fathoms. It is known that the measurements have a standard deviation of 65 fathoms. Does the result cast doubt on the accuracy of the chart at the 1% level of significance? State your assumptions.

¶ We assume that the measurements constitute a random sample from a $N(\mu, 65^2)$ distribution, where μ is the mean depth of the sea bed. Taking

$$H_O: \mu = 1515; \quad H_1: \mu \neq 1515,$$

the appropriate critical region of significance level 1% is

$$C = \{z: |z| > 2.576\}$$

where

$$z = \frac{\bar{x} - 1515}{65/\sqrt{25}}$$

The mean of the 25 measurements was 1546 and, therefore

$$z = \frac{1546 - 1515}{13} = 2.38.$$

This does not lie in the critical region and we conclude, at the 1% level, that there is no reason to doubt the accuracy of the chart.

3. The times of a 100-metre sprinter during last season were normally distributed with mean 10.7 seconds and standard deviation 0.15 seconds. In an attempt to improve the standard of his performances he gets a new coach before the start of the new season. The mean of the sprinter's times in the first four races of this season is 10.6 seconds. Assuming that this season's times are still normally distributed with unchanged variance, carry out a test at the 10% significance level to see if the change of coach has been beneficial.

¶ Let X denote the time taken by the sprinter to run 100 metres in the new season. We assume that X is $N(\mu, 0.15^2)$ and we take

$$H_O: \mu = 10.7; \quad H_1: \mu < 10.7.$$

The appropriate critical region of significance level 10% is given by

$$C = \{z: z < -z_{0.9} = -1.282\},$$

where

$$z = \frac{\bar{x} - 10.7}{0.15/\sqrt{4}}.$$

Since $\bar{x} = 10.6$,

$$z = \frac{10.6 - 10.7}{0.15/\sqrt{4}} = -1.33.$$

This value lies in the critical region and we conclude at the 10% level that the change of coach has been beneficial.

4. A device for measuring the wavelength of radiation is known to produce measurements with a standard deviation of 0.005 microns. Ten independent measurements of the wavelength of radiation from a certain source, known to be 1.455 microns, had a mean of 1.462 microns. Is the device biased?

¶ Let X denote the measured wavelength. Assume that X is $N(\mu, 0.005^2)$ and take

$$H_0: \mu = 1.455 \text{ (device unbiased)};$$
$$H_1: \mu \neq 1.455 \text{ (device biased)}.$$

Using a significance level of 1%, the appropriate critical region is

$$C = \{z: |z| > z_{.995} = 2.576\},$$

where

$$z = \frac{\bar{x}-1.455}{0.005/\sqrt{10}} \ .$$

Since $\bar{x} = 1.462$

$$z = \frac{1.462-1.455}{0.005/\sqrt{10}} = 4.43.$$

This value is significant at the 1% level and we conclude at this level that the device is biased.

5. A firm has two precision grinding machines, A and B, which produce cylindrical rods of mean diameter 2.500 cm. The diameters of the rods produced by machine A are normally distributed with standard deviation 0.01 cm and the diameters of the rods produced by machine B are normally distributed with standard deviation 0.015 cm. The composition of the steel the firm receives from its supplier is changed slightly. Random samples of size 10 from the output of machines A and B had mean diameters of 2.521 cm and 2.552 cm respectively. Assuming that the variability of the diameters of the rods produced is unchanged, test the hypothesis that the mean diameters produced by the two machines are still equal.

¶ Let X,Y denote respectively the diameters of randomly selected rods from machines A and B. We assume that X is $N(\mu_x, 0.01^2)$ and Y is $N(\mu_y, 0.015^2)$. Let

$$H_0: \mu_x = \mu_y;$$
$$H_1: \mu_x \neq \mu_y.$$

Using a significance level of 1%, the appropriate critical region
is

$$C = \{z: |z| > z_{.995} = 2.576\},$$

where, in the usual notation,

$$z = \frac{\bar{x} - \bar{y}}{\sqrt{\frac{\sigma_x^2}{m} + \frac{\sigma_y^2}{n}}}$$

Now, $\bar{x} = 2.521$, $\bar{y} = 2.552$, $\sigma_x = 0.01$, $\sigma_y = 0.015$, $m = 10$ and $n = 10$
so that

$$z = \frac{2.521 - 2.552}{\sqrt{\frac{0.01^2}{10} + \frac{0.015^2}{10}}} = 5.44 \ .$$

This value is highly significant and we conclude that the mean
diameters of cylinders produced by machines A and B are different.

6. Jim and John are keen members of the Aberponti Onion Growing
    Society, and each claims to grow the biggest onions. To test
    their claims, the Secretary of the society gives each of them
    12 onion sets at the beginning of the growing season and they
    plant these in their gardens. At the end of the season, Jim
    has 12 onions with a total weight of 13.25 kg and John has
    11 onions with a total weight of 12.69 kg (the neighbour's
    cat spoiled the remaining onion). The Secretary knows from
    past experience that the standard deviation of the weights
    of these onions is 0.05 kg, independently of the mean weight.
    Formulate and test suitable hypotheses, using a 5% significance
    level, and state your assumptions and conclusions.

¶   Let X,Y denote respectively the weights of onions grown by
    Jim and John. We assume that X is $N(\mu_x, 0.05^2)$ and Y is
    $N(\mu_y, 0.05^2)$. Let

$$H_0: \mu_x = \mu_y; \quad H_1: \mu_x \neq \mu_y.$$

The appropriate critical region of significance level 5% is
given by

$$C = \{z: |z| > z_{.975} = 1.96\},$$

where, in the usual notation,

$$z = \frac{\bar{x} - \bar{y}}{\sqrt{\frac{\sigma_x^2}{m} + \frac{\sigma_y^2}{n}}}$$

Now, $\bar{x}$ = 13.25/12, $\bar{y}$ = 12.69/11, $\sigma_x = \sigma_y$ = 0.05, m = 12 and
n = 11, so that

$$z = \frac{13.25/12 - 12.69/11}{\sqrt{0.05^2/12 + 0.05^2/11}} = -2.37 .$$

This value is significant at the 5% level and we conclude at
this level that the mean weights of onions produced by Jim and
John are different. To be more specific, John's onions are
heavier on average than Jim's.

Apart from the assumptions of normality, we have assumed that
the weights of the onions are independent.

7. Measurements of the refractive index of glass made by a certain
   refractometer are known to be subject to an error which is
   normally distributed with zero mean and standard deviation 0.004.
   Two samples of glass fragments were examined to see if they
   could have come from the same source. The refractive index of
   each fragment was measured and the results were as follows:

   Sample I : 1.522, 1.526, 1.519, 1.530, 1.525, 1.527;
   Sample II: 1.532, 1.527, 1.521, 1.529, 1.531.

   If the fragments in the first sample came from a broken window
   at the scene of a burglary and those in the second sample were
   found on a suspect's clothing, formulate suitable null and
   alternative hypotheses. Test the null hypothesis at the 10%
   level of significance and state your conclusions carefully.
   (Assume that fragments of glass from the same source have the
   same refractive index.)

¶ Let X,Y denote respectively the measured refractive indices
   of glass fragments from the broken window and from the
   suspect's clothing. We assume that X is $N(\mu_x, 0.004^2)$ and
   Y is $N(\mu_y, 0.004^2)$. Let

   $$H_0: \mu_x = \mu_y; \quad H_1 : \mu_x \neq \mu_y.$$

   The appropriate critical region of significance level 10% is

   $$C = \{z: |z| > z_{.95} = 1.645\},$$

   where, in the usual notation,

   $$z = \frac{\bar{x} - \bar{y}}{\sqrt{\frac{\sigma_x^2}{m} + \frac{\sigma_y^2}{n}}}$$

Here $\bar{x} = \dfrac{1.522 + 1.526 + \ldots + 1.527}{6} = 1.52483$

and $\bar{y} = \dfrac{1.532 + 1.527 + \ldots + 1.531}{5} = 1.528$.

Also, $\sigma_x = \sigma_y = 0.004$, $m = 6$ and $n = 5$ so that

$$z = \frac{1.52\dot{4}83 - 1.528}{\sqrt{0.004^2/6 + 0.004^2/5}} = -1.31 \ .$$

This value is not significant at the 10% level and we cannot conclude that the samples come from sources with different refractive indices. We cannot, of course, infer that they come from the same source, although we might well suspect this.

8. Let $X_1, X_2, \ldots, X_n$ be a random sample from a normal distribution with unknown mean μ and known variance σ^2. The hypotheses

$$H_o: \ \mu = \mu_o; \quad H_1: \ \mu \neq \mu_o$$

are to be tested at significance level α. Write down the critical region and show that the null hypothesis is accepted if, and only if, the $100(1-\alpha)\%$ confidence interval for μ contains μ_o.

¶   The appropriate critical region with significance level α is given by

$$C = \{z: \ z < -z_\gamma \ \text{or} \ z > z_\gamma\},$$

where $\gamma = 1 - \tfrac{1}{2}\alpha$

and

$$z = \frac{\bar{x} - \mu_o}{\sigma/\sqrt{n}} \ .$$

The acceptance region for H_o is therefore given by

$$C' = \{z: \ -z_\gamma \leqslant z \leqslant z_\gamma\}.$$

Now the inequality in C' can be manipulated as follows:

$$-z_\gamma \leqslant z \leqslant z_\gamma$$

$$\Leftrightarrow \quad -z_\gamma \leqslant \frac{\bar{x} - \mu_o}{\sigma/\sqrt{n}} \leqslant z_\gamma$$

$$\Leftrightarrow \quad -z_\gamma \frac{\sigma}{\sqrt{n}} \leqslant \bar{x} - \mu_o \leqslant z_\gamma \frac{\sigma}{\sqrt{n}}$$

$$\Leftrightarrow \bar{x} - z_{\gamma}\frac{\sigma}{\sqrt{n}} \le \mu_{0} \le \bar{x} + z_{\gamma}\frac{\sigma}{\sqrt{n}} \ . \tag{1}$$

Now since the $100(1-\alpha)\%$ confidence interval for μ is

$$[\bar{x} - z_{\gamma}\frac{\sigma}{\sqrt{n}} \ , \ \bar{x} + z_{\gamma}\frac{\sigma}{\sqrt{n}}] \ ,$$

it follows that inequality (1) states that this interval contains μ_{0}. H_{0} is therefore accepted if and only if the confidence interval for μ contains μ_{0}.

Exercises 9.4 Applications of the Central Limit Theorem

1. A self-taught golfer knows from past experience that the number of strokes she takes to complete a round of golf has a mean of 84.1 and a standard deviation of 2.6. She decides to try to improve her game by taking lessons with her club professional. Her mean number of strokes in 25 subsequent rounds is 83.1. Using the Central Limit Theorem and a significance level of 5%, test the null hypothesis that the overall standard of her game is unaltered against the alternative that it has improved. It may be assumed that the standard deviation of the number of strokes per round is unaffected by the lessons.

¶   Let μ denote the mean number of strokes taken to complete a round after the lessons and take

$$H_{0} : \mu = 84.1; \quad H_{1}: \mu < 84.1.$$

Assuming that scores in successive rounds are independent and identically distributed, the mean number of strokes in 25 rounds is approximately $N(\mu, 2.6^{2}/25)$. The appropriate critical region of significance level 5% is therefore

$$C = \{z: z < -z_{.95} = -1.645\},$$

where

$$z = \frac{\bar{x}-84.1}{2.6/\sqrt{25}} \ .$$

Since $x = 83.1,$

$$z = \frac{83.1-84.1}{0.51} = -1.92.$$

This value is significant at the 5% level and we conclude at this level that the overall standard of her game has improved.

2. A certain type of electric light bulb is designed to have a mean lifetime of 1200 hours. Tests on 50 bulbs from a certain batch gave a mean life of 1150 hours and sample standard deviation 150 hours. What evidence is there that this particular batch is substandard?

¶ Let X denote the lifetime of bulbs in this batch, and let $E(X) = \mu$.

We take
$$H_o: \mu = 1200; \quad H_1: \mu < 1200.$$

We now assume that the sample size is large enough so that

(i) the Central Limit Theorem can be applied,

(ii) the population standard deviation can be replaced by the sample standard deviation.

Then the appropriate critical region of significance level 1% is

$$C = \{z: z < -z_{.99} = -2.326\},$$

where
$$z = \frac{\bar{x}-1200}{150/\sqrt{50}} \ .$$

Since $\bar{x} = 1150$,
$$z = \frac{1150 - 1200}{150/\sqrt{50}} = 2.36 \ .$$

This value is significant at the 1% level and we conclude at this level that the batch is substandard.

3. In a study to assess the effect of fluoride in toothpaste, 100 children used a toothpaste containing fluoride over a period of three years and 100 children used a toothpaste not containing fluoride over the same period. The two types of toothpaste had the same appearance and flavour so that the children did not know which they were using. Over the period the group using the fluoride toothpaste averaged 6.7 new cavities per child while the other group averaged 7.5 new cavities per child. The sample standard deviations for the groups were 2.8 and 2.3 respectively. Using a significance level of 5%, test the hypothesis that the use of fluoride in toothpaste

has no beneficial effect against the alternative that it reduces the number of cavities.

¶ Let X,Y denote respectively the number of new cavities produced in children using toothpaste with and without fluoride, and let $E(X) = \mu_x$, $E(Y) = \mu_y$.

We test

$$H_0: \mu_x = \mu_y; \quad H_1: \mu_x < \mu_y .$$

We assume that the sample sizes are large enough so that

(i)   the Central Limit Theorem can be applied,

(ii)   the population standard deviations can be replaced by the sample standard deviations.

The appropriate critical region of significance level 5% is

$$C = \{z: z < -z_{.95} = -1.645\}$$

where, in the usual notation,

$$z = \frac{\bar{x} - \bar{y}}{\sqrt{\frac{\sigma_x^2}{m} + \frac{\sigma_y^2}{n}}}$$

Here $\bar{x} = 6.7$, $\bar{y} = 7.5$, $m = n = 100$ and we take $\sigma_x = 2.8$, $\sigma_y = 2.3$, so that

$$z = \frac{6.7 - 7.5}{\sqrt{2.8^2/100 + 2.3^2/100}} = -2.21.$$

This value is significant at the 5% level and we conclude at this level that fluoride in toothpaste has a beneficial effect.

4. In a survey, 100 women aged between 45 and 55 from locality A and 100 women in the same age group from locality B were asked how many times they had consulted their doctor during the previous twelve months. The results are summarized below.

Number of visits	0	1	2	3	4	5	6	7	8	9	10	11	12	13	14
Locality A	6	7	4	8	14	16	7	4	10	6	2	4	8	2	2
Locality B	3	3	3	4	8	8	12	16	10	10	6	5	6	3	3

Is there a significant difference at the 1% level between the two localities in the mean number of times that women in this age group see their doctor?

¶ Let X,Y denote respectively the number of consultations with the doctor by randomly selected patients in localities A and B, and let $E(X) = \mu_x$ and $E(Y) = \mu_y$.

Let

$$H_o : \mu_x = \mu_y; \quad H_1 : \mu_x \neq \mu_y.$$

We assume that the samples are large enough so that

(i)   the Central Limit Theorem can be applied,

(ii)   the population standard deviations can be replaced by the sample standard deviations.

The appropriate critical region of significance level 1% is

$$C = \{z: \quad z > z_{.995} = 2.576\},$$

where, in the usual notation,

$$z = \frac{\bar{x} - \bar{y}}{\sqrt{\frac{\sigma_x^2}{m} + \frac{\sigma_y^2}{n}}}$$

We now calculate the means and estimate the variances from the two samples.

Locality A

$$\sum f_i x_i = 593, \sum f_i x_i^2 = 4859$$

whence

$$\bar{x} = \frac{\sum f_i x_i}{100} = 5.93$$

and

$$\hat{\sigma}_x^2 = \frac{100}{99} \frac{\sum f_i x_i^2}{100} - \bar{x}^2 = 13.561$$

Locality B

$$\sum f_i y_i = 715, \sum f_i y_i^2 = 6209$$

whence $\bar{y} = 7.15$

and

$$\hat{\sigma}_y^2 = \frac{100}{99} \frac{\sum f_i y_i^2}{100} - \bar{y}^2 = 11.078 .$$

Using these values

$$z = \frac{5.93 - 7.15}{\sqrt{\frac{13.561}{100} + \frac{11.078}{100}}} = -2.46 .$$

This value is not significant at the 1% level and we cannot conclude at this level that there is a difference between localities A and B in the mean number of consultations per year.

5. The best 128 British junior tennis players born in 1970 were invited to play in a national tournament. A coach noticed that 28 of these players have their birthdays in January. Calculate the proportion of players born in January and show that this is significantly greater than $\frac{1}{12}$ at the 0.1% level. Can you offer an explanation for this phenomenon?

¶   Let p denote the probability that a top junior player has a January birthday, and let p denote the proportion of players in the sample whose birthdays are in January.
We test
$$H_o: p = \frac{1}{12}; \quad H_1: p > \frac{1}{12} .$$
The appropriate critical region of significance level 0.1% is
$$C = \{z: z > z_{.999} = 3.09\},$$
where
$$z = \frac{(\hat{p} - \frac{1}{12})\sqrt{128}}{\sqrt{\frac{1}{12}(1 - \frac{1}{12})}} .$$

Since
$$\hat{p} = \frac{28}{128}$$
we find that
$$z = 5.54.$$

This value is significant at the 0.1% level and we conclude at this level that the proportion of top junior players with a birthday in January exceeds $\frac{1}{12}$. The explanation is that these players are the oldest in their age group and so have, on average, a physical advantage over players born later in the year.

6. A drug company claims in an advertisement that at least 60% of people suffering from a certain complaint gain instant relief by using their product. In a random sample examined by a sceptical committee of doctors, 106 patients out of 200 did gain instant relief. Using a 5% significance level, test the validity of this claim.

¶ Let p denote the probability that a randomly selected person suffering from the complaint gains instant relief and let $\hat{p}$ denote the proportion in the sample gaining instant relief.

We test

$$H_0: p \geq 0.6; \quad H_1: p < 0.6.$$

Using a significance level of 5%, the appropriate critical region is

$$C = \{z: z < -z_{.95} = -1.645\},$$

where

$$z = \frac{(\hat{p}-0.6)\sqrt{200}}{\sqrt{0.6(1-0.6)}}.$$

Since $\hat{p} = \frac{106}{200} = 0.53$

it follows that

$$z = -2.02.$$

This value is significant at the 5% level and we conclude at this level that the percentage of people suffering from the complaint who gain instant relief is less than 60%.

7. A city is served by two rival radio stations, City Radio and City Broadcasting. In a survey commissioned by City Radio it was found that 52% of a sample of 450 listeners preferred City Radio to City Broadcasting. In an independent survey commissioned by City Broadcasting, 52% of a sample of 450 listeners preferred City Broadcasting. Is there sufficient evidence to question the impartiality of these surveys at a 5% significance level?

¶ Let p_1, p_2 denote the proportions of listeners who prefer City Radio in the populations sampled by the surveys commissioned by City Radio and City Broadcasting respectively. Ruling out the possibility that $p_1 < p_2$, we test

$$H_0: p_1 = p_2; \quad H_1; p_1 > p_2$$

(If $p_1 > p_2$ then at least one of the surveys is not impartial.)

The appropriate critical region of significance level 5% is

$$C = \{z: z > z_{.95} = 1.645\}$$

where

$$z = \frac{\hat{P}_1 - \hat{P}_2}{\sqrt{\hat{p}(1-\hat{p})(\frac{1}{m} + \frac{1}{n})}}$$

and $\hat{p}_1$, $\hat{p}_2$ are the respective estimates of p_1, p_2 from the two samples of sizes m, n and

$$\hat{p} = \frac{m\hat{p}_1 + n\hat{p}_2}{m+n}$$

is the estimate of p, the common value of p_1 and p_2 under H_o. Here, $\hat{p}_1$ = 0.52, $\hat{p}_2$ = 0.48, m = n = 450 so that $\hat{p}$ = 0.5 and

$$z = \frac{0.52-0.48}{\sqrt{0.5 \times 0.5(1/450 + 1/450)}} = 1.2.$$

This value is not significant at the 5% level so that there is no reason at this level to doubt the impartiality of the surveys.

8. In a routine safety check, the background level of radiation in a laboratory was measured every 15 seconds for 25 minutes. The frequency distribution of the 100 radioactive counts obtained is as follows.

Count	0	1	2	3	4	5	6	7	8	9	10	11	12
Frequency	1	4	8	14	20	15	15	10	5	4	2	1	1

Using a significance level of approximately 5%, test the hypothesis that the mean count in 15 seconds does not exceed the maximum specified value of 4.5 against the alternative that it does.

¶   Let X denote the radioactive count in a 15 second period, and let E(X) = μ and Var(X) = σ^2. We assume that the sample size is large enough to enable

(i)   the Central Limit Theorem to be used,

(ii) σ^2 to be replaced by the sample variance.

We test

$$H_o: \mu \leqslant 4.5$$

against $H_1: \mu > 4.5$.

The appropriate critical region of significance level 5% is

$$C = \{z: z > z_{.95} = 1.645\}$$

where $z = \dfrac{\bar{x}-4.5}{\sigma/\sqrt{100}}$

For these data,

$$\bar{x} = \frac{\sum f_i x_i}{100} = 4.96$$

and the estimate of σ^2 is

$$\hat{\sigma}^2 = \frac{100}{99} \frac{\sum f_i x_i^2}{100} - \bar{x}^2 = 5.41.$$

Thus, replacing σ by $\hat{\sigma}$, we find that

$$z = \frac{4.96-4.5}{\sqrt{5.41/100}} = 1.98.$$

This value is significant at the 5% level and we conclude at this level that the maximum specified radiation level is exceeded.

N.B. If we were to assume that X is Poisson distributed then, since the mean and variance are equal for the Poisson distribution, we would not need to estimate σ and we would have

$$z = \frac{4.96-4.5}{\sqrt{4.5/100}} = 2.17.$$

The conclusion would be the same in this example however.

9. The independent Poisson random variables X and Y have means μ_1 and μ_2 respectively. In order to test the hypothesis $H_0: \mu_1 = \mu_2$ against the alternative $H_1: \mu_1 > \mu_2$, random samples $X_1, X_2, \ldots, X_m$ and $Y_1, Y_2, \ldots, Y_n$ are obtained from the distributions of X and Y. Show that a suitable critical region of significance level α is given by

$$C = \{w: w > z_{1-\alpha}\},$$

where

$$W = \frac{\bar{X}-\bar{Y}}{\sqrt{\frac{m\bar{X}+n\bar{Y}}{m+n}\left(\frac{1}{m} + \frac{1}{n}\right)}},$$

$\bar{X}$ and $\bar{Y}$ denote the respective sample means and m and n are large enough to enable the Central Limit Theorem to be applied.

¶ Let $\bar{X}, \bar{Y}$ denote respectively the sample means of the X and Y samples. Then, using the Central Limit Theorem, it follows for large m, n that $\bar{X}$ is $N(\mu_1, \frac{\mu_1}{m})$ and $\bar{Y}$ is $N(\mu_2, \frac{\mu_2}{n})$, since, for the Poisson distribution, the variance is equal to the mean. It follows that $\bar{X}-\bar{Y}$ is $N(\mu_1-\mu_2,\ \mu_1/m+\mu_2/n)$.

Thus, under H_o,

$$\frac{\bar{X}-\bar{Y}}{\sqrt{\dfrac{\mu}{m}+\dfrac{\mu}{n}}}$$

is approximately $N(0,1)$ where μ is the unknown common value of μ_1 and μ_2. Finally we replace μ by its estimate obtained by pooling the two samples. This is

$$\hat{\mu} = \frac{m\bar{X}+n\bar{Y}}{m+n}\ .$$

Thus, assuming that the error in doing this is negligible, we find that

$$W = \frac{\bar{X}-\bar{Y}}{\sqrt{\dfrac{m\bar{X}+n\bar{Y}}{m+n}\left(\dfrac{1}{m}+\dfrac{1}{n}\right)}}$$

is approximately $N(0,1)$ when H_o is true. This is the required result.

10. In a study carried out by telephone engineers, 77 out of 100 monitored local calls lasted for less than 3 minutes. It is believed that the duration of such calls has an exponential distribution with probability density function

$$f(x) = \lambda e^{-\lambda x} \qquad \text{if } x \geqslant 0,$$
$$= 0 \qquad \text{otherwise.}$$

Test the hypotheses

$$H_o:\ \lambda=0.5;\quad H_1:\ \lambda<0.5,$$

using a 5% significance level. Explain in words the hypotheses and your conclusion.

¶ Let X denote the number of calls out of 100 that last for less than 3 minutes. Then X is $B(100,p)$ where

$$p = P(X<3) = \int_0^3 \lambda e^{-\lambda x}\ dx = 1 - e^{-3\lambda}.$$

When H_o is true,

$$p = 1-e^{-1.5} = 0.7768$$

and, using the normal approximation to the binomial, the appropriate critical region of significance level 5% is

$$C = \{z:\ z < -z_{.95} = -1.645\}$$

where $\quad z = \dfrac{(\hat{p}-0.7768)\sqrt{100}}{\sqrt{0.7768(1-0.7768)}}$

and $\hat{p}$ is the observed proportion of calls lasting less than 3 minutes.

Since $\hat{p}$ = 77/100, we find that z = -0.16. This value is not significant at the 5% level and we do not reject H_o: λ = 0.5 (mean call length is 2 minutes) in favour of H_1: λ < 0.5 (mean call length exceeds 2 minutes).

Exercises 9.5 Means of Normal Distributions in Small Samples

1. A certain pipette is supposed to dispense 5 ml of a fluid each time it is used. It was used eight times and the amount of fluid dispensed on each occasion was measured accurately. The results, in ml, were

> 5.083, 4.796, 4.813, 4.717, 5.013, 4.826, 4.635, 5.136.

Using a 5% significance level, test the null hypothesis that the pipette dispenses 5 ml of fluid on average against the alternative that it does not.

¶ Let X denote the amount dispensed and assume that X is $N(\mu,\sigma^2)$. We test the hypotheses

$$H_o: \mu = 5; \quad H_1: \mu \neq 5.$$

Under H_o, assuming that we have a random sample,

$$T = \frac{\bar{X}-5}{S/\sqrt{n}}$$

has a Student's t-distribution with n-1 degrees of freedom, where n is the sample size and $\bar{X}$ and S are the sample mean and sample standard deviation. Here n = 8 and, using Table 3, the appropriate critical region having a significance level of 5% is

$$C = \{t: |t| > t_{0.975}(7) = 2.365\}.$$

We find that the values of $\bar{X}$ and S are 4.8774 and 0.17946 respectively. Therefore

$$t = \frac{4.8774-5}{0.17946/\sqrt{8}} = -1.9327 .$$

As this value does not belong to the critical region, H_o is not rejected at the 5% level.

2. Steel girders produced by a certain foundry are claimed to have a mean breaking strength of 1000 tons. Nine girders were tested to destruction and the maximum loads, in tons, were

    910, 980, 1020, 900, 950, 1010, 960, 850, 975.

    Assuming that the breaking strengths are normally distributed and using a 2½% significance level, test the above claim against the alternative that the mean breaking strength is less than 1000 tons.

¶ We take the hypotheses to be

$$H_o: \mu = 1000; \quad H_1: \mu < 1000,$$

where μ is the mean breaking strength. The sample size is 9. So, using Table 3, the appropriate critical region having a significance level of 2½% is

$$C = \{t: t < t_{0.975}(8) = -2.306\},$$

where, in the usual notation,

$$t = \frac{\bar{x}-1000}{s/\sqrt{9}}$$

For the given data,

$$\bar{x} = 950.5\dot{5}, \quad s = 55.02525$$

so that

$$t = \frac{950.5\dot{5}-1000}{55.02525/3} = -2.6955.$$

This t-value belongs to C and so is significant at the 2½% level. We conclude, at this level, that the mean breaking strength is less than 1000 tons.

3. A wholesale greengrocer decides to buy a field of winter cabbages if he can convince himself that their mean weight exceeds 1.2 kg. Accordingly he cuts 12 cabbages at random and weighs them with the following results (in kg):

    1.26, 1.19, 1.17, 1.24, 1.23, 1.25,
    1.20, 1.18, 1.23, 1.21, 1.19, 1.17.

    Should the greengrocer buy the cabbages? Use a 10% level of significance.

¶ We take the hypotheses to be

$$H_o: \mu \leqslant 1.2; \quad H_1: \mu > 1.2,$$

where μ is the mean weight of a randomly selected cabbage. Assuming that the weights are normally distributed and using Table 3, a suitable critical region having a 10% significance level is

$$C = \{t: t > t_{0.90}(11) = 1.363\}$$

where, in the usual notation,

$$t = \frac{\bar{x} - 1.2}{s/\sqrt{12}}$$

For the given data,

$$\bar{x} = 1.21, \quad s = 0.031334$$

and we find that

$$t = 1.1055.$$

This t-value is not significant at the 10% level and the greengrocer should not buy the cabbages.

4. Two ingots of high quality magnet steel were delivered to a factory. Six independent determinations of the percentage of cobalt in each ingot were made but, because of a failure of the measuring apparatus, one observation is missing. The remaining results are as follows.

> Ingot 1: 23.5, 22.8, 22.7, 22.6, 23.7, 23.9.
> Ingot 2: 22.0, 22.6, 23.1, 22.8, 23.0.

Is there a difference between the cobalt content of the two ingots? Use a 5% significance level and state all assumptions made.

¶ Let X,Y denote the measured percentages of cobalt in Ingot 1 and Ingot 2 respectively and assume that X is $N(\mu_x, \sigma^2)$ and Y is $N(\mu_y, \sigma^2)$. We test the hypotheses

$$H_o: \mu_x = \mu_y; \quad H_1: \mu_x \neq \mu_y.$$

Under H_o,

$$T = \frac{\bar{X} - \bar{Y}}{\hat{\sigma}\sqrt{\frac{1}{m} + \frac{1}{n}}}$$

has Student's distribution with m+n-2 degrees of freedom, where
m,n denote the sample sizes, $\bar{X}, \bar{Y}$ are the sample means and

$$\hat{\sigma}^2 = \frac{(m-1)S_x^2 + (n-1)S_y^2}{m+n-2}$$

where S_x^2, S_y^2 are the sample variances.

A suitable critical region having a significance level of
5% is

$$C = \{t: \ |t| > t_{0.975}(m+n-2) = 2.262\},$$

since m = 6, n = 5.   We find that $\bar{x}$ = 23.2, $\bar{y}$ = 22.7, s_x^2 = 0.32,
s_y^2 = 0.19 and $\hat{\sigma}$ = 0.5121.

Thus

$$\frac{\bar{x}-\bar{y}}{\hat{\sigma}\sqrt{\frac{1}{m} + \frac{1}{n}}} = 1.6125.$$

This computed value is not significant at the 5% level and
there is no reason to believe that there is a difference between
the cobalt contents of the two ingots.

5. A market gardener, wishing to compare the effectiveness of two
    fertilizers, used one fertilizer throughout the growing season
    on half of his plants and used the second one on the other half.
    The yields of the surviving plants are shown below, measured
    in kilograms.

    Fertilizer A   6.72, 9.17, 7.43, 6.53, 10.20, 6.88, 6.28, 6.73,
                   7.38, 6.95, 7.03, 8.05, 7.57, 6.90, 7.63.

    Fertilizer B   7.73, 10.34, 8.59, 5.71, 5.42, 7.94, 8.29,
                   7.63, 9.41, 9.35, 9.62, 8.94.

    Stating all assumptions made, test at a 10% significance level
    the hypothesis that the fertilizers are equally effective
    against the alternative that they are not.

¶   Let X,Y denote the yields using the first and second fertilizers
    respectively and assume that X is $N(\mu_x, \sigma^2)$ and Y is $N(\mu_y, \sigma^2)$.
    We test the hypotheses

    $$H_o: \ \mu_x = \mu_y; \quad H_1: \ \mu_x \neq \mu_y.$$

    Assuming that we have independent random samples from the
    distributions of X and Y,

$$T = \frac{\bar{X}-\bar{Y}}{\hat{\sigma}\sqrt{\frac{1}{m} + \frac{1}{n}}}$$

has Student's t-distribution under H_o with m+n-2 degrees of freedom where m,n denote the sample sizes, $\bar{X},\bar{Y}$ are the sample means and

$$\hat{\sigma}^2 = \frac{(m-1)S_x^2 + (n-1)S_y^2}{m+n-2}$$

where S_x^2, S_y^2 are the sample variances.

A suitable critical region having a significance level of 10% is

$$C = \{t: |t| > t_{0.95} (m+n-2) = 1.708\},$$

since m = 15, n = 12. We find that $\bar{x}$ = 7.43, $\bar{y}$ = 8.2475, s_x^2 = 1.0891, s_y^2 = 2.2368 and $\hat{\sigma}$ = 1.2626.

Thus

$$t = \frac{\bar{x}-\bar{y}}{\hat{\sigma}\sqrt{\frac{1}{m} + \frac{1}{n}}} = -1.672.$$

This computed value is not significant at the 10% level and we do not reject H_o.

6. In a test on two different models of 1300 cc cars, the following distances, in kilometres, were travelled using 10 litres of petrol.

      Model 1:   126.2,   126.7,   128.3,   125.8,   130.5.

      Model 2:   130.2,   128.1,   131.4,   127.8,   129.6.

What evidence is there that Model 2 is more economical than Model 1?

¶ Let X,Y denote respectively the distances travelled on 10 litres of petrol by a randomly selected car of Model 1 and a randomly selected car of Model 2 and assume that X is $N(\mu_x, \sigma^2)$ and Y is $N(\mu_y, \sigma^2)$. We take the hypotheses to be

$$H_o: \mu_x = \mu_y; \quad H_1: \mu_x < \mu_y.$$

The sample sizes are m = n = 5. Thus a suitable critical region with a significance level of 10% is

$$C = \{t: t < -t_{0.9}(m+n-2) = -1.397\}$$

where, in the usual notation,

$$t = \frac{\bar{x}-\bar{y}}{\hat{\sigma}\sqrt{\frac{1}{m} + \frac{1}{n}}}.$$

We find that $\bar{x} = 127.5$, $\bar{y} = 129.42$, $s_x^2 = 3.715$, $s_y^2 = 2.232$ and $\hat{\sigma} = 1.7244$. Therefore,

$$t = -1.7605.$$

This computed value is significant at the 10% level and we conclude at this level that Model 2 is more economical than Model 1. The evidence is not very strong however. If, for example, we had used a 5% significance level, the computed value would not have been significant since $t_{0.95}(8) = 1.860$.

7. In a study of the effect of a drug on guinea pigs, the body temperatures of eight guinea pigs were taken immediately before treatment and again 24 hours later. The results were as follows.

Guinea Pig	1	2	3	4	5	6	7	8
Temperature before (°C)	38.1	38.3	38.4	37.9	38.6	38.5	38.2	38.5
Temperature Afterwards (°C)	38.8	38.7	38.4	38.4	38.5	39.0	38.5	38.2

Does the drug affect the mean body temperature of guinea pigs? Use a 5% significance level and state all assumptions made.

¶ A paired comparison test is appropriate here. From the data the temperature increases are as follows.

Guinea Pig	1	2	3	4	5	6	7	8
Temperature increase	0.7	0.4	0	0.5	-0.1	0.5	0.3	-0.3

Let X denote the increase in temperature of a randomly selected guinea pig and assume that X is $N(\mu, \sigma^2)$. We test the hypotheses

$$H_0: \mu = 0; \quad H_1: \mu \neq 0.$$

Assuming that the temperature increases are a random sample from the distribution of X,

$$T = \frac{\bar{X}}{S/\sqrt{n}}$$

has Student's t-distribution under H_0 with $n-1$ degrees of freedom, where n denotes the sample size and $\bar{X}$ and S^2 denote the sample mean and variance. A suitable critical region having a significance level of 5% is

$$C = \{t: |t| > t_{.975}(n-1) = 2.365\},$$

since $n = 8$. From the data, $\bar{x} = 0.25$ and $s = 0.3464$, so that

$$t = 2.041.$$

The computed value is not significant so that we cannot conclude that the drug affects the body temperature of guinea pigs.

8. Eight young English county cricket batsmen were awarded scholar-
ships which enabled them to spend the winter in Australia playing
club cricket. Their first-class batting averages in the preceding
and following seasons were as follows.

Batsman	1	2	3	4	5	6	7	8
Average before	29.43	21.21	31.23	36.27	22.28	30.06	27.60	43.19
Average after	31.26	24.95	29.74	33.43	28.50	30.35	29.16	47.24

Is there a significant improvement in their batting averages
between seasons? Could any change be attributed to the winter
practice?

¶   We consider the increases in the batting averages and use a
paired comparison test.

Batsman	1	2	3	4	5	6	7	8
Increase	1.83	3.74	-1.49	-2.84	6.22	0.29	1.56	4.05

Let X denote the increase in the batting average of a randomly
selected batsman and assume that X is $N(\mu, \sigma^2)$. We test the
hypotheses

$$H_o: \mu = 0; \quad H_1: \mu > 0.$$

Under H_o,

$$T = \frac{\bar{X}}{S/\sqrt{n}}$$

has Student's t-distribution with n-1 degrees of freedom, where
n denotes the sample size and $\bar{X}$ and S^2 denote the sample mean and
variance.   A suitable critical region having significance
level α is

$$C = \{t: t > t_{1-\alpha}(n-1) = t_{1-\alpha}(7)\},$$

since n = 8. From the data, $\bar{x} = 1.67$ and s = 2.998 so that

$$t = 1.58.$$

Since $t_{0.9}(7) = 1.415$ but $t_{0.95}(7) = 1.895$, we see that the
computed value is significant at the 10% level but not at the
5% level.

The winter practice is only one of several factors which might
improve the batting average. For example, the second summer
might be a good one with truer pitches than in the previous
summer.

9. In an industrial experiment, 35 workmen performed a certain job by one method and 30 other workmen performed it by a different method, the time taken to complete the job being recorded for each workman. Frequency distributions were formed for the two sets of results as follows.

Time (mins)	75-80	80-85	85-90	90-85	95-100	100-105	105-110
Method 1	3	6	8	9	6	2	1
Method 2	0	3	9	11	3	2	2

Is Method 1 faster than Method 2 on average? Use a 5% significance level and state your assumptions carefully.

¶ Let X,Y denote the times taken to do the job by Method 1 and Method 2 respectively. Assume that X is $N(\mu_x, \sigma^2)$ and Y is $N(\mu_y, \sigma^2)$. We test the hypotheses

$$H_0: \mu_x = \mu_y; \quad H_1: \mu_x < \mu_y.$$

Under H_0, assuming that we have two independent random samples from the distributions of X and Y,

$$T = \frac{\bar{X} - \bar{Y}}{\hat{\sigma}\sqrt{\frac{1}{m} + \frac{1}{n}}}$$

has Student's t-distribution with m+n-2 degrees of freedom where m,n denote the sample sizes, $\bar{X}, \bar{Y}$ the sample means and

$$\hat{\sigma}^2 = \frac{(m-1) S_x^2 + (n-1) S_y^2}{m+n-2}$$

where S_x^2, S_y^2 are the sample variances. A suitable critical region having a 5% significance level is

$$C = \{t: t < -t_{0.95}(m+n-2) = -1.670\},$$

since m = 35 and n = 30. Using the midpoints of the intervals, we find that $\bar{x} = 90.214$, $\bar{y} = 92.16$, $s_x^2 = 54.9160$, $s_y^2 = 42.9885$ and $\hat{\sigma} = 7.0303$ so that

$$t = -1.12.$$

The computed value is not significant at the 5% level and we cannot conclude at this level that Method 1 is faster than Method 2 on average.

10. A poultry scientist proposed a new diet for increasing egg production. A group of 16 hens was divided randomly into two groups of 8 hens. One group was fed on the old diet and

the other on the new diet. Let $x_1, x_2, \ldots, x_8$ denote the annual yields from the hens on the old diet and $y_1, y_2, \ldots, y_8$ those from the hens on the new diet. It was found that

$$\sum_{i=1}^{8} x_i = 1960, \quad \sum_{i=1}^{8} x_i^2 = 480776,$$

$$\sum_{i=1}^{8} y_i = 2088, \quad \sum_{i=1}^{8} y_i^2 = 545391.$$

Test the null hypothesis that the mean annual yield per hen has increased by at most 10 against the alternative that it has increased by more than 10 at the 5% level of significance.

¶ Let X,Y denote respectively the annual yield using the old diet and the new diet and assume that X is $N(\mu_x, \sigma^2)$ and Y is $N(\mu_y, \sigma^2)$. We test the hypotheses

$$H_0: \mu_y - \mu_x \leq 10; \quad H_1: \mu_y - \mu_x > 10 .$$

Since the sample sizes are m = n = 8, a suitable critical region having a significance level of 5% is

$$C = \{t: t > t_{0.95}(m+n-2) = 1.761\},$$

where, in the usual notation,

$$t = \frac{\bar{y} - \bar{x} - 10}{\hat{\sigma}\sqrt{\frac{1}{m} + \frac{1}{n}}} .$$

We find that

$$\bar{x} = 1960/8 = 245, \quad \bar{y} = 2088/8 = 261,$$

$$s_x^2 = \frac{8}{7}\left(\frac{480776}{8} - 245^2\right) = 82.2857, \quad s_y^2 = \frac{8}{7}\left(\frac{545391}{8} - 261^2\right) = 60.4286.$$

Thus

$$\hat{\sigma} = \left[\frac{7 \times 82.2857 + 7 \times 60.4286}{14}\right]^{\frac{1}{2}} = 8.4473$$

so that

$$t = 1.4206.$$

The computed value is not significant at the 5% level and we cannot conclude at this level that the mean yield has increased by more than 10.

Exercises 9.6 The Power Function

1. A random variable X has the distribution $N(\mu,9)$. A random sample of size n is taken from the distribution of X. It is desired to use the sample mean to test the hypothesis H_o: $\mu=10$ against H_1: $\mu>10$ at the 5% level of significance. Construct such a test and obtain an expression for its power function in terms of n. Hence find the smallest value of n for which the probability of rejecting H_o when $\mu=13$ exceeds 0.99.

¶   A suitable critical region is $\bar{X} > k$ where k is a constant. The Type I error probability is given by

$$\begin{aligned} \alpha &= P(\text{Reject } H_o | H_o \text{ true}) \\ &= P(\bar{X} > k | \bar{X} \text{ is } N(10, \tfrac{9}{n})) \\ &= 1 - \Phi(\tfrac{\sqrt{n}}{3}(k-10)) . \end{aligned}$$

$$\Phi(\tfrac{\sqrt{n}}{3}(k-10)) = 1-\alpha = 0.95.$$

Thus

$$\tfrac{\sqrt{n}}{3}(k-10) = 1.645$$

whence
$$k = 10 + \frac{4.935}{\sqrt{n}} .$$

The power function is given by

$$\begin{aligned} \pi(\mu) &= P(\text{Reject } H_o;\ \mu) \\ &= P(\bar{X} > k | \bar{X} \text{ is } N(\mu, \tfrac{9}{n})) \\ &= 1 - \Phi(\tfrac{\sqrt{n}}{3}(k-\mu)) \\ &= 1 - \Phi(1.645 + \tfrac{\sqrt{n}}{3}(10-\mu)) \end{aligned}$$

We require $\pi(13) > 0.99$,

i.e. $\Phi(1.645 + \tfrac{\sqrt{n}}{3}(10-13)) < 0.01$

$$1.645 - \sqrt{n} < -2.326$$

$$\sqrt{n} > 3.971$$

$$n > 15.77.$$

The minimum value of n is therefore 16.

2. A technique for measuring the pH values of chemical solutions produces measurements that are normally distributed with mean equal to the true value and standard deviation 0.2. Four independent measurements are made of the pH value of a

certain solution. Construct a two-tailed test with significance level 0.05 of the null hypothesis that the solution has
a pH value of 7.0. Find its power function.

Suppose that the true pH value is 7.2. Calculate the probability that the test will detect the fact that the true value
is not 7.0. How many measurements should be made if this
probability is to be 0.95?

¶   Denote the pH value by μ and its measurement by X. Then X
is $N(\mu,0.04)$. We test the hypotheses

$$H_o: \mu = 7.0; \quad H_1: \mu \neq 7.0$$

with a critical region of the form $|\bar{X}-7| > k$. For a random
sample of size n the power function is given by

$$\begin{aligned}
\pi(\mu) &= P(\text{Reject } H_o; \mu) \\
&= P(|\bar{X}-7| > k; \mu) \\
&= 1-P(\frac{-k-\mu+7}{0.2/\sqrt{n}} < \frac{\bar{X}-\mu}{0.2/\sqrt{n}} < \frac{k-\mu+7}{0.2/\sqrt{n}} ; \mu) \\
&= 1-\Phi(\frac{k-\mu+7}{0.2/\sqrt{n}}) + \Phi(\frac{-k-\mu+7}{0.2/\sqrt{n}}).
\end{aligned}$$

For a significance level of 0.05 we require

$$\pi(7) = 2\Phi(\frac{-k}{0.2} \sqrt{n}) = 0.05.$$

Thus $\quad \dfrac{k\sqrt{n}}{0.2} = 1.96 \qquad$ i.e. $k = \dfrac{0.392}{\sqrt{n}}$.

When $n = 4$, $k = 0.196$ so that

$$\pi(\mu) = \Phi(-10(7.196-\mu)) + \Phi(10(6.804-\mu)).$$

We are required to calculate $\pi(7.2)$.

$$\pi(7.2) = \Phi(0.04) + \Phi(-3.96) = 0.5160.$$

To find the value of n such that $\pi(7.2) = 0.95$, we have

$$\Phi(-1.96 + \sqrt{n}) + \Phi(-1.96-\sqrt{n}) = 0.95.$$

Neglecting the second term on the left hand side, this
becomes

$$\Phi(-1.96 + \sqrt{n}) = 0.95$$

and the required value of n is 13.

3.   Bags of sugar of nominal weight 1 kg are filled automatically
by a dispenser that delivers amounts that are normally distributed with standard deviation 2 gm. The mean is required to

be at least 1.005 kg. The output is sampled hourly to check
that the requirement is being satisfied. The inspection scheme
consists of selecting five bags and concluding that the requirement is not being satisfied if, and only if, all five bags weigh
less than 1.005 kg. Find the significance level and sketch the
power function of this scheme. (It may be assumed that the
weights of successive bags are independent.)

¶   Let X be the weight (in grams) of sugar delivered. Then X is
$N(\mu, 4)$ where μ is the mean weight delivered. We test the
hypotheses

$$H_0: \mu \geq 1005; \quad H_1: \mu < 1005$$

and H_0 is rejected in favour of H_1 if and only if all five bags
weigh less than 1005 grams. Therefore the power function is
given by

$$\pi(\mu) = [P(X < 1005; \mu)]^5$$
$$= [\Phi(\frac{1005-\mu}{2})]^5.$$

Since H_0 is composite, the significance level α is the maximum
value of the power function on the interval $\mu \geq 1005$. Therefore, since $\pi(\mu)$ is a decreasing function of μ,

$$\alpha = \pi(1005) = [\Phi(0)]^5 = 1/32.$$

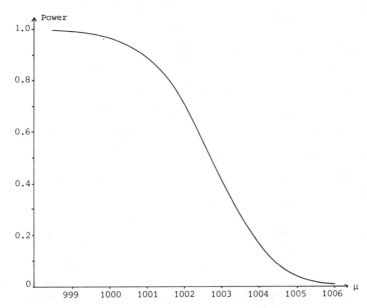

4. The manager of a casino buys a new roulette wheel, but he suspects that the zero does not appear as often as it should; for a perfect wheel, the probability p of a zero is 1/37. He therefore decides to test the null hypothesis H_0: $p = \frac{1}{37}$ against the alternative H_1: $p < \frac{1}{37}$. To do this, he spins the wheel 370 times and decides to accept H_1 if the number of zeros is less than 8. Use a suitable Poisson approximation to find the significance level of the test and write down an expression for the power function. Calculate the value of p for which it equals 0.95.

¶ Let X denote the number of zeros obtained in 370 spins. Then X is B(370,p). We test the hypotheses

$$H_0: p = \frac{1}{37}; \quad H_1: p < \frac{1}{37} .$$

The critical region is given to be $X \leq 7$. Therefore the significance level is

$$\alpha = P(H_0 \text{ rejected} \mid H_0 \text{ true})$$

$$= \sum_{x=0}^{7} {}^{370}C_x \left(\frac{1}{37}\right)^x \left(\frac{36}{37}\right)^{370-x}$$

$$\approx \sum_{x=0}^{7} e^{-10} \frac{10^x}{x!}$$

$$= 0.22022.$$

The power function is given by

$$\pi(p) = P(\text{Reject } H_0; p)$$

$$= \sum_{x=0}^{7} {}^{370}C_x \, p^x (1-p)^{370-x}$$

$$\approx \sum_{x=0}^{7} e^{-370p} \frac{(370p)^x}{x!} .$$

Interpolating in Poisson tables we find that $\pi(p) = 0.95$ when

$$370p = 3.978$$

$$\text{i.e.} \quad p = 0.0108.$$

5. The time to failure of a certain electrical component is
    known to be distributed with probability density function

$$f(t) = \lambda e^{-\lambda t} \qquad \text{if } t \geqslant 0,$$
$$= 0 \qquad \text{otherwise.}$$

In order to test the null hypothesis H_0: $\lambda = 2$ against the
alternative H_1: $\lambda > 2$, a random sample of times to failure
$T_1, T_2, \ldots, T_n$ is obtained. Let W and Z respectively denote
the sample minimum and sample maximum. A test with a 5%
significance level is required. Consider the test with a
critical region of the form $W < k$. Find the value of k in
terms of n for which the test has a 5% significance level
and obtain an expression for the power function of the test.
Carry out the same exercise for a test whose critical region
has the form $Z < k$. Which is the better test?

¶   Denote the power function of the test with critical region
$W < k$ by $\pi_1(\lambda)$.

$$\begin{aligned}
\pi_1(\lambda) &= P(W < k;\ \lambda) \\
&= 1 - P(W \geqslant k;\ \lambda) \\
&= 1 - P(T_i \geqslant k\ (i=1\ldots n);\ \lambda) \\
&= 1 - [P(T_1 \geqslant k;\ \lambda)]^n \\
&= 1 - e^{-n\lambda k}.
\end{aligned}$$

For a significance level of 5% we require

$$\pi_1(2) = 1 - e^{-2nk} = 0.05.$$

Therefore $k = -\dfrac{1}{2n} \log_e 0.95$

and $\pi_1(\lambda) = 1 - \exp(\dfrac{\lambda}{2} \log_e 0.95)$

$$= 1 - (0.95)^{\lambda/2}.$$

Consider now the test with critical region $Z < k$. Let
its power function be denoted by $\pi_2(\lambda)$.

$$\begin{aligned}
\pi_2(\lambda) &= P(Z < k;\ \lambda) \\
&= P(T_i < k\ (i=1,\ldots,n);\ \lambda) \\
&= [P(T_1 < k;\ \lambda)]^n \\
&= (1 - e^{-\lambda k})^n.
\end{aligned}$$

We require

$$\pi_2(2) = (1 - e^{-2\lambda})^n = 0.05.$$

Therefore $k = -\dfrac{1}{2} \log_e(1 - 0.05^{\frac{1}{n}})$

and $\qquad \pi_2(\lambda) = [1-\exp(\frac{\lambda}{2} \log_e(1-0.05^{\frac{1}{n}}))]^n$

$\qquad\qquad\quad = [1-(1-0.05^{\frac{1}{n}})^{\lambda/2}]^n.$

Computation of the two power functions shows that, for $n \geq 2$, the test based on Z is more powerful and therefore better than the one based on W. For n = 1 the two tests are of course the same but the test based on W does not become more powerful as n increases. Taking, for example, n = 10, we find the following power curves.

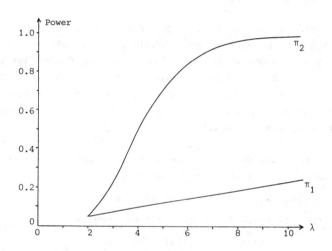

Miscellaneous Problems

1. It is claimed that at most 20% of accidents suffered by workers in a certain occupation are classified as serious. In a random sample of 250 cases, 60 were classified as serious. Test the claim at the 5% level of significance.

¶   Let p denote the probability that an accident is serious. We test the hypotheses

$\qquad\qquad H_0: p \leq 0.2; \quad H_1: p > 0.2$

at the 5% level using the critical region

$\qquad\qquad C = \{z: z > z_{0.95} = 1.645\},$

where $z = \dfrac{(\hat{p}-0.2)\sqrt{250}}{\sqrt{0.2(1-0.2)}}$

and $\hat{p}$ is the proportion of serious accidents in the sample. Here

$$\hat{p} = \frac{60}{250} = 0.24$$

and $z = \dfrac{(0.24-0.2)\sqrt{250}}{\sqrt{0.2(1-0.2)}} = 1.581.$

The computed z-value does not belong to the critical region, and although the observed proportion is 24%, the claim cannot be rejected at the 5% significance level.

2. A fruit wholesaler claims that the average weight of the bunches of bananas he supplies is at least 800 gm. A retailer weighs a random sample of 25 bunches. He finds that the sample mean is 779 gm and the sample variance is 6400 gm². Does the retailer have a case for renegotiating the price with the wholesaler? (Assume that weights of bunches of bananas are normally distributed.)

¶ Let the distribution of the weights of bunches of bananas be $N(\mu,\sigma^2)$. We test the hypotheses

$$H_o:\ \mu \geq 800; \quad H_1:\ \mu < 800$$

at the 10% level using the critical region

$$C = \{t:\ t < -t_{0.9}(24) = -1.318\}$$

where, in the usual notation,

$$t = \frac{\bar{x}-800}{s/\sqrt{25}}$$

It is given that $\bar{x} = 779$ and $s^2 = 6400 = 80^2$. Therefore

$$t = \frac{779-800}{80/\sqrt{25}} = -1.3125.$$

The computed t-value does not belong to the critical region and there is no case for renegotiating the price with the wholesaler.

3. A lathe is adjusted to produce parts of diameter 10 cm. A random sample of 15 parts gave a mean of 9.93 cm and a standard deviation of 0.12 cm. Test the null hypothesis that the lathe is producing parts of mean diameter 10 cm against the alternative that it is not. Use a 5% significance level and assume that the diameters are independent and normally distributed.

¶ Let X denote the diameter of a randomly chosen part and suppose that X is $N(\mu, \sigma^2)$. We test the hypotheses

$$H_o: \mu = 10; \quad H_1: \mu \neq 10$$

at the 5% level using the critical region

$$C = \{t: |t| > t_{0.975}(14) = 2.145\}$$

where, in the usual notation,

$$t = \frac{\bar{x}-10}{s/\sqrt{15}}.$$

It is given that $\bar{x} = 9.93$ and $s = 0.12$. Therefore

$$t = \frac{9.93-10}{0.12/\sqrt{15}} = 2.259.$$

This value belongs to the critical region and we conclude, at the 5% level, that the mean diameter is not equal to 10.

4. The numbers of a certain kind of crustacean were counted at 60 one square metre sites along a coastline, 30 facing South and 30 facing North. The results were as follows:

South facing sites

28, 27, 31, 45, 21, 10, 30, 32, 25, 38,

27, 28, 30, 35, 27, 41, 11, 22, 34, 26,

35, 30, 27, 38, 26, 30, 14, 42, 39, 30.

North facing sites

27, 15, 38, 16, 21, 18, 20, 26, 30, 21,

24, 19, 27, 30, 31, 41, 32, 28, 27, 15,

14, 21, 22, 19, 25, 27, 30, 21, 22, 24.

Does the crustacean tend to prefer one type of site to the other? Use a significance level of approximately 1%.

¶ Let X,Y denote respectively the numbers of crustaceans per square metre in South facing and North facing sites.

We test the hypotheses

$$H_o: \mu_x = \mu_y; \quad H_1: \mu_x \neq \mu_y$$

where μ_x, μ_y are the means of X,Y respectively. Using the Central Limit Theorem and replacing the unknown variances by the corresponding sample variances s_x^2 and s_y^2, the critical region

$$C = \{z: |z| > z_{0.995} = 2.576\},$$

where $z = \dfrac{\bar{x}-\bar{y}}{\sqrt{(s_x^2+s_y^2)/30}}$

gives a two-tailed test whose significance level is approximately 1%.

From the data we find that

$$\bar{x} = 29.3, \quad \bar{y} = 24.36,$$

$$s_x^2 = 69.5966, \quad s_y^2 = 42.4471.$$

Therefore

$$z = \frac{29.3-24.36}{\sqrt{(69.5966+42.4471)/30}} = 2.553.$$

This is almost significant at the 1% level and we conclude that there is strong evidence that the crustacean prefers one type of site to the other.

5.   Of 172 mice, 60 were selected at random and vaccinated against a certain disease. All 172 mice were then infected with the disease. It was found that 22 vaccinated mice died as a result of the infection whereas there were 56 deaths in the unvaccinated group. Test at the 5% level of significance the hypothesis that the vaccine does not reduce the mortality rate against the alternative that it does.

¶   Let p_1, p_2 denote the respective probabilities that a vaccinated and an unvaccinated mouse dies from the disease. Let $\hat{p}_1, \hat{p}_2$ denote their estimates and let

$$\hat{p} = \frac{60\hat{p}_1 + 112\hat{p}_2}{172}.$$

We test the hypotheses

$$H_0: p_1 = p_2; \quad H_1: p_1 < p_2$$

at (approximately) the 5% level using the critical region

$$C = \{z: z < -z_{0.95} = -1.645\}$$

where $z = \dfrac{\hat{p}_1-\hat{p}_2}{\sqrt{\hat{p}(1-\hat{p})(1/60 + 1/112)}}$.

We have

$$\hat{p}_1 = \frac{22}{60}, \quad \hat{p}_2 = \frac{56}{112}, \quad \hat{p} = \frac{22+56}{172} = \frac{78}{172}$$

and we find that

$$z = -1.674.$$

This z-value belongs to the critical region and so the null hypothesis is rejected at (approximately) the 5% level of significance. We conclude, therefore, that the vaccine reduces the mortality rate.

6. Nine tyres of brand A had a mean life of 26000 miles with a standard deviation of 3000 miles. Nine tyres of brand B had a mean life of 23400 miles with a standard deviation of 3200 miles. Tyres of brand A are more expensive than those of brand B. Using a 5% significance level, is there sufficient evidence to conclude that the more expensive tyres have the longer mean life? State your assumptions.

¶ Let X,Y denote respectively the lifetimes of randomly selected tyres of brands A and B. Assume that X is $N(\mu_x, \sigma^2)$, Y is $N(\mu_y, \sigma^2)$ and the mileages of the nine tyres of brand A and the nine tyres of brand B are random samples from the distributions of X and Y with means $\bar{X}, \bar{Y}$ and variances S_x^2, S_y^2 respectively.

We test the hypotheses

$$H_o: \mu_x = \mu_y; \quad H_1: \mu_x > \mu_y.$$

Under H_o,

$$T = \frac{\bar{X} - \bar{Y}}{\hat{\sigma}\sqrt{\frac{1}{m} + \frac{1}{n}}}$$

has Student's t-distribution with m+n-2 degrees of freedom, where the sample sizes are m and n and

$$\hat{\sigma}^2 = \frac{(m-1)S_x^2 + (n-1)S_y^2}{m+n-2}.$$

Here m = n = 9 and the appropriate critical region is

$$C = \{t: t > 1.746\},$$

since, from Table 3, $t_{0.95}(16) = 1.746$.

We find that

$$t = \frac{26000 - 23400}{\sqrt{\frac{8 \times 3000^2 + 8 \times 3200^2}{16}(\frac{1}{9} + \frac{1}{9})}} = 1.778$$

This value is significant at the 5% level and we conclude at this level that the more expensive tyres do have the longer mean life.

7. In order to examine the question of whether the time of day
    affects candidates' performances in examinations, ten pairs
    of identical twins were given an arithmetic test. One twin
    of each pair was chosen at random and given the test in the
    morning. The remaining twins were not allowed to talk to
    the first group and took the test in the afternoon. The
    marks were as follows.

Twins	1	2	3	4	5	6	7	8	9	10
Morning	68	78	67	72	56	73	50	76	64	65
Afternoon	66	85	68	67	58	71	48	70	57	65

Use an appropriate t-test to examine the null hypothesis
that time of day does not affect examination performance.

¶   We apply a single-sample t-test to the differences between
    the morning and afternoon marks.

Twins	1	2	3	4	5	6	7	8	9	10
Difference	2	-7	-1	5	-2	2	2	6	7	0

Let X denote the difference between the morning and afternoon
marks for a randomly selected pair of twins. We assume that
X is $N(\mu, \sigma^2)$ and test the hypotheses

$$H_0: \mu = 0; \quad H_1: \mu \neq 0.$$

The sample mean and standard deviation are 1.4 and 4.1687.
Therefore

$$t = \frac{1.4}{4.1687} \sqrt{10} = 1.062.$$

As this does not lie in the critical region

$$C = \{t: |t| > t_{0.9}(9) = 1.383\},$$

the null hypothesis is not rejected even at the 20% level
of significance.

8. A government offers industrial companies financial aid in order
    to reduce sulphurous emissions from their plants. The following
    table gives the emissions (in tons) from ten large industrial
    plants on a particular day before aid was available and on the
    corresponding day two years later when aid had been available
    for eighteen months.

Plant	1	2	3	4	5	6	7	8	9	10
Before	8.3	6.8	5.9	3.4	5.6	6.7	4.3	5.4	9.5	6.0
After	9.2	5.6	5.0	3.4	4.6	6.7	3.7	6.0	8.5	5.8

Can a claim that the government's policy has had no effect be rejected at the 10% level of significance? State your assumptions.

¶   We apply a single-sample t-test to the decreases in emissions over the two-year period.

Plant	1	2	3	4	5	6	7	8	9	10
Decrease	-0.9	1.2	0.9	0	1.0	0	0.6	-0.6	1.0	0.2

Let X denote the decrease in emission over the two-year period for a randomly selected plant. We assume that X is $N(\mu, \sigma^2)$ and test the hypotheses

$$H_o: \mu = 0; \quad H_1: \mu > 0.$$

The sample mean and standard deviation are 0.34 and 0.7199. Therefore

$$t = \frac{0.34}{0.7199}\sqrt{10} = 1.494.$$

As this lies in the critical region

$$C = \{t: t > t_{0.9}(9) = 1.383\},$$

the null hypothesis is rejected at the 10% level of significance. Thus the claim is rejected at this level provided we assume that the government's policy is the only possible cause of the decrease.

9.   The random variable X is $N(\mu, 1)$. It is desired to test the null hypothesis $H_o: \mu = 0$ against the alternative hypothesis $H_1: \mu = 1$ using a random sample of size 10 from the distribution of X. The null hypothesis is to be rejected if 8 or more observations are positive. Find the Type I and Type II error probabilities of this procedure.

An alternative test is to reject H_o if the sample mean $\bar{X}$ exceeds a constant k. Find the value of k which gives the same Type I error probability as the first test. Determine the corresponding Type II error probability. Which is the better test?

¶ Let Y denote the number of positive scores.

Since

$$P(X > 0|H_o) = 0.5$$

and $P(X > 0|H_1) = P(X-1 > -1|H_1) = \Phi(1) = 0.84134,$

Y is $B(10,0.5)$ under H_o but $B(10,0.84134)$ under H_1.

The Type I error probability of the first procedure is

$$\alpha = P(Y \geqslant 8|H_o)$$

$$= \sum_{x=8}^{10} {}^{10}C_x \, 0.5^{10}$$

$$= 0.05469.$$

The corresponding Type II error probability is

$$\beta = P(Y \leqslant 7|H_1)$$

$$= \sum_{x=0}^{7} {}^{10}C_x (0.84134)^x (0.15866)^{10-x}$$

$$= 0.2028.$$

(N.B. If binomial tables are used with linear interpolation, the answer obtained is 0.2045.)

For the second procedure we require

$$\alpha = P(\bar{X} > k|H_o) = 1-\Phi(k\sqrt{10}) = 0.05469$$

i.e. $k\sqrt{10} = 1.601$

or $k = 0.5063.$

With this value of k, the Type II error probability is

$$\beta = P(\bar{X} \leqslant 0.5063|H_1)$$

$$= \Phi((0.5063-1)\sqrt{10}) = \Phi(-1.56) = 0.05938.$$

The second test is better since the tests have the same Type I error probability but the second test has the smaller Type II error probability.

10. A nurseryman sells two different grades of wallflower seed, A and B, which are indistinguishable by eye. Eighty per cent of Grade A seeds produce red flowers; the corresponding figure for Grade B seeds is sixty per cent. He finds an unlabelled sack of seeds in a storeroom. He plants 100 of these seeds and decides to label the sack 'Grade A'

if at least 70 seeds produce a red flower and otherwise to label it 'Grade B'. Assuming that all the seeds germinate, calculate the Type I and Type II error probabilities if the null hypothesis is that they are Grade A seeds.

What decision rule should he adopt if he wants the probability of correctly labelling the sack to be as near to 0.99 as possible if the sack contains Grade B seeds? What then is the probability of correctly labelling the sack if the sack contains Grade A seeds?

¶ Let X denote the number of red flowers produced from 100 seeds. Then X is $B(100, p)$ and we test the hypotheses

$$H_0: p = 0.8 \text{ (Grade A)};$$
$$H_1: p = 0.6 \text{ (Grade B)}.$$

For the given rule the Type I error probability is

$$\alpha = P(X \leq 69 | H_0) = 0.00606$$

and the Type II error probability is

$$\beta = P(X \geq 70 | H_1) = 0.02478.$$

Consider now the critical region $X \leq k$. We wish to choose k so that β is as close to 0.01 as possible. We find that $\beta = 0.01478$ if $k = 70$ and $\beta = 0.00843$ if $k = 71$. The required value of k is therefore 71. With this value of k,

$$\alpha = P(X \leq 71 | H_0) = 0.02002$$

and the required probability is

$$1-\alpha = 1-0.02002 = 0.97998.$$

11. Fourteen independent experiments are carried out in order to test the various predictions of a psychological theory. If a prediction is rejected at the 5% level of significance in one case while the results in the other thirteen experiments are non-significant, is there reason to doubt the theory's validity?

¶ Let H_0 denote the null hypothesis that the theory is correct. Then, since for each experiment a 5% level of significance is used, it follows that for each experiment, if H_0 is true,

P(correct conclusion) = 0.95
P(incorrect conclusion) = 0.05.

The probability that one rejection out of 14 occurs if H_o is true is

$$14 \times 0.05 \times 0.95^{13} = 0.36.$$

This is not a rare event so that there is no reason to doubt the truth of H_o.

12.   A company makes a product that uses three similar components. The behaviour of each component is independent of the behaviour of the other components and an item of the product works if and only if none of its components is defective. The company's records show that only 62.5% of the items work when they are assembled for the first time. The supplier of the components claims that only 5% of the components are defective when supplied and says that the high failure rate is caused by damage to the components when the product is assembled. The company rejects this claim and makes the counterclaim that only 5% of the components are damaged on assembly.

In order to settle the dispute, a random sample of 100 supplied components is examined before assembly and X are found to be defective. The supplier's claim will be accepted if $X \leqslant 7$; otherwise the supplier's claim will be rejected in favour of the company's counterclaim. Find the probabilities of both kinds of error for this test procedure.

¶   Let p_1 denote the probability that a supplied component is non-defective and let p_2 denote the probability that it is not damaged on assembly. Then

$$(p_1 p_2)^3 = 0.625.$$

If $p_1 = 0.95$ then $p_2 = 0.9$.
If $p_2 = 0.95$ then $p_1 = 0.9$.

Therefore we test H_o: $p_1 = 0.95$ against H_1: $p_1 = 0.9$ or, equivalently, H_o: $q_1 = 0.05$ against H_1: $q_1 = 0.1$, where $q_1 = 1 - p_1$.

Since X is $B(100, q_1)$, the Type I error probability is

$$\alpha = P(X \geqslant 8 | H_o)$$

$$= 1 - \sum_{x=0}^{7} {}^{100}C_x (0.05)^x (0.95)^{100-x}$$

$$= 0.12796$$

and the Type II error probability is

$$= P(X \le 7 | H_1)$$

$$= \sum_{x=0}^{7} {}^{100}C_x (0.1)^x (0.9)^{100-x}$$

$$= 0.20605.$$

13. A random sample of size 25 was taken from a normal distribution $N(1,4)$ with probability $\frac{1}{2}$ or from a normal distribution $N(2,4)$ with probability $\frac{1}{2}$. A decision about which distribution was sampled is to be based on the value of the sample mean. A loss of 15 units is incurred if it is decided that the sample came from the $N(1,4)$ distribution when in fact it came from the $N(2,4)$ distribution. A loss of 5 units is incurred if it is decided that it came from the $N(2,4)$ distribution when in fact it came from the $N(1,4)$ distribution. The reward for a correct decision is the avoidance of a loss. Find the decision rule that minimises the expected loss.

¶ Suppose that the random sample is taken from the distribution of a random variable X. It is given that X is $N(\mu,4)$ where μ is 1 or 2. The problem is to decide between H_o: $\mu = 1$ and H_1: $\mu = 2$ and we reject H_o in favour of H_1 if and only if the sample mean $\bar{X}$ exceeds some constant k.

Let L denote the loss. Then the expected loss is given by

$$E(L) = 15P(\bar{X} \le k | H_1) + 5P(\bar{X} > k | H_o)$$

$$= 15\Phi\left(\frac{k-2}{2/\sqrt{25}}\right) + 5\Phi\left(-\frac{k-1}{2/\sqrt{25}}\right).$$

We wish to minimise this function with respect to k. Now

$$\frac{dE(L)}{dk} = 15 \times \frac{5}{2}\phi\left(\frac{5}{2}(k-2)\right) - 5 \times \frac{5}{2}\phi\left(\frac{5}{2}(k-1)\right),$$

where $\phi(x) = \Phi'(x) = \frac{1}{\sqrt{2\pi}} e^{-\frac{1}{2}x^2}$.

Equating this to zero we obtain.

$$3\phi\left(\frac{5}{2}(k-2)\right) = \phi\left(\frac{5}{2}(k-1)\right).$$

Taking logarithms and simplifying, this becomes

$$\log_e 3 = -\frac{25}{8}(2k-3)$$

i.e. $k = \frac{3}{2} - \frac{4}{25}\log_e 3 = 1.3242.$

We find that $\dfrac{d^2 E(L)}{dk^2}$ is positive for this value of k. Therefore the expected loss is minimised by rejecting H_O if and only if $\bar{X} > 1.3242$.

14. A random variable X has the distribution $N(\mu, 9)$. A random sample of size n is taken from the distribution of X. It is desired to use the sample mean $\bar{X}$ to test H_O: $|\mu| \leqslant 3$ against H_1: $|\mu| > 3$, using a critical region of the form $|\bar{X}| > k$. The test is to have a significance level of 5%. Find the required value of k in terms of n and obtain an expression for the power function.

¶ The power function is given in terms of k by

$$\pi(\mu) = P(H_O \text{ rejected}; \mu)$$

$$= P(|\bar{X}| > k; \mu)$$

$$= P(\bar{X} > k; \mu) + P(\bar{X} < -k; \mu)$$

$$= \Phi(\sqrt{n}(\mu-k)/3) + \Phi(-\sqrt{n}(\mu+k)/3)$$

As the null hypothesis H_O is composite we define the significance level to be the largest possible probability of falsely rejecting H_O. Now $\pi(\mu)$ is maximised on the interval $|\mu| \leqslant 3$ when $|\mu| = 3$. Therefore we require

$$\pi(3) = 0.05$$

i.e. $\Phi(\sqrt{n}(3-k)/3) + \Phi(-\sqrt{n}(3+k)/3) = 0.05$.

Neglecting the second term on the left hand side, we have

$$\Phi(-\sqrt{n}(3-k)/3) = 0.05$$

so that $\dfrac{\sqrt{n}}{3}(3-k) = 1.645$.

Therefore $k = 3 + \dfrac{4.935}{\sqrt{n}}$.

Finally

$$\pi(\mu) = \Phi(\tfrac{\sqrt{n}}{3}(\mu-3)-1.645) + \Phi(-\tfrac{\sqrt{n}}{3}(\mu+3)-1.645).$$

15. Suppose that the random variable X is uniformly distributed on the interval $[0, \theta]$. Let Z denote the maximum of a random sample of size 10 from the distribution of X. It is required to test the hypothesis H_O: $\theta=1$ against the alternative H_1: $\theta \neq 1$ using the critical region $|Z-1| > k$, where k is a suitable constant. Given that a significance level of 0.1 is required, calculate k and sketch the power function of the test.

¶ The power function is

$$\pi(\theta) = P(|Z-1|>k;\theta) = P(Z>1+k;\theta) + P(Z<1-k;\theta) \qquad (k > 0).$$

We require $\pi(1) = 0.1$.

Now $\quad P(Z>1+k;\theta) = 0$ if $\theta=1$.

Therefore $\quad \pi(1) = P(Z<1-k|\theta=1) = (1-k)^{10} = 0.1$

so that $\qquad k = 1-0.1^{0.1} = 0.20567$

and $\qquad \pi(\theta) = P(Z>1.20567;\theta) + P(Z<0.79433;\theta)$.

For $\theta \leq 0.79433$, $\pi(\theta) = P(Z<0.79433) = 1$.

For $0.79433 < \theta \leq 1.20567$,

$$\pi(\theta) = P(Z<0.79433) = (\frac{0.79433}{\theta})^{10} = \frac{0.1}{\theta^{10}} \; .$$

For $\theta > 1.20567$,

$$\pi(\theta) = 1 - (\frac{1.20567}{\theta})^{10} + \frac{0.1}{\theta^{10}} \; .$$

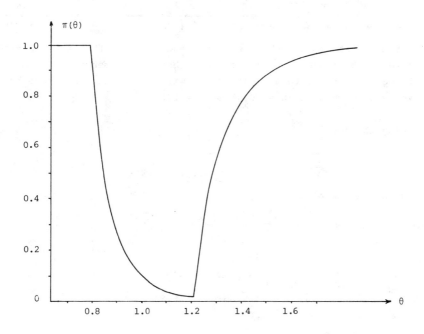

10

Regression and Correlation

Exercises 10.2 Least Squares Regression

1. The electrical resistance y of a length of wire is known to depend linearly upon its temperature x. Measurements of the resistance at different temperatures were made with the following results.

Temperature (°C)	2	10	15	19	24
Measured resistance (ohms)	1.324	1.368	1.391	1.415	1.435

Estimate the relationship between y and x, given that the temperature can be measured accurately but that measurements of resistance are subject to a random error with zero mean. Estimate the value of y when (i) x = 20, (ii) x = 24.

¶ Using the data,
$$\sum x_i = 70, \qquad \sum x_i^2 = 1266,$$
$$\sum y_i = 6.933, \quad \sum x_i y_i = 98.518.$$

As the sample size n is 5,

$$s_{xx} = \sum x_i^2 - \left(\sum x_i\right)^2 / n$$
$$= 1266 - 70^2/5$$
$$= 286$$

and
$$s_{xy} = \sum x_i y_i - \sum x_i \sum y_i / n$$
$$= 98.518 - 70 \times 6.933/5$$
$$= 1.456.$$

The slope estimate is given by
$$\hat{m} = \frac{s_{xy}}{s_{xx}} = \frac{1.456}{286} = 0.005091.$$

The estimated relationship is

$$y-\bar{y} = \hat{m}(x-\bar{x})$$

i.e. $\quad y-6.933/5 = \dfrac{1.456}{286}\ (x-70/5)$

or $\quad\quad\quad\quad y = 0.005091x + 1.3153.$

(i) When $x = 20$ the estimate of y is

$$\hat{y} = 0.005091 \times 20 + 1.3153 = 1.417.$$

(ii) When $x = 24$ the estimate of y is

$$\hat{y} = 0.005091 \times 24 + 1.3153 = 1.437.$$

Note that the measured resistance at 24°C, namely 1.435 ohms, is also an unbiased estimate of the resistance at that temperature. The least squares estimate is to be preferred, however, as it makes use of all the measurements. In fact the variance of the least squares estimator at 24°C is

$$\left(\frac{1}{5} + \frac{(24-14)^2}{286}\right)\sigma^2 = 0.55\sigma^2,$$

where σ^2 denotes the variance of a single measurement. Thus the efficiency of a single measurement at 24°C relative to the least squares estimator is only 55%.

2. The production manager at a factory wishes to investigate how the noise level affects the time taken to assemble a product. He conducts an experiment in which the times taken by ten workers to assemble the product under pre-set noise levels are recorded. The results were as follows.

Noise level (dB)	50	50	60	60	60	70	70	70	80	80
Assembly time (mins)	10	14	13	16	18	16	18	20	19	25

Plot a scatter diagram of these data. Calculate the equation of the least squares regression line of assembly time on noise level, and draw this on your scatter diagram. Find also a point estimate for the mean assembly time corresponding to a noise level of 65 dB.

¶ The scatter diagram is as follows

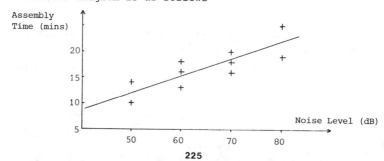

Let   x = noise level,

         y = assembly time .

Then

$$\sum x_i = 650, \qquad \sum x_i^2 = 43300,$$
$$\sum y_i = 169, \qquad \sum x_i y_i = 11320$$

and, as the sample size n is 10,

$$s_{xx} = \sum x_i^2 - \left(\sum x_i\right)^2/n$$
$$= 43300 - 650^2/10$$
$$= 1050,$$

$$s_{xy} = \sum x_i y_i - \sum x_i \sum y_i/n$$
$$= 11320 \ - 650 \times 169/10$$
$$= 335.$$

The slope estimate is given by

$$\hat{m} = \frac{s_{xy}}{s_{xx}} = \frac{335}{1050} = 0.3190.$$

The least squares regression line of y on x is

$$y - \bar{y} = \hat{m}(x - \bar{x})$$

i.e. $y - 169/10 = \dfrac{335}{1050} (x - 650/10)$

or $y = 0.3190x - 3.8381.$

This line is drawn on the scatter diagram.

The least squares estimate of the mean assembly time at a noise level of 65 dB is

$$\hat{y} = 0.3190 \times 65 - 3.8381 = 16.9 \text{ minutes.}$$

3. The price per case of a certain Chateau bottled claret depends upon age, and the following prices were noted in a catalogue.

Age (years), x	3	5	6	8	9	12
Price/case (£),y	42	58	68	80	92	132

Draw a scatter diagram, and calculate the line of regression of y on x.   Mark this line on your diagram and use it to predict the price/case of a 10 year old claret from the same Chateau.

¶ The scatter diagram is as follows

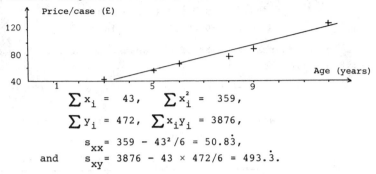

$$\sum x_i = 43, \qquad \sum x_i^2 = 359,$$

$$\sum y_i = 472, \qquad \sum x_i y_i = 3876,$$

$$s_{xx} = 359 - 43^2/6 = 50.8\dot{3},$$

and $s_{xy} = 3876 - 43 \times 472/6 = 493.\dot{3}.$

The slope estimate is

$$\hat{m} = \frac{493.\dot{3}}{50.8\dot{3}} = 9.7049$$

and the least squares regression line of y on x is

$$y - 472/6 = \frac{493.\dot{3}}{50.8\dot{3}} (x - 43/6)$$

i.e. $y = 9.7049x + 9.1148.$

This line is drawn on the scatter diagram.   The least squares estimate of the price/case of a 10 year old claret is

$$\hat{y} = 9.7049 \times 10 + 9.1148 = 106.2.$$

4. Dawn temperatures were recorded at 10 locations in a mountainous region.   Let x_i denote the altitude in metres of the ith location and let y_i denote the measured temperature there in °C.   The results were as follows.

x	225	413	421	290	684	1659	1452	1273	999	981
y	18	11	16	14	13	7	6	11	13	10

Find the least squares regression line of y on x and estimate the mean temperature at an altitude of 840 metres.

¶

$$\sum x_i = 8397, \qquad \sum x_i^2 = 9391867,$$

$$\sum y_i = 119, \qquad \sum x_i y_i = 85406,$$

$$s_{xx} = 9391867 - 8397^2/10 = 2340906.11,$$

and $s_{xy} = 85406 - 8397 \times 119/10 = -14518.3.$

The slope estimate is

$$\hat{m} = -\frac{14518.3}{2340906.11} = -0.006202$$

and the least squares regression line of y on x is

$$y - 119/10 = -0.006202(x - 8397/10)$$

i.e. $$y = -0.006202x + 17.1078.$$

The least squares estimate of the mean temperature at an altitude of 840 metres is

$$\hat{y} = -0.006202 \times 840 + 17.1078 = 11.9\,°C.$$

5. An inaccurate weighing machine gave the following readings when standard weights were placed upon it.

Weight, x(kg)	10	10	10	20	20	20	30	30	30
Reading, y(kg)	17.2	12.9	13.2	24.8	24.7	21.5	33.6	32.5	33.0

Draw a scatter diagram of these data and obtain the least squares regression line of y on x. Draw this line on your diagram. Use your line to estimate the weight of an object which gives a reading of 28.2 kg.

¶   The scatter diagram is as follows

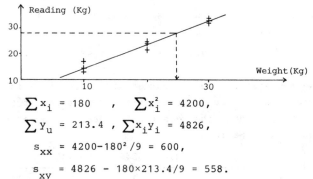

$$\sum x_i = 180 \quad , \quad \sum x_i^2 = 4200,$$

$$\sum y_u = 213.4 \quad , \quad \sum x_i y_i = 4826,$$

$$s_{xx} = 4200 - 180^2/9 = 600,$$

and $$s_{xy} = 4826 - 180 \times 213.4/9 = 558.$$

The slope estimate is

$$\hat{m} = \frac{558}{600} = 0.93$$

and the least squares regression line of y on x is

$$y - 213.4/9 = 0.93(x - 180/9)$$

i.e. $$y = 0.93x + 5.111.$$

This line can be used to 'calibrate' the weighing machine, i.e. to correct the readings when the machine is used to measure unknown weights. Thus, if an object of unknown weight x gives a reading of 28.2 kg, we estimate its weight to be

$$\hat{x} = \frac{28.2-5.111}{0.93} = 24.8 \text{ kg.}$$

The procedure is illustrated by the broken line in the figure.

6. The speed v (m/sec) of an object is related to time t (secs) by the equation

$$v = u + at$$

where   u = initial speed,
          a = acceleration (assumed constant).

In order to estimate a and u, v was measured at times 0,1,2,3 and 4 with the following results.

t	0	1	2	3	4
v	4.2	5.6	7.3	8.8	10.0

Given that measurements of v are subject to a normally distributed error with zero mean and standard deviation 0.1, calculate 95% confidence intervals for a and u. Compare your confidence interval for u with the one based on the single observation on v at time t=0.

$$\sum t_i = 10 \quad , \quad \sum t_i^2 = 30,$$
$$\sum v_i = 35.9, \quad \sum t_i v_i = 86.6,$$
$$\begin{aligned} s_{tt} &= \sum t_i^2 - (\sum t_i)^2/n \\ &= 30 - 10^2/5 \\ &= 10, \end{aligned}$$

and

$$\begin{aligned} s_{tv} &= \sum t_i v_i - \sum t_i \sum v_i/n \\ &= 86.6 - 10 \times 35.9/5 \\ &= 14.8. \end{aligned}$$

The least squares estimate of a is

$$\hat{a} = \frac{s_{tv}}{s_{tt}} = \frac{14.8}{10} = 1.48$$

and the 95% confidence interval for a is given by

$$[\hat{a}-1.96\sigma/\sqrt{s_{tt}}, \quad \hat{a}+1.96\sigma/\sqrt{s_{tt}}]$$

i.e. $[1.48-1.96 \times 0.1/\sqrt{10}, \ 1.48+1.96 \times 0.1/\sqrt{10}]$

or $[1.42, 1.54]$

Furthermore

$$\begin{aligned} \hat{u} &= \sum v_i/n - \hat{a}\sum t_i/n \\ &= 35.9/5 - 1.48 \times 10/5 \\ &= 4.22. \end{aligned}$$

The 95% confidence interval for u is given by

$$[\hat{u}-1.96\sigma\sqrt{1/n+\bar{t}^2}/s_{tt}, \quad \hat{u}+1.96\sigma\sqrt{1/n+\bar{t}^2}/s_{tt}]$$

i.e. $[4.22-1.96\times0.1\sqrt{1/5+2^2}/10, \quad 4.22+1.96\times0.1\sqrt{1/5+2^2}/10]$

or $\qquad\qquad\qquad [4.07, 4.37]$

Since the v measurements have a standard deviation of 0.1 and since v=u when t=0, the 95% confidence interval for u based on the observation at t=0 is

$$[4.2-1.96\times0.1, 4.2+1.96\times0.1]$$

i.e. $\qquad\qquad\qquad [4.00, 4.40].$

As is to be expected, this interval is wider than the one based on the least squares estimate.

7. An experiment on the solubility of a certain chemical at different temperatures gave the following results.

Temperature (°C)	0	4	10	15	21	30	45
Measured Solubility (g)	60.2	65.1	70.3	75.2	81.2	85.1	100.2

Find the least squares regression line of solubility on temperature and estimate the solubility at a temperature of 25°C. Calculate a 95% confidence interval for this solubility assuming that the measurements have a random error which is normally distributed with zero mean and standard deviation 1.5.

¶ Using the data and letting x = temperature, y = solubility,

$$\sum x_i = 125, \quad \sum x_i^2 = 3707,$$
$$\sum y_i = 537.3, \quad \sum x_i y_i = 10858.6,$$

It follows that, with n=7,

$$s_{xx} = 3707 - 125^2/7 = 1474.86,$$

and $\qquad s_{xy} = 10858.6 - 125\times537.3/7 = 1263.96.$

The slope estimate is

$$\hat{m} = \frac{1263.96}{1474.86} = 0.8570$$

and the least squares regression line of y on x is

$$y-537.3/7 = 0.8570(x-125/7)$$

i.e. $\qquad\qquad\qquad y = 0.8570x + 61.4535.$

The least squares estimate of the solubility at a temperature of 25°C is

$$\hat{y} = 0.8570 \times 25 + 61.4535 = 82.9.$$

The 95% confidence interval for y for a particular value $x = x_o$ is

$$[\hat{y} - 1.96\sigma\sqrt{1/n + (\bar{x} - x_o)^2/s_{xx}}, \quad \hat{y} + 1.96\sigma\sqrt{1/n + (\bar{x} - x_o)^2/s_{xx}}]$$

Thus the required interval is

$$[82.9 - 1.96 \times 1.5\sqrt{1/7 + (25 - 125/7)^2/1474.86},$$
$$82.9 + 1.96 \times 1.5\sqrt{1/7 + (25 - 125.7)^2/1474.86}]$$

i.e.   [81.6, 84.1].

8. The specific heat y of a certain substance is believed to follow
    a relationship of the form

$$y = mx + c,$$

    where x denotes the temperature in °C. Measurements were made
    at six different temperatures, with the following results.

Temperature	10	20	30	40	50	60
Measured specific heat	0.112	0.121	0.126	0.139	0.146	0.150

Use the method of least squares to estimate m and c. Find a 95%
confidence interval for the specific heat at 45°C, given that
the measurements of y are subject to error with zero mean and
standard deviation 0.002.

¶   Using the data,

$$\sum x_i = 210 \quad , \qquad \sum x_i^2 = 9100 \quad ,$$
$$\sum y_i = 0.794, \quad \sum x_i y_i = 29.18.$$

It follows that with n=6,

$$s_{xx} = 9100 - 210^2/6 = 1750,$$

and $$s_{xy} = 29.18 - 210 \times 0.794/6 = 1.39.$$

The slope estimate is

$$\hat{m} = \frac{s_{xy}}{s_{xx}} = \frac{1.39}{1750} = 0.0007943.$$

$$\bar{x} = \sum x_i/n = 210/6 = 35,$$

$$\bar{y} = \sum y_i/n = 0.794/6 = 0.132\overset{.}{3}$$

and the intercept estimate is

$$\hat{c} = \bar{y} - \hat{m}\bar{x}$$
$$= 0.132\dot{3} - 0.0007943 \times 35$$
$$= 0.1045.$$

The 95% confidence interval for y for a particular value $x = x_0$ is

$$[\hat{y} - 1.96\sigma\sqrt{1/n + (x_0 - \bar{x})^2/s_{xx}}, \quad \hat{y} + 1.96\sigma\sqrt{1/n + (x_0 - \bar{x})^2/s_{xx}}]$$

Given $x_0 = 45°C$,

$$\hat{y} = 0.0007943 \times 45 + 0.1045 = 0.1402$$

and the required interval is

$$[0.1402 - 1.96 \times 0.002\sqrt{1/6 + (45-35)^2/1750},$$
$$0.1402 + 1.96 \times 0.002\sqrt{1/6 + (45-35)^2/1750}]$$

i.e. $\qquad\qquad [0.138, \ 0.142].$

9. Observations Y_i of a variable y are made at pre-determined values $i = 1, 2, \ldots, n$ of a variable x. Given that the relationship between x and y is
$$y = mx + c,$$
show that the least squares estimators for m, c are

$$\hat{m} = \frac{6}{n(n^2 - 1)} \sum (2i - n - 1) Y_i,$$

$$\hat{c} = \frac{2}{n(n-1)} \sum (2n - 3i + 1) Y_i.$$

Derive an expression for the variance of $\hat{m}$ in terms of n and σ^2, the variance of the error associated with the measurements Y_i.

¶ In this case,

$$\sum x_i = \sum_{i=1}^{n} i = \frac{1}{2} n(n+1),$$

$$\sum x_i^2 = \sum_{i=1}^{n} i^2 = \frac{1}{6} n(n+1)(2n+1).$$

Thus $\qquad s_{xx} = \sum x_i^2 - \frac{1}{n} \left(\sum x_i \right)^2$

$$= \frac{1}{6} n(n+1)(2n+1) - \frac{n^2(n+1)^2}{4n}$$

$$= \frac{n(n^2 - 1)}{12},$$

and

$$s_{xy} = \sum x_i y_i - \sum x_i \sum y_i / n$$

$$= \sum_{i=1}^{n} iy_i - \frac{n(n+1)}{2n} \sum_{i=1}^{n} y_i$$

$$= \frac{1}{2} \left[\sum_{i=1}^{n} (2i-n-1)y_i \right].$$

Therefore the slope estimate is given by

$$\hat{m} = \frac{s_{xy}}{s_{xx}}$$

$$= \frac{6}{n(n^2-1)} \sum_{i=1}^{n} (2i-n-1)\, y_i.$$

The corresponding estimator is therefore

$$\hat{m} = \frac{6}{n(n^2-1)} \sum_{i=1}^{n} (2i-n-1)\, Y_i.$$

The intercept estimate is given by

$$\hat{c} = \sum y_i / n - \hat{m} \sum x_i / n$$

$$= \frac{\displaystyle\sum_{i=1}^{n} y_i}{n} - \frac{6}{n(n^2-1)} \sum_{i=1}^{n} (2i-n-1) \cdot \frac{n(n+1)}{2n}$$

$$= \frac{\displaystyle\sum_{i=1}^{n} y_i(n-1-6i+3n+3)}{n(n-1)}$$

$$= \frac{2}{n(n-1)} \sum_{i=1}^{n} (2n-3i+1)\, y_i.$$

The corresponding estimator is

$$\hat{c} = \frac{2}{n(n-1)} \sum_{i=1}^{n} (2n-3i+1)\, Y_i.$$

Consider

$$\text{Var}(\hat{m}) = \frac{36}{n^2(n^2-1)^2} \sum_{i=1}^{n} (2i-n-1)^2\, \text{Var}(Y_i)$$

$$= \frac{36\sigma^2}{n^2(n^2-1)^2} \left[4\sum_{i=1}^{n} i^2 - 4(n+1)\sum_{i=1}^{n} i + (n+1)^2 \sum_{i=1}^{n} 1 \right]$$

$$= \frac{36\sigma^2}{n^2(n^2-1)^2}\left[\frac{4n(n+1)(2n+1)}{6} - 4(n+1)\frac{n(n+1)}{2} + (n+1)^2n\right]$$

$$= \frac{36\sigma^2}{n^2(n^2-1)^2}\cdot\frac{n(n+1)}{3}[4n+2-6n-6+3n+3]$$

$$= \frac{12\sigma^2}{n(n^2-1)}\ .$$

10. A series of measurements on a pair of variables gave the results (x_1,y_1), (x_2,y_2),...,(x_n,y_n).

If $\qquad\qquad \zeta_i = \dfrac{(x_i-a)}{b}$

and $\qquad\qquad \eta_i = \dfrac{(y_i-d)}{e}$,

where a,b,d,e are constants, show that

(i) $\quad \bar{x} = b\bar{\zeta} + a$, $\qquad$ (ii) $\quad \bar{y} = e\bar{\eta} + d$,

(iii) $\quad s_{xx} = b^2 s_{\zeta\zeta}$, $\qquad$ (iv) $\quad s_{yy} = e^2 s_{\eta\eta}$,

(v) $\quad s_{xy} = bes_{\zeta\eta}$,

where $\bar{x},\bar{y},s_{xx},s_{yy}$ and s_{xy} have their usual meaning and

$$\bar{\zeta} = \sum \zeta_i/n, \qquad\qquad \bar{\eta} = \sum \eta_i/n,$$

$$s_{\zeta\zeta} = \sum(\zeta_i-\bar{\zeta})^2, \qquad s_{\eta\eta} = \sum(\eta_i-\bar{\eta})^2$$

$$s_{\zeta\eta} = \sum(\zeta_i-\bar{\zeta})(\eta_i-\bar{\eta}).$$

¶ (i) Since

$$x_i = b\zeta_i + a$$

it follows that

$$\sum \frac{x_i}{n} = \sum \frac{b\ \zeta_i}{n} + \sum \frac{a}{n}$$

or $\quad \bar{x} = b\ \bar{\zeta} + a$

(ii) Similarly,

$$y_i = e\ \eta_i + d$$

$$\sum \frac{y_i}{n} = \sum \frac{e\eta_i}{n} + \sum \frac{d}{n}$$

or $\qquad \bar{y} = e\bar{\eta} + d$

(iii) $\begin{aligned} s_{xx} &= \sum(x_i - \bar{x})^2 \\ &= \sum(b\zeta_i + a - b\bar{\zeta} - a)^2 \\ &= b^2 \sum(\zeta_i - \bar{\zeta})^2 \\ &= b^2 s_{\zeta\zeta} \end{aligned}$

(iv) $\begin{aligned} s_{yy} &= \sum(y_i - \bar{y})^2 \\ &= \sum(e\eta_i + d - e\bar{\eta} - d)^2 \\ &= e^2 \sum(\eta_i - \bar{\eta})^2 \\ &= e^2 s_{\eta\eta} \end{aligned}$

(v) $\begin{aligned} s_{xy} &= \sum(x_i - \bar{x})(y_i - \bar{y}) \\ &= \sum(b\zeta_i + a - b\bar{\zeta} - a)(e\eta_i + d - e\bar{\eta} - d) \\ &= be \sum(\zeta_i - \bar{\zeta})(\eta_i - \bar{\eta}) \\ &= bes_{\zeta\eta} \end{aligned}$

11. Measurements of the velocity of sound in air at different temperatures gave the following results

Air temperature, x(°C)	30	45	60	75	90
Measured velocity of sound, y (m/sec)	351	359	367	377	384

Transform these data using the method given in Exercise 10,
taking a=60, b=15, d=360 and e=1. Calculate $\bar{\zeta}$, $\bar{\eta}$, $s_{\zeta\zeta}$, $s_{\zeta\eta}$ and
deduce the values of $\bar{x}$, $\bar{y}$, s_{xx}, s_{xy}. Hence find the least
squares regression line of y on x.

¶   Using the given transformation, the data become

ζ	-2	-1	0	1	2
η	-9	-1	7	17	24

Thus $\bar{\zeta} = 0$, $\bar{\eta} = 7.6$.

Also, $s_{\zeta\zeta} = \sum \zeta^2 - n\bar{\zeta}^2 = 10$,

and $s_{\zeta\eta} = \sum \zeta\eta - n\bar{\zeta}\bar{\eta} = 84$.

Thus, using the results of Exercise 10,

$$\bar{x} = b\bar{\zeta} + a = 60,$$
$$\bar{y} = e\bar{\eta} + d = 367.6,$$

$$s_{xx} = b^2 s_{\zeta\zeta} = 2250,$$

$$s_{xy} = be\ s_{\zeta\eta} = 1260.$$

Thus the slope estimate of the regression line of y on x is

$$\hat{m} = \frac{s_{xy}}{s_{xx}} = \frac{1260}{2250} = 0.56.$$

The least squares regression line of y on x is

$$y - \bar{y} = \hat{m}(x - \bar{x})$$

i.e. $y - 367.6 = 0.56(x - 60)$

or $y = 0.56x + 334.$

12. Suppose that for i=1,2,...,n,

$$y_i = mx_i + \varepsilon_i,$$

where the ε_i's are independent random error terms with zero mean and m is an unknown constant. Show that the least squares estimate of m is given by

$$\hat{m} = \frac{\sum x_i y_i}{\sum x_i^2}$$

where y_i is the value taken by Y_i. Deduce that the least squares line does not, in general, pass through the centroid of the data.

¶   Let $q = \sum (y_i - \hat{m}\ x_i)^2$

Then the least squares estimate of m is the value of $\hat{m}$ which minimises q.

Now $\dfrac{dq}{d\hat{m}} = -2 \sum (y_i - \hat{m}\ x_i) x_i$

and $\dfrac{d^2 q}{d\hat{m}^2} = 2 \sum x_i^2.$

The equation $\dfrac{dq}{d\hat{m}} = 0$

i.e. $\sum (y_i - \hat{m}\ x_i) x_i = 0,$

gives $\sum x_i y_i = \hat{m} \sum x_i^2$

or $\hat{m} = \dfrac{\sum x_i y_i}{\sum x_i^2}.$

Since
$$\frac{d^2 q}{d\hat{m}^2} > 0$$

(excluding the trivial case $\sum x_i^2 = 0$), this gives a minimum as required.

The equation of the least squares line is
$$y = x \, \frac{\sum x_i y_i}{\sum x_i^2} \, .$$

The condition for this to pass through the centroid $(\bar{x}, \bar{y})$ is

$$\bar{y} = \bar{x} \, \frac{\sum x_i y_i}{\sum x_i^2} \, ,$$

i.e.
$$\frac{\sum y_i}{n} = \frac{\sum x_i}{n} \cdot \frac{\sum x_i y_i}{\sum x_i^2}$$

or
$$\sum x_i^2 \sum y_i = \sum x_i \sum x_i y_i \, .$$

This is not true in general. So the least squares line does not necessarily pass through the centroid in this case.

13. Suppose that
$$Y_i = mi + \varepsilon_i \quad (i = 1, 2, \ldots, n),$$

where $\varepsilon_1, \varepsilon_2, \ldots, \varepsilon_n$ are independent $N(0, \sigma^2)$ random variables and m is constant. Show that the least squares estimator of m is given by
$$\hat{m}_1 = \frac{6 \sum i Y_i}{n(n+1)(2n+1)}$$

and that $\hat{m}_1$ is unbiased with variance

$$\frac{6\sigma^2}{n(n+1)(2n+1)} \, .$$

Show further that, for $n \geqslant 2$,
$$\hat{m}_2 = \frac{Y_n - Y_1}{(n-1)}$$

is another unbiased estimator for m and that the efficiency of $\hat{m}_2$ relative to $\hat{m}_1$ is

$$\frac{3(n-1)^2}{n(n+1)(2n+1)} \, .$$

Deduce that $\hat{m}_1$ is the better estimator for all permissible values of n.

¶ Let y_i be the observed value of Y_i and (as in Exercise 12) define

$$q = \sum_{i=1}^{n} (y_i - \hat{m}_1 i)^2.$$

Then the least squares estimate of m is the value of $\hat{m}_1$ which minimises q.

Now

$$\frac{dq}{d\hat{m}_1} = -2 \sum_{i=1}^{n} (y_i - \hat{m}_1 i) \times i$$

and

$$\frac{d^2 q}{d\hat{m}_1^2} = 2 \sum_{i=1}^{n} i^2 > 0.$$

The equation $\dfrac{dq}{d\hat{m}_1} = 0$

i.e.

$$\sum_{i=1}^{n} i(y_i - \hat{m}_1 i) = 0,$$

gives

$$\hat{m}_1 = \frac{\sum_{i=1}^{n} i\, y_i}{\sum_{i=1}^{n} i^2}$$

$$= \frac{6 \sum_{i=1}^{n} i\, y_i}{n(n+1)(2n+1)}$$

and since $\dfrac{d^2 q}{d\hat{m}_1^2} > 0$, this gives a minimum.

The corresponding estimator for m is

$$\hat{m}_1 = \frac{6 \sum i Y_i}{n(n+1)(2n+1)}$$

Now

$$E(\hat{m}_1) = \frac{6 \sum i E(Y_i)}{n(n+1)(2n+1)}$$

$$= \frac{6 \sum i.mi}{n(n+1)(2n+1)}$$

$$= \frac{6m \sum i^2}{n(n+1)(2n+1)}$$

$$= \frac{6m}{n(n+1)(2n+1)} \cdot \frac{n(n+1)(2n+1)}{6}$$

$$= m$$

so that $\hat{m}_1$ is unbiased for m.

Also, $\quad \text{Var}(\hat{m}_1) = \dfrac{36}{n^2(n+1)^2(2n+1)^2} \sum i^2 \, \text{Var}(Y_i)$

$$= \dfrac{36\sigma^2 \sum i^2}{n^2(n+1)^2(2n+1)^2}$$

$$= \dfrac{36\sigma^2}{n^2(n+1)^2(2n+1)^2} \cdot \dfrac{n(n+1)(2n+1)}{6}$$

$$= \dfrac{6\sigma^2}{n(n+1)(2n+1)} \cdot$$

Now consider

$$\hat{m}_2 = \dfrac{Y_n - Y_1}{n-1}$$

$$E(\hat{m}_2) = \dfrac{E(Y_n) - E(Y_1)}{n-1}$$

$$= \dfrac{mn - m}{n-1}$$

$$= m.$$

Thus $\hat{m}_2$ is unbiased for m.

Also, $\quad \text{Var}(\hat{m}_2) = \dfrac{1}{(n-1)^2} \, \text{Var}(Y_n - Y_1)$

$$= \dfrac{1}{(n-1)^2} \, [\text{Var}(Y_n) + \text{Var}(Y_1)]$$

$$= \dfrac{2\sigma^2}{(n-1)^2} \cdot$$

The efficiency of $\hat{m}_2$ relative to $\hat{m}_1$ is given by

$$\text{Eff} = \dfrac{\text{Var}(\hat{m}_1)}{\text{Var}(\hat{m}_2)}$$

$$= \dfrac{6\sigma^2}{n(n+1)(2n+1)} \cdot \dfrac{(n-1)^2}{2\sigma^2}$$

$$= \dfrac{3(n-1)^2}{n(n+1)(2n+1)} \cdot$$

We are required to show that this is less than 1 for $n \geq 2$.

Consider the expression in the form

$$\text{Eff} = \dfrac{3}{(2n+1)} \cdot \dfrac{n^2 - 2n + 1}{n^2 + n}$$

For $n \geq 2$,

$$3 < 2n+1$$

and $\quad n^2 - 2n + 1 < n^2 + n.$

Thus, for n $\geqslant$ 2,

Eff < 1.

14. The variables y and x are related by the equation
$$y = mx.$$
Observations on y at a number of given values of x gave the following results.

x	1	2	3	4	5	6
y	2.0	6.6	9.8	11.2	15.0	18.1

Draw a scatter diagram of these data and calculate

(i) $\hat{m}$, the least squares estimate of m,

(ii)   the 95% confidence interval for m, given that the y measurements are subject to a normally distributed error of zero mean and standard deviation 0.5.

Mark on your diagram (a) the least squares line, (b) the lines corresponding to the upper and lower limits of the confidence interval for m.

¶ (i)   From the data we find that
$$\sum x_i^2 = 91, \qquad \sum x_i y_i = 273.$$
Thus,
$$\hat{m} = \frac{\sum x_i y_i}{\sum x_i^2}$$
$$= 3.$$

(ii)   Using the result in Exercise 13,
$$\text{Var}(\hat{m}) = \frac{6\sigma^2}{n(n+1)(2n+1)}$$

Thus the standard error of $\hat{m}$ is given by
$$\text{SE}(\hat{m}) = \sigma\sqrt{6/(n(n+1)(2n+1))}$$
$$= 0.5\sqrt{6/(6\times7\times13)}$$
$$= \frac{0.5}{\sqrt{91}}.$$

The 95% confidence interval for m is therefore
$$[\hat{m}-1.96\ \text{SE}(\hat{m}),\ \hat{m}+1.96\ \text{SE}(\hat{m})]$$
i.e $[3 - \dfrac{1.96\times0.5}{\sqrt{91}},\ 3 + \dfrac{1.96\times0.5}{\sqrt{91}}]$
or $[2.897, 3.103].$

These data are illustrated below

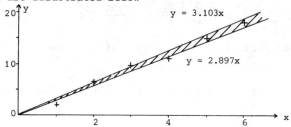

We are '95% confident' that the true line relating y to x lies within the shaded area.

15. Measurements on y for given values of x were as follows.

x	1.0	2.5	4.0	6.0	7.5	10.0
y	3.5	6.0	14.2	18.2	21.1	26.0

Plot a scatter diagram of these results. Calculate the equation of the least squares regression line of y on x and mark this on your diagram. It is subsequently decided on physical grounds that the regression line passes through the origin, i.e. the intercept c is zero. Calculate the modified equation of the least squares regression line and mark it on your diagram.

¶ From the data we find that

$$\sum x_i = 31, \quad \sum x_i^2 = 215.5,$$
$$\sum y_i = 89, \quad \sum x_i y_i = 602.75.$$

Thus
$$s_{xx} = 215.5 - 31^2/6$$
$$= 55.\dot{3},$$

and
$$s_{xy} = 602.75 - 31 \times 89/6$$
$$= 142.916\dot{6}.$$

The slope estimate is therefore
$$\hat{m} = \frac{142.916\dot{6}}{55.\dot{3}} = 2.5828.$$

The least squares regression line of y on x is
$$y - \bar{y} = \hat{m}(x - \bar{x})$$

i.e. $y - 89/6 = 2.5828(x - 31/6)$

or $y = 2.5828x + 1.4887.$

Suppose now that the line is constrained to pass through the origin. For this model,

$$\hat{m} = \frac{\sum x_i y_i}{\sum x_i^2} = \frac{602.75}{215.5} = 2.7970.$$

The modified least squares line is therefore

$$y = 2.7970x.$$

The following scatter diagram illustrates these results

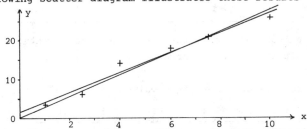

16. The braking distance y of a car is approximately related to its speed x by the formula

$$y = kx^2,$$

where k is a constant depending on the efficiency of the braking system. The following results were obtained in a series of trials on a particular car.

Speed, x (mph)	30	45	60	70	80
Braking distance, y(ft)	46.2	100.1	182.2	243.8	321.5

Draw a scatter diagram in which y is plotted against x^2 and calculate the least squares estimate of k. Plot the corresponding line on your diagram and estimate the braking distance for a speed of 50 mph.

¶ Let $z = x^2$ so that the modified data are

z	900	2025	3600	4900	6400
y	46.2	100.1	182.2	243.8	321.5

For these data,

$$\sum z_i^2 = 82840625, \sum z_i y_i = 4152422.5.$$

The least squares estimate of k is therefore

$$\hat{k} = \frac{\sum z_i y_i}{\sum z_i^2}$$
$$= \frac{4152422.5}{82840625}$$
$$= 0.050125.$$

The following diagram illustrates these results:

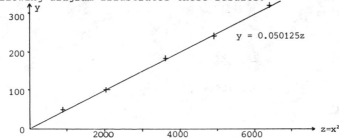

The least squares estimate of the braking distance from 50 mph is

$$\hat{y} = 0.050125 \times 50^2 = 125.3.$$

17. The stopping distance y of a car, i.e. the distance travelled between the driver seeing an emergency and the car coming to rest, is approximately related to the speed x by the formula

$$y = ax + bx^2,$$

where a and b are constants. (Here, ax represents the 'thinking distance' and bx^2 represents the 'braking distance'.)
A series of trials gave the following results for a particular driver in a particular car.

Speed, x (mph)	50	60	70	80	90
Stopping distance, y(ft)	173.4	240.6	312.9	402.0	496.3

By writing the relationship in the form

$$z = a + bx,$$

where z = y/x, calculate the least squares estimates of a and b.
Draw a scatter diagram of the (x,y) data and mark on it the curve defined by your estimated values of a and b.
Does this curve pass through $(\bar{x},\bar{y})$, the centroid of the data?

¶ The transformed data are

x	50	60	70	80	90
z	3.468	4.01	4.47	5.025	5.514

Using these data

$$\sum x_i = 350, \qquad \sum x_i^2 = 25500,$$
$$\sum z_i = 22.4874, \qquad \sum x_i z_i = 1625.2.$$

Thus $s_{xx} = 25500 - 350^2/5 = 1000,$

and $\quad s_{xz}$ = 1625.2$-$350×22.4874/5 = 51.0789.

Thus

$$\hat{b} \;=\; \frac{s_{xz}}{s_{xx}}$$

$$=\; \frac{51.0789}{1000}$$

$$=\; 0.05108.$$

Also, $\quad \hat{a} \;=\; \bar{z} - \hat{b}\,\bar{x}$

$$=\; \frac{22.4874}{5} - 0.05108 \times \frac{350}{5}$$

$$=\; 0.9220.$$

The following diagram illustrates these results.

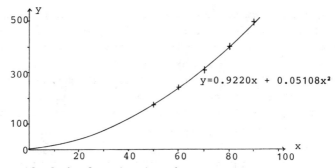

$$y=0.9220x + 0.05108x^2$$

The centroid of the data is given by

$$\bar{x} \;=\; \frac{\sum x_i}{n} \;=\; \frac{350}{5} \;=\; 70,$$

$$\bar{y} \;=\; \frac{\sum y_i}{n} \;=\; \frac{1625.2}{5} \;=\; 325.04.$$

Consider

$$\bar{y} - \hat{a}\bar{x} - \hat{b}\bar{x}^2 \;=\; 325.04 - 0.9220 \times 70 - 0.05108 \times 70^2$$

$$=\; 10.21$$

$$\neq\; 0.$$

The curve does not therefore pass through $(\bar{x}, \bar{y})$.

18. The variables x and y satisfy a relationship of the form
$$y = ax^b,$$
where a,b are unknown constants. Measurements on y for given values of x were as follows.

x	0.8	1.1	1.5	1.9	2.4	3.0
y	1.36	2.63	4.76	7.92	11.73	19.60

Estimate a and b by taking logarithms to any convenient base
and using the method of least squares.

¶   Taking logarithms to base e,

$$\log y = \log a + b \log x.$$

Putting $\zeta = \log x$, $\eta = \log y$,

the relationship becomes

$$\eta = \log a + b\zeta,$$

which is linear.

The transformed data are

ζ	-0.22314	0.09531	0.40547	0.64185	0.87547	1.09861
η	0.30749	0.96698	1.56025	2.06939	2.46215	2.97553

Using these data,

$$\sum \zeta_i = 2.89357, \qquad \sum \zeta_i^2 \quad 2.60865,$$

$$\sum \eta_i = 10.34179, \qquad \sum \zeta_i \eta_i = 7.40891.$$

It follows that

$$s_{\zeta\zeta} = 2.60865 - 2.89357^2/6 = 1.21320$$

and $s_{\zeta\eta} = 7.40891 - 2.89357 \times 10.34179/6 = 2.42147$

Thus $\hat{b} = s_{\zeta\eta}/s_{\zeta\zeta} = \dfrac{2.42147}{1.21320} = 1.99594.$

If   c = log a, then

$$\hat{c} = \bar{\eta} - \hat{b}\,\bar{\zeta}$$
$$= 10.34179/6 - 1.99594 \times 2.89357/6$$
$$= 0.76107.$$

Since $a = e^c$, it follows that

$$\hat{a} = e^{\hat{c}} = e^{0.76107} = 2.1406.$$

19.   The selling price y of a certain model of car is approximately
related to age x by the formula

$$y = \lambda e^{-\mu x},$$

where λ and μ are constants.   The following prices were noted
in a showroom.

Age, x (months)	2	12	14	26	9	30	18
Selling price, y (£)	4100	3200	3000	2400	3600	2000	2950

Taking logarithms to base e, use the method of least squares to estimate λ and μ. What selling price would you expect for a 20 month old car of this model?

¶ Taking logarithms to base e,

$$\log y = \log \lambda - \mu x$$

or $\qquad z = mx + c,$

where $\qquad z = \log y,$

$$m = -\mu$$

and $\qquad c = \log \lambda.$

Transforming the y data, we obtain

x	2	12	14	26	9	30	18
z	8.3187	8.0709	8.0064	7.7832	8.1887	7.6009	7.9896

Using these data,

$$\sum x_i = 111 \quad , \quad \sum x_i^2 = 2325 \quad ,$$
$$\sum z_i = 55.9584, \quad \sum x_i z_i = 873.4791,$$

whence $\quad s_{xx} = 2325 - 111^2/7$

$$= 564.8571,$$

and $\quad s_{xz} = 873.4791 - 111 \times 55.9584/7$

$$= -13.8612$$

and $\qquad \hat{m} = \dfrac{-13.8612}{564.8571} = -0.02454.$

Since $\qquad \mu = -m$

it follows that

$$\hat{\mu} = 0.0245 \text{ (to 4 decimal places).}$$

Furthermore,

$$\hat{c} = \bar{z} - \hat{m}\,\bar{x}$$

$$= 55.9584/7 + 0.02454 \times 111/7$$

$$= 8.3832.$$

Since $\qquad c = \log \lambda$

it follows that

$$\lambda = e^c,$$

whence $\qquad \hat{\lambda} = e^{\hat{c}} = e^{8.3832} = 4373.$

The estimated relationship is therefore

$$\hat{y} = 4373\, e^{-0.02454x}$$

Putting x = 20,
$$\hat{y} = 4373\ e^{-0.02454 \times 20}$$
$$= 2677.$$

N.B. If the value of $\hat{m}$ had been rounded to -0.0245 and this value had been used to calculate $\hat{\lambda}$ and $\hat{y}$, the incorrect values 4370 and 2679 would have been obtained. Such premature rounding should be avoided.

20. The length y of an elastic string is given in terms of its tension x by the formula
$$y = mx + c$$
where m , c are constants. Measurement of x can be made accurately, but measurements of y are subject to an error which may be assumed to be normally distributed with zero mean and unknown variance σ^2. The following measurements were made.

x (Newtons)	5.0	7.5	10.0	12.5	15.0
y (metres)	1.23	1.39	1.52	1.66	1.81

Find the least squares estimates of m and c and calculate

(i)   an unbiased estimate of σ^2,

(ii)   a 95% confidence interval for the unstretched length of the string, i.e. the length corresponding to zero tension.

¶   From the data,
$$\sum x_i = 50\ , \qquad \sum x_i^2 = 562.5\ ,$$
$$\sum y_i = 7.61, \qquad \sum x_i y_i = 79.675.$$

Thus $s_{xx} = 562.5 - 50^2/5$
$$= 62.5,$$

and $s_{xy} = 79.675 - 50 \times 7.61/5$
$$= 3.575.$$

It follows that
$$\hat{m} = \frac{3.575}{62.5} = 0.0572\ .$$

Furthermore,
$$\hat{c} = \bar{y} - \hat{m}\ \bar{x}$$
$$= \frac{7.61}{5} - 0.0572 \times \frac{50}{5}$$
$$= 0.95.$$

(i)   An unbiased estimate for σ^2 is given by

$$\hat{\sigma}^2 = \frac{1}{n-2}(s_{yy}-s_{xy}^2/s_{xx}).$$

Now $\sum y_i^2$ = 11.7871

so that s_{yy} = 11.7871 - 7.61²/5
               = 0.20468.

Thus $\hat{\sigma}^2 = \frac{1}{3}(0.20468 - \frac{3.575^2}{62.5})$

               = 0.000063.

(ii)   We now require to find a 95% confidence interval for
c since this is the unstretched length. The required interval
is given by

$$\left[\hat{c}-t_{0.975}(n-2)\hat{\sigma}\sqrt{\frac{1}{n}+\frac{\bar{x}^2}{s_{xx}}}, \quad \hat{c}+t_{0.975}(n-2)\hat{\sigma}\sqrt{\frac{1}{n}+\frac{\bar{x}^2}{s_{xx}}}\right]$$

Since $t_{0.975}(3)$ = 3.182 and $\bar{x}$ = 10, this reduces to

$$\left[0.95-3.182 \times \sqrt{0.000063}\sqrt{\frac{1}{5}+\frac{10^2}{62.5}}, \quad 0.95+3.182 \times \sqrt{0.000063}\sqrt{\frac{1}{5}+\frac{10^2}{62.5}}\right]$$

i.e.   [0.916, 0.984].

21. An experiment was conducted at an agricultural research institute
to investigate the relationship between Y, the daily growth of a
certain plant (in millimetres), and the mean daily temperature x
(in °C). The data collected were as follows.

x	9.0	9.3	9.1	10.8	11.4	8.1	9.2	8.3	8.4	9.9	9.6	6.3	9.4	7.8
y	3.1	3.6	3.4	4.0	4.4	3.2	3.3	2.9	3.0	3.8	3.4	2.5	3.7	3.1

Plot a scatter diagram of these data. Assuming that a suitable
model is

$$E(Y) = mx + c,$$

where m and c are constants, calculate the least squares
estimates of m and c and mark the least squares line on your
diagram. Obtain 90% confidence intervals for E(Y) corresponding
to the following values of x.

6.5, 7.0, 7.5, 8.0, 8.5, 9.0, 9.5, 10.0, 10.5, 11.0.

For which value of x is the 90% confidence interval for E(Y)
narrowest?

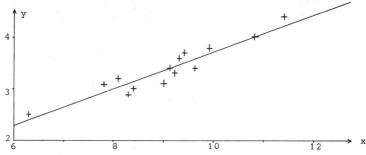

For these data,

$$\sum x_i = 126.6, \qquad \sum x_i^2 = 1165.66,$$
$$\sum y_i = 47.4, \qquad \sum x_i y_i = 436.2,$$

whence $s_{xx} = 1165.66 - 126.6^2/14 = 20.83428,$

and $s_{xy} = 436.2 - 126.6 \times 47.4/14 = 7.56857.$

Thus $\hat{m} = \dfrac{7.56857}{20.83428} = 0.363275.$

Also $\hat{c} = \bar{y} - \hat{m}\,\bar{x}$
$$= 47.4/14 - 0.363275 \times 126.6/14$$
$$= 0.10067.$$

Since σ is not given we must estimate its value from the data. Now

$$\sum y_i^2 = 163.58$$

and $s_{yy} = 163.58 - 47.4^2/14 = 3.09714.$

Therefore $\hat{\sigma}^2 = \dfrac{1}{n-2}(s_{yy} - s_{xy}^2/s_{xx})$
$$= \dfrac{1}{12}(3.09714 - 7.56857^2/20.83428)$$
$$= 0.028972$$

and $\hat{\sigma} = \sqrt{0.028972} = 0.17021.$

The 90% confidence interval for the value of y for a particular value of x is

$$[\hat{y} - t_{0.95}(n-2)\hat{\sigma}\sqrt{1/n + (x-\bar{x})^2/s_{xx}}, \; \hat{y} + t_{0.95}(n-2)\hat{\sigma}\sqrt{1/n + (x-\bar{x})^2/s_{xx}}]$$

where $\hat{y} = \hat{m}x + \hat{c}.$

As $n = 14$, $t_{0.95}(n-2) = t_{0.95}(12) = 1.782.$

Evaluating the interval for the various values of x we obtain the following table.

x	90% Confidence interval for y
6.5	[2.27, 2.65]
7.0	[2.49, 2.80]
7.5	[2.69, 2.96]
8.0	[2.90, 3.11]
8.5	[3.10, 3.28]
9.0	[3.29, 3.45]
9.5	[3.47, 3.64]
10.0	[3.63, 3.84]
10.5	[3.79, 4.04]
11.0	[3.94, 4.25]

It can be seen from the general expression for the confidence interval that this interval is narrowest when $x=\bar{x}$, i.e. when $x=126.6/14 = 9.04$.

22. An enthusiastic gardener, who grows tomatoes in a greenhouse, decided to investigate the relationship between the yield of a plant and the number of times it is watered during the growing season. He took 8 plants, watered them at different intervals throughout the season, and measured their yields. His results were as follows.

Number of waterings, x	20	25	30	35	40	45	50	55
Yield, y (lbs)	6.3	6.8	6.9	7.3	7.4	7.8	7.5	6.9

Find the least squares regression line of y on x and test the null hypothesis that watering has no effect on average yield against the alternative that the average yield is increased at a 5% significance level. Comment on any assumptions that you make in order to test these hypotheses.

¶ For these data,

$$\sum x_i = 300, \qquad \sum x_i^2 = 12300,$$
$$\sum y_i = 56.9, \qquad \sum x_i y_i = 2160.$$

Thus $s_{xx} = 12300 - 300^2/8 = 1050,$

and $s_{xy} = 2160 - 300 \times 56.9/8 = 26.25.$

The slope estimate is given by

$$\hat{m} = \frac{26.25}{1050} = 0.025.$$

The least squares regression line of y on x is
$$y-\bar{y} = \hat{m}(x-\bar{x})$$
i.e. $y-56.9/8 = 0.025(x-300/8)$
or $y = 0.025x + 6.175.$

Since σ is unknown, we must estimate its value.
Now
$$\sum y_i^2 = 406.29$$
and $s_{yy} = 406.29-56.9^2/8 = 1.58875.$

Thus $\hat{\sigma}^2 = \dfrac{1}{n-2} \, (s_{yy}-s_{xy}^2/s_{xx})$
$$= \frac{1}{6} \, (1.58875-26.25^2/1050)$$
$$= 0.15542$$

and $\hat{\sigma} = \sqrt{0.15542} = 0.39423.$

We now test the hypotheses
$$H_0:m=0; \quad H_1:m>0.$$

We find that
$$\frac{\hat{m}}{\hat{\sigma}} \, \sqrt{s_{xx}} = \frac{0.025\sqrt{1050}}{0.39423} = 2.055$$
but, from tables of Student's t distribution,

$$t_{0.95}(6) = 1.943.$$

Thus H_0 is rejected at the 5% level of significance in favour of the alternative that watering does increase the average yield.

This analysis assumes that the yields are normally and independently distributed with constant variance and that the average yield is a linear function of the number of waterings. An examination of the data suggests that this last assumption may not be valid. The observed yields increase with the number of waterings up to a point but then decrease, possibly due to chance but possibly due to over-watering.

23. A consumer council wishes to investigate the seasonal variation in price of a 'basket' of basic commodities. To do this, the mean monthly price of the basket was recorded over a two-year period, with the following results.

Month, Year I	Jan	Feb	Mar	Apr	May	Jun	Jul	Aug	Sep	Oct	Nov	Dec
Mean Price	348	350	341	346	340	325	318	324	350	335	346	351

Month, Year II	Jan	Feb	Mar	Apr	May	Jun	Jul	Aug	Sep	Oct	Nov	Dec
Mean Price	346	342	350	355	340	324	322	326	346	352	348	355

The following model is proposed to represent the situation:

$$E(P) = \alpha + \beta s,$$

where P denotes the mean monthly price and s is a variable which takes the value 1 for the months of June, July and August and 0 otherwise.

(a)   Find the least squares estimates of α and β.

(b)   Using a 1% significance level, test the claim that prices fall during the months of June, July and August.

¶   The transformed data are

s	0	0	0	0	0	1	1	1	0	0	0	0
p	348	350	341	346	340	325	318	324	350	335	346	351

s	0	0	0	0	0	1	1	1	0	0	0	0
p	346	342	350	355	340	324	322	326	346	352	348	355

(i)   For these data,

$$\sum s_i = 6 \quad , \quad \sum s_i^2 = 6 \quad ,$$
$$\sum p_i = 8180, \quad \sum s_i p_i = 1939.$$

It follows that

$$\hat{\beta} = \frac{1939 - 6 \times 8180/24}{6 - 6^2/24} = -\frac{106}{4.5} = -23.\dot{5}$$

and

$$\hat{\alpha} = 8180/24 + 23.\dot{5} \times 6/24 = 346.7\dot{2}.$$

(ii)   We now wish to test the hypotheses

$$H_0 : \beta = 0; \quad H_1 : \beta < 0.$$

We first compute $\hat{\sigma}$:

$$p_i^2 = 2791058,$$
$$s_{pp} = 2791058 - 8180^2/24 = 3041.333,$$
$$\hat{\sigma}^2 = \frac{1}{22}(3041.333 - 106^2/4.5) = 24.7475,$$
$$\hat{\sigma} = \sqrt{24.7475} = 4.97468.$$

Therefore the value of the t-statistic is

$$\frac{-23.\dot{5}}{4.97468}\sqrt{4.5} = -10.04$$

and this is considerably less than the critical t-value, namely
$$-t_{0.99}(22) = -2.508.$$

We conclude that prices tend to fall during the summer months.

24. Plot an accurate scatter diagram of the following points.

x	1	2	3	10	14
y	2	3	1	16	8

Calculate the least squares regression line of y on x and mark this on your diagram.

Some text books give the following method for drawing the least squares line. Calculate the centroid G of the data and mark this on your diagram. Draw a line through G parallel to the y-axis. This divides the data into two sets of points. Calculate the centroids G_1, G_2 of these two sets of points and mark these on your diagram. Finally, draw a line through G passing as close as possible to G_1 and G_2. This, allegedly, is the required regression line of y on x.

Carry out this procedure for the above data and show that it gives the wrong answer.

¶ For these data,

$$\sum x_i = 30, \qquad \sum x_i^2 = 310,$$
$$\sum y_i = 30, \qquad \sum x_i y_i = 283.$$

Thus, $s_{xx} = 310 - 30^2/5 = 130$,

and $s_{xy} = 283 - 30 \times 30/5 = 103$.

It follows that the slope estimate is given by

$$\hat{m} = \frac{103}{130} = 0.7923.$$

The least squares regression line of y on x is therefore given by

$$y - \bar{y} = \hat{m}(x - \bar{x})$$
$$\text{or } y - \frac{30}{5} = \frac{103}{130}\left(x - \frac{30}{5}\right)$$
$$\text{i.e. } y = 0.7923x + 1.2462$$

This is illustrated in the scatter diagram below.

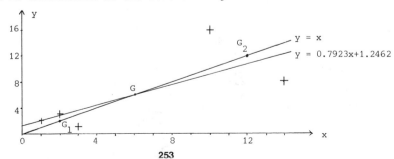

The centroid G is the point (6,6). Furthermore, G_1 is (2,2) and G_2 is (12,12).

Since G, G_1 and G_2 are collinear, the line through G passing as close as possible to G_1 and G_2 is the line passing through all three points, i.e. the line $y = x$.

This is not the correct regression line of y on x.

25. Suppose that
$$Y_i = mx_i + \varepsilon_i \quad (i=2,3,\ldots,n),$$
where $\varepsilon_1, \varepsilon_2, \ldots, \varepsilon_n$ are independent $N(0,\sigma^2)$ random errors and m is a constant. Two possible methods of estimating m from n pairs of observations $(x_1,y_1), (x_2,y_2), \ldots, (x_n,y_n)$ are as follows.

(i)   Choose the value of m which minimises
$$\sum (y_i - mx_i)^2$$

(ii)   Choose m to be the gradient of the line which joins the origin to the centroid $(\bar{x}, \bar{y})$ of the data.

Show that both these methods give unbiased estimates of m and that if $\hat{m}_1, \hat{m}_2$ denote the respective estimators, then
$$\mathrm{Var}(\hat{m}_1) = \frac{\sigma^2}{\sum x_i^2}$$

and
$$\mathrm{Var}(\hat{m}_2) = \frac{n\sigma^2}{(\sum x_i)^2}$$

By considering $s_{xx} = \sum x_i^2 - n\bar{x}^2$, show that $\hat{m}_1$ is more efficient than $\hat{m}_2$.

¶   (i)   The least squares estimator of m is
$$\hat{m}_1 = \frac{\sum x_i Y_i}{\sum x_i^2}.$$
(See Exercise 12).

(ii) $$\hat{m}_2 = \frac{\bar{Y}}{\bar{x}} = \frac{\sum Y_i}{\sum x_i}.$$

Consider $E(\hat{m}_1) = \dfrac{\sum x_i E(Y_i)}{\sum x_i^2} = \dfrac{m \sum x_i^2}{\sum x_i^2} = m.$

Also $E(\hat{m}_2) = \dfrac{\sum E(Y_i)}{\sum x_i} = \dfrac{m \sum x_i}{\sum x_i} = m.$

Thus both $\hat{m}_1$ and $\hat{m}_2$ are unbiased.

Consider
$$\text{Var}(\hat{m}_1) = \frac{\sum x_i^2 \, \text{Var}(Y_i)}{(\sum x_i^2)^2} = \frac{\sigma^2}{\sum x_i^2} \, .$$

Also
$$\text{Var}(\hat{m}_2) = \frac{\sum \text{Var}(Y_i)}{(\sum x_i)^2} = \frac{n\sigma^2}{(\sum x_i)^2}$$

Now
$$s_{xx} = \sum(x_i - \bar{x})^2 \geqslant 0.$$

Thus
$$\sum x_i^2 \geqslant n\,\bar{x}^2 = \frac{1}{n}(\sum x_i)^2$$

or
$$\frac{n}{(\sum x_i)^2} \geqslant \frac{1}{\sum x_i^2} \, .$$

Therefore $\text{Var}(\hat{m}_2) \geqslant \text{Var}(\hat{m}_1)$.

Equality occurs only if $x_1 = x_2 = \ldots = x_n$ (since then $s_{xx}=0$). Ignoring this trivial case,

$$\text{Var}(\hat{m}_2) > \text{Var}(\hat{m}_1),$$

which means that $\hat{m}_1$ is more efficient than $\hat{m}_2$.

Exercises 10.3 Correlation

1. The attendance figures (x) and numbers of programmes sold (y) at the first eight home matches of a football club were as follows:

Match	1	2	3	4	5	6	7	8
Attendance (x)	12302	15693	9609	11325	18901	13857	9829	11361
Sales (y)	5943	7552	4833	6352	8356	6620	5428	6980

Plot a scatter diagram of these data. Calculate the least squares regression lines of y on x and x on y and mark them on your diagram.

The club secretary expects a crowd of 25,000 at the next match which is a 'local derby'. Use the appropriate regression line to predict the number of programmes sold at this match. Comment on the reliability of this prediction.

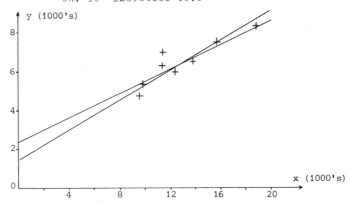

For these data, with n=8,

$$\sum x_i = 102877, \sum y_i = 52064, \quad \bar{x} = 12859.625, \quad \bar{y} = 6508,$$

$$\sum x_i^2 = 1393143771, \sum y_i^2 = 347888466, \quad x_i y_i = 692322707.$$

It follows that

$$s_{xx} = \sum x_i^2 - n\bar{x}^2 = 70184129.88,$$

$$s_{yy} = \sum y_i^2 - n\bar{y}^2 = 9055954,$$

$$s_{xy} = \sum x_i y_i - n\bar{x}\bar{y} = 22799191.$$

N.B.   The numbers above are too large to be handled by some calculators, but the data can be coded - see Question 10, Exercises 10.2.

The equations of the least squares regression lines are

<u>y on x</u> $y - \bar{y} = \dfrac{s_{xy}}{s_{xx}} (x - \bar{x})$

i.e. $y = 0.32485x + 2330.6$

<u>x on y</u> $x - \bar{x} = \dfrac{s_{xy}}{s_{yy}} (y - \bar{y})$

i.e. $x = 2.5176y - 3524.9$

These are drawn on the scatter diagram.
The appropriate line for estimating y given x = 25,000 is the y on x line. Putting x = 25,000 we find that
$$y = 0.32485 \times 25000 + 2330.6 = 10452.$$
This prediction is unreliable for at least two reasons:

(i)   The attendance figure of 25,000 is itself a prediction.

(ii)   x = 25,000 lies outside the range of collected data and 'extrapolated' estimates should always be viewed with suspicion.

2.   In a certain school the first-formers sit a numeracy test at the beginning of the year. The following table gives the marks in this test and the marks in the end of year mathematics examination for ten pupils in a class.

Pupil	1	2	3	4	5	6	7	8	9	10
Exam mark	62	83	71	76	69	72	56	60	69	63
Test mark	101	132	109	123	117	125	107	112	131	127

An eleventh member of the class had a mark of 120 in the numeracy test but was unable to sit the mathematics examination due to illness. Estimate the mark that would have been obtained.

¶   Let x = test mark; y = exam mark. Then we require to find the regression line of y on x. For these data,

$$\sum x_i = 1184, \quad \sum y_i = 681, \quad \bar{x} = 118.4, \quad \bar{y} = 68.1,$$

$$\sum x_i^2 = 141232, \quad \sum x_i y_i = 81130.$$

It follows that

$$s_{xx} = \sum x_i^2 - n\bar{x}^2 = 1046.4,$$
$$s_{xy} = \sum x_i y_i - n\bar{x}\bar{y} = 499.6.$$

The equation of the least squares regression line of y on x is

$$y - \bar{y} = \frac{s_{xy}}{s_{xx}} (x - \bar{x})$$

i.e. y = 0.47745x + 11.57.

To estimate the mark that the eleventh member of the class would have obtained, put x = 120. This gives

$$y = 0.47745 \times 120 + 11.57 \approx 69.$$

3.   Plot a scatter diagram and calculate the sample correlation coefficient for each of the following sets of data

(a)

x	1	2	2.5	2.5	3.5	4	4.5	4.5	5.5	6.5
y	2	1.5	2	2.5	3	2.5	3	4	3.5	4

(b)

x	-2.4	1.2	0.0	-0.5	0.8	1.8	-1.9	-2.0
y	4.6	6.3	2.1	5.0	4.6	4.1	2.8	6.1

(c)

x	2.3	3.6	4.2	6.4	7.1	8.1	9.2	10.0
y	4.6	5.1	3.7	4.2	2.6	1.4	1.5	1.1

¶   (a)

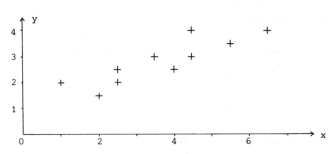

$$\sum x_i = 36.5, \quad \sum y_i = 28, \quad \bar{x} = 3.65, \quad \bar{y} = 2.8,$$

$$\sum x_i^2 = 158.75, \quad \sum y_i^2 = 85, \quad \sum x_i y_i = 113.5.$$

Thus with n=10,

$$s_{xx} = \sum x_i^2 - n\bar{x}^2 = 25.525,$$

$$s_{yy} = \sum y_i^2 - n\bar{y}^2 = 6.6,$$

$$s_{xy} = \sum x_i y_i - n\bar{x}\bar{y} = 11.3$$

and $$r = \frac{s_{xy}}{\sqrt{s_{xx}s_{yy}}} = 0.8706.$$

(b)

$$\sum x_i = -3, \quad \sum y_i = 35.6, \quad \bar{x} = -0.375, \quad \bar{y} = 4.45,$$

$$\sum x_i^2 = 18.94, \quad \sum y_i^2 = 173.28, \quad \sum x_i y_i = -12.44.$$

Thus with n=8

$$s_{xx} = \sum x_i^2 - n\bar{x}^2 = 17.815,$$

$$s_{yy} = \sum y_i^2 - n\bar{y}^2 = 14.86,$$

$$s_{xy} = \sum x_i y_i - n\bar{x}\bar{y} = 0.91$$

and $\quad r = \dfrac{s_{xy}}{\sqrt{s_{xx}s_{yy}}} = 0.0559.$

(c)

$$\sum x_i = 50.9, \quad \sum y_i = 24.2, \quad \bar{x} = 6.3625, \quad \bar{y} = 3.025,$$

$$\sum x_i^2 = 377.51, \quad \sum y_i^2 = 90.68, \quad \sum x_i y_i = 125.96.$$

Thus with n=8,

$$s_{xx} = \sum x_i^2 - n\bar{x}^2 = 53.65875,$$

$$s_{yy} = \sum y_i^2 - n\bar{y}^2 = 17.475,$$

$$s_{xy} = \sum x_i y_i - n\bar{x}\bar{y} = -28.0125$$

and $\quad r = \dfrac{s_{xy}}{\sqrt{s_{xx}s_{yy}}} = -0.9148.$

4. Fifteen first-formers were given examinations in two subjects, A and B. The results were as follows.

Pupil	1	2	3	4	5	6	7	8	9	10	11	12	13	14	15
Exam A	42	60	39	82	71	65	80	42	31	91	40	53	62	48	79
Exam B	76	51	50	63	41	39	62	53	40	83	71	63	31	71	42

Calculate the correlation coefficient of these data and interpret its value.

¶   Let x,y denote respectively the marks obtained in subjects A and B. For these data, n=15 and

$$\sum x_i = 885, \sum y_i = 836, \quad \bar{x} = 59, \quad \bar{y} = 55.7\dot{3},$$

$$\sum x_i^2 = 57079, \sum y_i^2 = 49966, \sum x_i y_i = 49620.$$

It follows that

$$s_{xx} = \sum x_i^2 - n\bar{x}^2 = 4864,$$
$$s_{yy} = \sum y_i^2 - n\bar{y}^2 = 3372.93329,$$
$$s_{xy} = \sum x_i y_i - n\bar{x}\bar{y} = 296$$

and

$$r = \frac{s_{xy}}{\sqrt{s_{xx}s_{yy}}} = 0.0731.$$

We see from Table 5 that this value is not significantly different from zero at any of the quoted levels. Thus these data are consistent with the hypothesis that marks in these two subjects are statistically independent. (Note that this conclusion depends upon assuming the data to be bivariate normal.)

5.   Two random variables X and Y were observed simultaneously on seven occasions. The observations were as follows.

x	2.2	-1.2	0.0	0.8	-2.4	1.4	-0.6
y	9.7	2.9	0.0	1.3	11.1	3.8	0.7

Calculate the sample correlation coefficient and interpret its value.

¶   For these data,

$$\sum x_i = 0.2, \sum y_i = 29.5, \quad \bar{x} = 0.02857, \quad \bar{y} = 4.2143,$$
$$\sum x_i^2 = 15, \quad \sum y_i^2 = 242.33, \quad \sum x_i y_i = -2.84.$$

With n=7,

$$s_{xx} = \sum x_i^2 - n\bar{x}^2 = 14.994$$
$$s_{yy} = \sum y_i^2 - n\bar{y}^2 = 118.009$$
$$s_{xy} = \sum x_i y_i - n\bar{x}\bar{y} = -3.683$$

and $\qquad r = \dfrac{s_{xy}}{\sqrt{s_{xx}s_{yy}}} = -0.0876.$

At first sight one might conclude that this value is not significantly different from zero and that X and Y are independent. However, an examination of a scatter diagram of the data suggests that there is a relationship between the variables but that it is non-linear.

6. Give possible explanations for the following observed correlations:

    (a) a negative correlation between the weekly number of visitors to a holiday resort and the number of hot drinks sold each week;

    (b) a negative correlation between the incidence of heart disease and the consumption of wine per person, per year;

    (c) a positive correlation between the number of births in Danish villages and the number of storks nesting in those villages.

¶   (a) The common factor here is the weather. As the weather improves, the number of visitors increases and the number of hot drinks sold decreases.

    (b) This suggests that drinking wine is beneficial in that it provides some protection against heart disease. This need not be the case however. For example, it may be that people who drink a lot of wine tend to die of cirrhosis of the liver before they have a chance to die of heart disease.

    (c) Even though the arrival of storks is a cause for celebration, it is unlikely that an increase in the number of storks causes an increase in the number of births. The common factor here is time. Both the number of storks and the number of births just happened to be increasing over the same period of time.

7. The heights and weights in random samples of ten male and ten female undergraduates were found to be as follows.

Males

Height (cm)	162	168	174	176	180	184	188	190	194	198
Weight (kg)	75	62	71	81	78	81	71	76	73	79

Females

Height (cm)	152	156	159	162	162	164	168	169	172	173
Weight (kg)	52	50	59	55	58	55	62	61	68	59

Plot scatter diagrams of these two data sets on the same axes using different symbols, such as + and ×, for males and females. Calculate (i) the sample correlation coefficients for males and females,

(ii) the sample correlation coefficient obtained by combining the two data sets.

Comment on your results.

¶

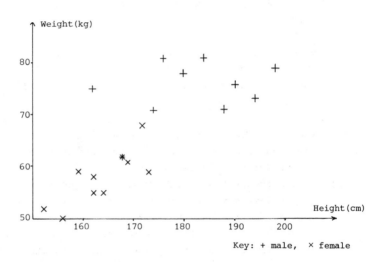

Key: + male, × female

Let X = height; Y = weight.

(i) Males

$$\sum x_i = 1814, \quad \sum x_i^2 = 330260,$$

$$\sum y_i = 747, \quad \sum y_i^2 = 56103, \quad \sum x_i y_i = 135712,$$

$$s_{xx} = 1200.4, \quad s_{yy} = 302.1, \quad s_{xy} = 206.2,$$

$$r = \frac{s_{xy}}{\sqrt{s_{xx} s_{yy}}} = 0.3424.$$

Females

$$\sum x_i = 1637, \sum x_i^2 = 268403,$$

$$\sum y_i = 579, \quad \sum y_i^2 = 33769, \quad \sum x_i y_i = 95039,$$

$$s_{xx} = 426.1, \quad s_{yy} = 244.9, \quad s_{xy} = 256.7,$$

$$r = \frac{s_{xy}}{\sqrt{s_{xx}s_{yy}}} = 0.7946.$$

(ii)   Males and Females

$$\sum x_i = 3451, \sum x_i^2 = 598663,$$

$$\sum y_i = 1326, \sum y_i^2 = 89872, \quad \sum x_i y_i = 230751,$$

$$s_{xx} = 3192.95, \quad s_{yy} = 1958.2, \quad s_{xy} = 1949.7,$$

$$r = \frac{s_{xy}}{\sqrt{s_{xx}s_{yy}}} = 0.7797.$$

If the two bivariate distributions of height and weight for males and females were the same then it would be legitimate to combine the two data sets in order to estimate the common correlation coefficient ρ. The results in (i) however, suggest that the correlation coefficients for males and females are different. Thus the combined sample correlation coefficient in (ii) is not an estimate of a common correlation coefficient and we are not entitled to say that the estimate of the correlation coefficient between height and weight is 0.7997. The high value of r in (ii) is obtained because there is a considerable difference between the means of the two bivariate distributions.

8. The n pairs of observations $(x_1, y_1), (x_2, y_2), \ldots, (x_n, y_n)$ are transformed linearly using the relationships

$$\zeta_i = \frac{x_i - a}{b}, \quad \eta_i = \frac{y_i - d}{e} \quad (i = 1, 2, \ldots, n).$$

Use the results of Question 10, Exercises 10.2, to show that the sample correlations coefficients between $(x_1, y_1), (x_2, y_2), \ldots, (x_n, y_n)$ and $(\zeta_1, \eta_1), (\zeta_2, \eta_2), \ldots, (\zeta_n, \eta_n)$ are equal if eb is positive and equal in magnitude but opposite in sign if eb is negative.

¶   Let r_{xy} and $r_{\zeta\eta}$ denote the respective sample correlation coefficients. Then, with the usual notation,

$$r_{xy} = \frac{s_{xy}}{\sqrt{s_{xx}s_{yy}}} .$$

Now, using the results of Question 10, Exercises 10.2,

$$s_{xx} = b^2 s_{\zeta\zeta}, \qquad s_{yy} = e^2 s_{\eta\eta}, \qquad s_{xy} = bes_{\zeta\eta}.$$

Thus,

$$r_{xy} = \frac{bes_{\zeta\eta}}{\sqrt{b^2 s_{\zeta\zeta}\ e^2 s_{\eta\eta}}}$$

$$= \frac{be}{|be|} \cdot \frac{s_{\zeta\eta}}{\sqrt{s_{\zeta\zeta}s_{\eta\eta}}} = \frac{be}{|be|}. r_{\zeta\eta}.$$

Thus $r_{xy} = r_{\zeta\eta}$ if eb is positive and $r_{xy} = -r_{\zeta\eta}$ if eb is negative.

9. A random sample of size n is taken from a bivariate normal distribution.
    (i)   What is the minimum value of n necessary to conclude that a sample correlation coefficient of 0.3705 differs significantly from zero at the 5% level?
    (ii) What is the minimum value of n necessary to conclude that a sample correlation coefficient of 0.3132 is significantly greater than zero at the 5% level?

¶   (i)   Using Table 5 with a two-tailed 5% significance level, we see that the critical values for n=28 and 29 are respectively 0.3739 and 0.3673. Thus, the minimum n for which 0.3705 is significant is 29.

    (ii) Using Table 5 with a one-tailed 5% significance level, we see that the critical values for n=28 and 29 are respectively 0.3172 and 0.3115. Thus the minimum n for which 0.3232 is significant is 29.

10. The average daily temperature and the number of hours of sunshine were recorded at a winter holiday resort on fourteen successive Christmas days with the following results

Sunshine (hrs)	4.1	1.0	2.3	3.1	0.0	5.1	5.6	8.2	7.6	3.1	3.2	4.9	6.1	1.2
Av. Temp (°C)	2.3	0.2	-1.6	-0.8	-2.9	2.6	3.2	4.1	3.8	0.4	-1.0	-3.3	0.0	-0.7

Calculate the sample correlation coefficient. Making appropriate assumptions, determine whether or not your value differs significantly from zero at the 1% level.

¶ Taking x = hours of sunshine, y = average temperature,

$$\sum x_i = 55.5, \quad \sum x_i^2 = 297.59,$$

$$\sum y_i = 6.3, \quad \sum y_i^2 = 77.73 \quad \sum x_i y_i = 78.18,$$

$$s_{xx} = 77.572, \quad s_{yy} = 74.895, \quad s_{xy} = 53.205,$$

$$r = \frac{s_{xy}}{\sqrt{s_{xx} s_{yy}}} = 0.698.$$

Using Table 5, we see that the critical value for n=14 at the two-tailed 1% significance level is 0.6614. Our computed value of r is therefore significantly different from zero at this level.

We need to assume that these data constitute a random sample from a bivariate normal distribution.

11. Samples of rock from a number of mines were analysed for the presence of two rare minerals, A and B. The results (in micrograms per gram) were as follows:

Sample	1	2	3	4	5	6	7	8	9	10
A	27	122	180	83	18	150	15	76	59	200
B	16	85	72	49	24	75	58	130	15	187

Sample	11	12	13	14	15	16	17	18	19	20
A	140	7	192	101	62	98	20	30	153	175
B	80	23	94	100	75	26	55	105	150	125

Calculate the sample correlation coefficient and test to see if it is significantly greater than zero at the 1% level. Traces of mineral A are washed from the ground by rain water. Consequently the existence of A in a region is indicated by its presence in streams. Deposits of mineral B are more difficult to detect. Comment on the usefulness of mineral A as an indicator of mineral B.

¶ Let x = amount of A, y = amount of B.

$$\sum x_i = 1908, \quad \sum x_i^2 = 262704,$$

$$\sum y_i = 1544, \quad \sum y_i^2 = 160966, \quad \sum x_i y_i = 184328,$$

$$s_{xx} = 80680.8, \quad s_{yy} = 41769.2, \quad s_{xy} = 37030.4,$$

$$r = \frac{s_{xy}}{\sqrt{s_{xx} s_{yy}}} = 0.6379.$$

Using Table 5, we see that the critical value at the one-tailed 1% significance level is 0.5155. Our value is therefore signi- ficantly greater than zero at this level and mineral A can be used as an indicator of mineral B. It is not a completely reliable indicator however. Examining the data, we see, for example, that low concentrations of B can occur with high concentrations of A.

12. A random sample of 39 pairs of observations was taken from a bivariate normal distribution. Use the Fisher Z transformation to test the null hypothesis $H_o : \rho = 0.5$ at the 5% level of signi- ficance in the following cases:

(i) $H_1 : \rho \neq 0.5$ and $r = 0.70$,   (ii) $H_1 : \rho > 0.5$ and $r = 0.68$,

(iii) $H_1 : \rho < 0.5$ and $r = 0.32$.

¶   On each occasion we need to evaluate the quantity

$$(z - \tanh^{-1} \rho_o) \sqrt{n-3}$$

where $z = \tanh^{-1} r$, $n = 39$ and $\rho_o = 0.5$. In all cases,

$$\tanh^{-1} \rho_o = \tanh^{-1} 0.5 = 0.5493 \text{ (using Table 7)}.$$

(i) $z = \tanh^{-1} 0.7 = 0.8673$.

Thus

$$(z - \tanh^{-1} \rho_o) \sqrt{n-3} = (0.8673 - 0.5493) \times 6 = 1.908.$$

From Table 2, the critical value at the two-tailed 5% signifi- cance level is 1.96. The computed value is not significant at this level so that H_o is not rejected.

(ii) $z = \tanh^{-1} 0.68 = 0.8291$.

Thus

$$(z - \tanh^{-1} \rho_o) \sqrt{n-3} = (0.8291 - 0.5493) \times 6 = 1.6788.$$

Using Table 2, the critical value at the one-tailed 5% signifi- cance level is 1.645. The computed value exceeds this so that H_o is rejected.

(iii) $z = \tanh^{-1} 0.32 = 0.3316$.

Thus

$$(z - \tanh^{-1} \rho_o) \sqrt{n-3} = (0.3316 - 0.5493) \times 6 = -1.3062.$$

Using Table 2, the critical value at the one-tailed 5% significance level is -1.645. The computed value exceeds this (i.e.
is closer to zero) so that H_0 is not rejected.

13. The sample correlation coefficient for n pairs of observations
from a bivariate normal distribution was found to be 0.8.   In
testing $H_0:\rho=0.6$ against $H_1:\rho>0.6$, what is the minimum value of
n for which H_0 would be rejected at the 5% significance level?

¶   We must evaluate
$$(z-\tanh^{-1}\rho_0)\sqrt{n-3}$$
where $z = \tanh^{-1} r = \tanh^{-1} 0.8 = 1.0986$
and $\rho_0 = 0.6.$
so that
    $\tanh^{-1}\rho_0 = \tanh^{-1} 0.6 = 0.6931.$

Using Table 2, the critical value at the one-tailed 5% significance level is 1.645. Thus we require
$$(1.0986-0.6931)\sqrt{n-3} > 1.645$$
$$\text{or}\quad \sqrt{n-3} > 1.645/0.4055 = 4.057$$
i.e. $n>3 + 4.057^2 = 19.46.$

The required minimum value is therefore 20.

14. A random sample of size n is taken from a bivariate normal
distribution. Calculate a 95% confidence interval for the
population correlation coefficient ρ when

    (a) r=0,   (b) r=0.98,   (c) r=-0.85

in each of the following cases:

    (i) n=30, (ii) n=50,   (iii) n=100.

¶   We use the general result that an approximate 95% confidence
interval for ρ based on a computed value of r from a sample
of n pairs of observations is given by

    $$[\tanh(z-1.96/\sqrt{n-3}),\ \tanh(z+1.96/\sqrt{n-3})]$$
where $z = \tanh^{-1} r.$

(a) Here r=0 so that z=0. The interval is therefore
    $$[\tanh(-1.96/\sqrt{n-3}),\ \tanh(1.96/\sqrt{n-3})].$$

(i)   With n=30, this reduces to

    [tanh(-0.3252), tanh(0.3252)]

  or [-0.3142, 0.3142] (using Table 8).

(ii)   With n=50, this reduces to

    [tanh(-0.2859), tanh(0.2859)]

  or [-0.2783, 0.2783].

(iii)   With n=100, this reduces to

    [tanh(-0.1990), tanh(0.1990)]

  or [-0.1964, 0.1964].

(b)   Here r=0.98 so that (using Table 7) z=2.2976.
  The interval is therefore

$$[\tanh(2.2976-1.96/\sqrt{n-3}), \tanh(2.2976+1.96/\sqrt{n-3})].$$

(i)   With n=30, this reduces to

    [tanh(1.9204), tanh(2.6748)]

  or [0.9579, 0.9905].

(ii)   With n=50 this reduces to

    [tanh(2.0117), tanh(2.5835)]

  or [0.9648, 0.9887].

(iii)   With n=100, this reduces to

    [tanh(2.0986), tanh(2.4966)]

  or [0.9704, 0.9865].

(c)   Here r=-0.85, so that z=-1.2562. The interval is
  therefore

$$[\tanh(-1.2562-1.96/\sqrt{n-3}), \tanh(-1.2562+1.96/\sqrt{n-3})].$$

(i)   With n=30 this reduces to

    [tanh(-1.6334), tanh(-0.8790)]

  or [-0.9266, -0.7059].

(ii)   With n=50 this reduces to

[tanh(-1.5421), tanh(-0.9703)]

or   [-0.9125, -0.7488].

(iii)   With n=100 this reduces to

[tanh(-1.4552), tanh(-1.0572)]

or   [-0.8967, -0.7846].

15.   The marks obtained in Physics and Chemistry by one hundred
students taking a first-year university course in Natural
Science are summarized in the following bivariate table.

| | | Physics | | | | | | |
		90-99	80-89	70-79	60-69	50-59	40-49	30-39
	90-99	2	1					
	80-89	1	5	4	2			
	70-79		3	8	8	2		
Chemistry	60-69		1	7	9	7	1	
	50-59			2	8	6	3	1
	40-49			1	3	4	4	1
	30-39					2	2	2

Calculate the sample correlation coefficient r and obtain a
90% confidence interval for the product moment correlation
coefficient ρ.

¶   Here the mid-values of the classes are used in the calculation.

Let   x = Physics mark,   y = Chemistry mark.

$$\sum x_i = 6430, \sum x_i^2 = 432045,$$

$$\sum y_i = 6350, \sum y_i^2 = 425325, \sum x_i y_i = 422985,$$

$$s_{xx} = 18596, \ s_{yy} = 22100, \qquad s_{xy} = 14680,$$

$$r = \frac{s_{xy}}{\sqrt{s_{xx} s_{yy}}} = 0.7241.$$

An approximate 90% confidence interval for ρ is

$$[\tanh(z-1.645/\sqrt{n-3}), \ \tanh(z+1.645/\sqrt{n-3})]$$

where n=100 and $z = \tanh^{-1} r = \tanh^{-1}(0.7241) = 0.9163$.

The required interval is therefore

$$[\tanh(0.7493), \tanh(1.0833)]$$

i.e. $[0.6347, 0.7944]$.

16. A psychologist selected 30 boys and 30 girls at random and recorded the times taken by each child to complete two different aptitude tests. The sample correlation coefficient between the two times was found to be 0.79 for the boys and 0.89 for the girls. Let ρ_1 and ρ_2 denote the corresponding population correlation coefficients. Use the Fisher Z transformation to test $H_0: \rho_1 = \rho_2$ against $H_1: \rho_1 \neq \rho_2$ at the 5% level of significance.

¶ We use the result that, under H_0, the statistic

$$D = \frac{z_1 - z_2}{\sqrt{\dfrac{1}{n_1 - 3} + \dfrac{1}{n_2 - 3}}}$$

is approximately $N(0,1)$, where

$$z_1 = \tanh^{-1} R_1, \quad z_2 = \tanh^{-1} R_2;$$

R_1, R_2 being the two sample correlation coefficients and n_1, n_2 the respective sample sizes.

$$z_1 = \tanh^{-1} 0.79 = 1.0714,$$

$$z_2 = \tanh^{-1} 0.89 = 1.4219$$

and $n_1 = n_2 = 30$. The value of the D statistic is therefore

$$d = \frac{1.0714 - 1.4219}{\sqrt{\dfrac{1}{27} + \dfrac{1}{27}}} = -1.2878$$

Since the critical region is

$$C = \{d : |d| > 1.96\}$$

we accept H_0 at the 5% significance level.

17. It is required to use a random sample of size n from a bivariate normal distribution to test, at the 5% level, $H_0: \rho = 0$ against $H_1: \rho > 0$ using the critical region r>k, where r denotes the sample correlation coefficient and k is a suitably chosen constant.

Use Table 5 to obtain values of k in the cases n=10,15,20,25 and
30. Repeat the calculations using the Fisher Z transformation.
Comment on your results.

¶   The values of k can be read directly from Table 5 using a
one-tailed 5% significance level.

Using the Fisher Z-transformation, the critical region is

$$z\sqrt{n-3} > 1.645$$

i.e. $\tanh^{-1}r > 1.645/\sqrt{n-3}$

or $r > \tanh(1.645/\sqrt{n-3})$.

Therefore $k = \tanh(1.645/\sqrt{n-3})$.

We obtain the following values using Tables 5 and 8.

n	k using Table 5	k using Table 8
10	0.5494	0.5524
15	0.4409	0.4421
20	0.3783	0.3791
25	0.3365	0.3370
30	0.3061	0.3064

The values found using Table 5 are exact. The values
found using the Fisher Z transformation are approximate.
The table shows that the approximation improves as the
sample size increases.

18.   If θ denotes the angle between the least squares regression
lines of y on x and x on y, show that (in the usual notation)

$$\tan \theta = \frac{s_{xx}s_{yy} - s_{xy}^2}{s_{xy}(s_{xx}+s_{yy})} .$$

Deduce that the two lines coincide if and only if the sample
correlation coefficient r is equal to ± 1.

¶   The equations of the two regression lines are

$$y-\bar{y} = \frac{s_{xy}}{s_{xx}} (x-\bar{x})   \text{(y on x)}$$

$$x - \bar{x} = \frac{s_{xy}}{s_{yy}} \, (y - \bar{y}) \qquad \text{(x on y)}$$

The gradients of these two lines are given by

$$m_1 = \frac{s_{xy}}{s_{xx}}, \quad m_2 = \frac{s_{yy}}{s_{xy}}.$$

Therefore

$$\tan \theta = \frac{m_2 - m_1}{1 + m_1 m_2}$$

$$= \frac{s_{xx} s_{yy} - s_{xy}^2}{s_{xy}(s_{xx} + s_{yy})}.$$

The lines coincide if and only if

$$\tan \theta = 0$$

i.e. $s_{xx} s_{yy} - s_{xy}^2 = 0$

or $\qquad \dfrac{s_{xy}^2}{s_{xx} s_{yy}} = 1$

i.e. $\qquad r^2 = 1$ as required.

19. The probability density function of the sample correlation coefficient R based on a sample of n pairs of observations from a bivariate normal distribution is given by

$$f(r) = k_1 (1 - r^2)^{(n-4)/2} \quad \text{if } -1 \leq r \leq 1,$$
$$= 0 \qquad\qquad\qquad \text{otherwise}$$

where k_1 is a normalising constant. Use the method of transformations to show that

$$T = R \sqrt{\frac{n-2}{1-R^2}}$$

has probability density function

$$g(t) = k_2 \left(1 + \frac{t^2}{(n-2)}\right)^{-(n-1)/2} \quad (-\infty < t < \infty),$$

where k_2 is another normalising constant.

(N.B. This result shows that T has a Student's t-distribution with (n-2) degrees of freedom.)

¶   We note first that

$$t = r \sqrt{\frac{n-2}{1-r^2}}$$

is a monotonic increasing function mapping the interval $-1 \leq r \leq 1$ to $-\infty < t < \infty$. Therefore the density function of T is given by

$$g(t) = f(r) \frac{dr}{dt} .$$

Now

$$t^2 = \frac{r^2(n-2)}{1-r^2}$$

$$1-r^2 = \frac{n-2}{t^2+n-2}$$

$$= \left(1 + \frac{t^2}{n-2}\right)^{-1} .$$

Thus

$$f(r) = k_1 \left(1 + \frac{t^2}{n-2}\right)^{-(n-4)/2}$$

Furthermore,

$$r = \frac{t}{\sqrt{t^2+n-2}}$$

$$\frac{dr}{dt} = \frac{\sqrt{t^2+n-2} - \frac{1}{2}(t^2+n-2)^{-\frac{1}{2}} \cdot 2t^2}{t^2+n-2}$$

$$= \frac{n-2}{(t^2+n-2)^{3/2}}$$

$$= \left(1 + \frac{t^2}{n-2}\right)^{-3/2} \cdot \frac{1}{\sqrt{n-2}} .$$

Thus

$$g(t) = k_1 \left(1 + \frac{t^2}{n-2}\right)^{-(n-4)/2} \left(1 + \frac{t^2}{n-2}\right)^{-3/2} \cdot \frac{1}{\sqrt{n-2}}$$

$$= k_2 \left(1 + \frac{t^2}{n-2}\right)^{-(n-1)/2}$$

where

$$k_2 = \frac{k_1}{\sqrt{n-2}} .$$

20.   Suppose that X,Y have means μ_x, μ_y and variances σ_x^2, σ_y^2 respectively. Let ρ denote their correlation coefficient. Suppose that Y is to be predicted from X by means of the linear function

$$\hat{Y} = \mu_y + \rho \frac{\sigma_y}{\sigma_x} (X-\mu_x).$$

The error of the prediction is $Y-\hat{Y}$ and the mean squared error is $E[(Y-\hat{Y})^2]$. By considering the identity

$$E[(Y-\hat{Y})^2] = \text{Var}(Y-\hat{Y}) + [E(Y-\hat{Y})]^2,$$

show that

$$E[(Y-\hat{Y})^2] = (1-\rho^2)\sigma_y^2.$$

Deduce that (i) $-1 \leqslant \rho \leqslant 1$,

(ii) X and Y are linearly related if $\rho=\pm1$.

¶   Consider

$$\text{Var}(Y-\hat{Y}) = \text{Var}[(Y-\mu_y) - \rho\frac{\sigma_y}{\sigma_x}(X-\mu_x)]$$

$$= \text{Var}(Y - \rho\frac{\sigma_y}{\sigma_x}X) \quad \text{(Ignoring constants)}$$

$$= \text{Var}(Y) + \frac{\rho^2\sigma_y^2}{\sigma_x^2}\text{Var}(X) - \frac{2\rho\sigma_y}{\sigma_x}\text{Cov}(X,Y)$$

$$= \sigma_y^2 + \frac{\rho^2\sigma_y^2}{\sigma_x^2}\sigma_x^2 - \frac{2\rho\sigma_y}{\sigma_x}\rho\,\sigma_x\sigma_y = (1-\rho^2)\,\sigma_y^2 .$$

Also

$$E(Y-\hat{Y}) = E[(Y-\mu_y) - \rho\frac{\sigma_y}{\sigma_x}(X-\mu_x)]$$

$$= E(Y-\mu_y) - \rho\frac{\sigma_y}{\sigma_x}E(X-\mu_x)$$

$$= 0.$$

Thus $E[(Y-\hat{Y})^2] = (1-\rho^2)\,\sigma_y^2.$

(i) Since $E[(Y-\hat{Y})^2] \geqslant 0$,

$$(1-\rho^2)\,\sigma_y^2 \geqslant 0.$$

It follows that $-1 \leqslant \rho \leqslant 1$ (provided $\sigma_y^2 > 0$).

(ii) $E[(Y-\hat{Y})^2] = 0$ if $\rho = \pm 1$.

It follows that $Y = \hat{Y}$

i.e. $Y = \mu_y + \rho\frac{\sigma_y}{\sigma_x}(X-\mu_x)$

as required.

Exercises 10.4 Rank Correlation

1. The following table gives the Intelligence Quotients (IQ's) of
    ten randomly selected children, together with their parents'
    total annual incomes (in £1000's).

Child	A	B	C	D	E	F	G	H	I	J
IQ	122	94	100	140	119	115	104	126	114	98
Parents' Income	12.9	12.5	24.8	18.5	9.7	10.7	25.6	17.8	10.3	13.2

    Calculate the Spearman rank correlation coefficient between
    IQ and parents' income and comment.

¶   The ranks and their differences $|d|$ are as follows:

Child	A	B	C	D	E	F	G	H	I	J
IQ	8	1	3	10	7	6	4	9	5	2
Parents' Income	5	4	9	8	1	3	10	7	2	6
$|d|$	3	3	6	2	6	3	6	2	3	4

    It follows that

    $$\sum d_i^2 = 168$$

    $$\text{and} \quad r_s = 1 - \frac{6 \sum d_i^2}{n(n^2 - 1)}$$

    $$= 1 - \frac{6 \times 168}{10 \times 99}$$

    $$= -0.0182.$$

    This is clearly not significantly different from zero. There
    is no evidence of an association between IQ and parents' income.

2. In a Glamorous Granny contest, a judge placed the twelve
    contestants as shown in the following table.

Contestant	A	B	C	D	E	F	G	H	I	J	K	L
Place	1	9	7	6	5	2	4	11	3	8	10	12
Age	68	55	46	58	60	65	52	44	72	48	50	49

    The judge, who adjudicates many such contests, is suspected of
    being biased in favour of the more elderly contestants.
    Calculate the Spearman rank correlation coefficient between

placing and age and examine the hypothesis that the placings
are independent of age. State your conclusion in words.

¶ The ranks are as follows:

Contestant	A	B	C	D	E	F	G	H	I	J	K	L
Place	1	9	7	6	5	2	4	11	3	8	10	12
Age	11	7	2	8	9	10	6	1	12	3	5	4
$|d|$	10	2	5	2	4	8	2	10	9	5	5	8

It follows that
$$\sum d_i^2 = 512$$

and
$$r_s = 1 - \frac{6 \sum d_i^2}{n(n^2-1)}$$

$$= 1 - \frac{6 \times 512}{12 \times 143}$$

$$= -0.7902.$$

We now take

H_0: No association between place and age;

H_1: A tendency for low values of place number to
be associated with high values of age, and
vice versa.

We see, using Table 6, that this computed value is significant
even at the 0.5% one-tail significance level (critical value
= -0.7273). We conclude, therefore, that the judge is biased
in favour of the more elderly contestants.

3. The 17 first class county cricket teams contested two distinct
competitions in 1981, the Schweppes County Championship, based
on traditional 3-day matches, and the John Player League, based
on limited over matches. The following table gives the
position of each team in the two competitions:

Schweppes County Championship	John Player League
Top	Nottinghamshire	Essex
	Sussex	Somerset
	Somerset	Warwickshire
	Middlesex	Derbyshire
	Essex	Sussex
	Surrey	Hampshire
	Hampshire	⌈Kent
	Leicestershire	⟨Surrey
	Kent	⌊Yorkshire

Yorkshire	Worcestershire
Worcestershire	Glamorgan
Derbyshire	Lancashire
Gloucestershire	Nottinghamshire
Glamorgan	Leicestershire
Northamptonshire	Middlesex
Lancashire	Gloucestershire
Bottom Warwickshire	Northamptonshire

(The bracket { denotes a tie.)

Calculate the Spearman coefficient of correlation by ranks, and interpret its value.

¶   The ranks are as follows:

Team	Schweppes C.C.	J.P. League	$|d|$
Nottinghamshire	1	11.5	10.5
Sussex	2	5	3
Somerset	3	2	1
Middlesex	4	15	11
Essex	5	1	4
Surrey	6	8	2
Hampshire	7	6	1
Leicestershire	8	14	6
Kent	9	8	1
Yorkshire	10	8	2
Worcestershire	11	11.5	0.5
Derbyshire	12	4	8
Gloucestershire	13	16	3
Glamorgan	14	11.5	2.5
Northamptonshire	15	17	2
Lancashire	16	11.5	4.5
Warwickshire	17	3	14

It follows that

$$\sum d_i^2 = 603$$

and

$$r_s = 1 - \frac{6\sum d_i^2}{n(n^2-1)}$$

$$= 1 - \frac{6 \times 603}{17 \times 288}$$

$$= 0.2610.$$

This value is not significantly different from zero at any of the levels given in Table 6 (e.g. the one-tail critical value at a 10% level is 0.3271). We therefore conclude that there is no evidence of an association between a team's performances in the Schweppes County Championship and the John Player League.

4. Two sports journalists, A and B, attend a football match and each gives a mark out of 20 to the players in the home team. The marks are as follows:

Player	1	2	3	4	5	6	7	8	9	10	11
A	15	10	12	18	11	14	14	13	19	16	17
B	12	13	9	16	12	17	18	11	15	12	14

Is there a tendency for the journalists to agree about the quality of a player's performance? Calculate the Spearman rank correlation coefficient and test an appropriate null hypothesis at the 10% level of significance.

¶ The ranks are as follows:

Player	1	2	3	4	5	6	7	8	9	10	11
A	7	1	3	10	2	5.5	5.5	4	11	8	9
B	4	6	1	9	4	10	11	2	8	4	7
$|d|$	3	5	2	1	2	4.5	5.5	2	3	4	2

It follows that

$$\sum d_i^2 = 126.5$$

and

$$r_s = 1 - \frac{6 \sum d_i^2}{n(n^2-1)}$$

$$= 1 - \frac{6 \times 126.5}{11 \times 120}$$

$$= 0.425.$$

The one-tail 10% critical value is 0.4182. Since the computed value exceeds this, we conclude that (at this level) there is a measure of agreement between the two journalists.

5. The weights and shoe sizes of 14 men were measured with the following results.

Weight (kg)	74	82	68	58	63	87	91	64	76	84	71	70	77	83
Shoe size	8	9	6	7½	9	8	11	7½	10	10½	6½	8½	7	8½

Calculate the Spearman rank correlation coefficient and test whether or not it is significantly greater than zero at the 5% level.

¶ The ranks are as follows

Man	1	2	3	4	5	6	7	8	9	10	11	12	13	14
Weight	7	10	4	1	2	13	14	3	8	12	6	5	9	11
Shoe size	6.5	10.5	1	4.5	10.5	6.5	14	4.5	12	13	2	8.5	3	8.5
$|d|$	0.5	0.5	3	3.5	8.5	6.5	0	1.5	4	1	4	3.5	6	2.5

It follows that

$$\sum d_i^2 = 226$$

$$r_s = 1 - \frac{6 \sum d_i^2}{n(n^2-1)}$$

$$= 1 - \frac{6 \times 226}{14 \times 195}$$

$$= 0.5033.$$

The one tail 5% critical value is 0.4593. Since the computed value exceeds this, we conclude that (at the 5% level) there is a positive association between weight and shoe size.

6. The headmaster of a large school decides to see whether there is any relationship between performances in General Studies and in Mathematics. Ten of his sixth form students took examinations in both subjects and obtained the following marks

Student	A	B	C	D	E	F	G	H	I	J
General studies	40	46	50	45	51	55	52	49	54	78
Mathematics	43	39	45	55	60	50	41	53	60	84

Calculate both the sample (product moment) correlation coefficient r and the Spearman rank correlation coefficient r_S for these data. It was subsequently discovered that Student J had been cheating. Re-calculate both coefficients for the remaining nine students and comment on your results.

¶ Let x = General Studies mark; y = Mathematics mark.
Then
$$\sum x_i = 520, \qquad \sum x_i^2 = 27972,$$
$$\sum y_i = 530, \qquad \sum y_i^2 = 29666, \qquad \sum x_i y_i = 28570$$
and
$$s_{xx} = 27972 - 520^2/10 = 932,$$
$$s_{yy} = 29666 - 530^2/10 = 1576,$$
$$s_{xy} = 28570 - 520 \times 530/10 = 1010.$$
Thus
$$r = \frac{s_{xy}}{\sqrt{s_{xx} s_{yy}}} = 0.8334.$$

The ranking for the ten students is

	A	B	C	D	E	F	G	H	I	J
General Studies	1	3	5	2	6	9	7	4	8	10
Mathematics	3	1	4	7	8.5	5	2	6	8.5	10
$|d|$	2	2	1	5	2.5	4	5	2	0.5	0

Thus
$$\sum d_i^2 = 85.5,$$
$$r_s = 1 - \frac{6 \times 85.5}{10 \times 99} = 0.4818.$$

For the nine students excluding J,
$$\sum x_i = 442, \quad \sum x_i^2 = 21888,$$
$$\sum y_i = 446, \quad \sum y_i^2 = 22610, \quad \sum x_i y_i = 22018$$

and
$$s_{xx} = 21888 - 442^2/9 = 180.8\dot{8},$$
$$s_{yy} = 22610 - 446^2/9 = 508.2\dot{2},$$
$$s_{xy} = 22018 - 442 \times 446/9 = 114.4\dot{4}.$$

Thus
$$r = \frac{s_{xy}}{\sqrt{s_{xx} s_{yy}}} = 0.3775.$$

The ranking for the nine students is

	A	B	C	D	E	F	G	H	I
General Studies	1	3	5	2	6	9	7	4	8
Mathematics	3	1	4	7	8.5	5	2	6	8.5
$|d|$	2	2	1	5	2.5	4	5	2	2.5

Thus
$$\sum d_i^2 = 85.5,$$
$$r_s = 1 - \frac{6 \times 85.5}{9 \times 80} = 0.2875.$$

These calculations illustrate the fact that the effect of an 'outlier' such as J is greater on the product moment correlation coefficient r than on the Spearman rank correlation coefficient r_s.

7. When n pairs of observations $(x_1, y_1), \ldots, (x_n, y_n)$ were ranked in ascending order it was found that
$$u_i = i$$
and
$$v_i = n+1-i$$
where u_i denotes the rank of x_i and v_i denotes the rank of y_i (i=1,2,...,n). Show that the Spearman coefficient of rank correlation is equal to -1.

¶   With the usual notation,

$$d_i = v_i - u_i = n+1-2i$$

$$d_i^2 = (n+1-2i)^2$$

$$= (n+1)^2 - 4(n+1)i + 4i^2$$

$$\sum_{i=1}^{n} d_i^2 = n(n+1)^2 - 4(n+1)\sum_{i=1}^{n} i + 4\sum_{i=1}^{n} i^2$$

$$= n(n+1)^2 - 2n(n+1)^2 + \frac{2n(n+1)(2n+1)}{3}$$

$$= \frac{n(n^2-1)}{3}.$$

Thus

$$r_s = 1 - \frac{6\sum d_i^2}{n(n^2-1)}$$

$$= 1 - \frac{6}{n(n^2-1)} \cdot \frac{n(n^2-1)}{3}$$

$$= -1.$$

Here one set of ranks is the reverse of the other.

8.   Show that an alternative formula for the Spearman rank correlation coefficient of $(x_1,y_1),\ldots,(x_n,y_n)$ is given by

$$r_s = \frac{12\sum u_i v_i}{n(n^2-1)} - 3\left(\frac{n+1}{n-1}\right)$$

where u_i denotes the rank of x_i and v_i denotes the rank of y_i
$(i=1,2,\ldots,n)$.

¶   The basic definition of the Spearman rank correlation coefficient is

$$r_s = \frac{\sum u_i v_i - \frac{1}{n}\sum u_i \sum v_i}{\sqrt{[\sum u_i^2 - \frac{1}{n}(\sum u_i)^2][\sum v_i^2 - \frac{1}{n}(\sum v_i)^2]}}$$

Now

$$\sum_{i=1}^{n} u_i = \sum_{i=1}^{n} i = \frac{1}{2}n(n+1)$$

and

$$\sum_{i=1}^{n} u_i^2 = \sum_{i=1}^{n} i^2 = \frac{1}{6}n(n+1)(2n+1).$$

It follows that

$$\sum_{i=1}^{n} u_i^2 - \frac{1}{n} \left(\sum_{i=1}^{n} u_i \right)^2 = \frac{n(n+1)(2n+1)}{6} - \frac{n(n+1)^2}{4}$$

$$= \frac{n(n+1)[4n+2-3n-3]}{12}$$

$$= \frac{n(n^2-1)}{12} \; .$$

Similarly,

$$\sum_{i=1}^{n} v_i^2 - \frac{1}{n} \left(\sum_{i=1}^{n} v_i \right)^2 = \frac{n(n^2-1)}{12} \; .$$

Also

$$\frac{1}{n} \sum_{i=1}^{n} u_i \sum_{i=1}^{n} v_i = \frac{1}{n} \cdot \frac{n(n+1)}{2} \cdot \frac{n(n+1)}{2}$$

$$= \frac{n(n+1)^2}{4} \; .$$

Finally,

$$r_s = \frac{\sum u_i v_i - \frac{1}{4} n(n+1)^2}{\frac{1}{12} n(n^2-1)}$$

$$= \frac{12 \sum u_i v_i}{n(n^2-1)} - \frac{3(n+1)}{(n-1)} \; .$$

9. In calculating the Spearman rank correlation coefficient, show that the same value is obtained by ranking both variables in descending order as by ranking them in ascending order.

¶   Let (x_1, y_1), $(x_2, y_2), \ldots, (x_n, y_n)$ be a sample of n pairs of observations, and let u_i, v_i denote respectively the ranks of x_i, y_i where the ranking is done in ascending order. Then

$$r_s = 1 - \frac{6 \sum d_i^2}{n(n^2-1)}$$

where $d_i = v_i - u_i.$

Suppose now that the ranking is done in descending order and let u_i', v_i' be the new ranks of x_i, y_i respectively. Then

$$u_i' = n+1-u_i$$

and $v_i' = n+1-v_i.$

The new rank difference is given by

$$d'_i = v'_i - u'_i$$
$$= n+1-v_i-n-1+u_i$$
$$= u_i-v_i$$
$$= -d_i.$$

Thus $\qquad\qquad d'^2_i = d^2_i$

and $\qquad\qquad \sum d'^2_i = \sum d^2_i$

Thus the same value of r_s is obtained by using $u'_i, v'_i,$ and hence $d'_i,$ as by using u_i, v_i and d_i.

10. Two judges rank 3 wines (without ties) in order of preference. The rankings can be written in the following way.

Wine	A	B	C
Judge 1	1	2	3
Judge 2	v_1	v_2	v_3

Here (v_1, v_2, v_3) is a permutation of the integers $(1,2,3)$. Calculate the 6 possible values of r_s, the Spearman rank correlation coefficient, corresponding to the 6 possible permutations. Under the null hypothesis (H_0) of independence, these 6 permutations are all equally likely. Deduce the distribution of r_s under H_0. Repeat your calculations for ranking 4 wines.

¶ The six permutations and the corresponding values of r_s are as follows

$v_1 v_2 v_3$	r_s
1 2 3	1
1 3 2	$\frac{1}{2}$
2 3 1	$-\frac{1}{2}$
2 1 3	$\frac{1}{2}$
3 1 2	$-\frac{1}{2}$
3 2 1	-1

The six permutations are equally likely under H_0. Therefore the distribution of r_s under H_0 is

r_s	-1	$-\frac{1}{2}$	$\frac{1}{2}$	1
Prob.	$\frac{1}{6}$	$\frac{1}{3}$	$\frac{1}{3}$	$\frac{1}{6}$

In the case of ranking four wines there are 4! = 24 permutations of 1234. The possible values of r_s and the permutations which give rise to these values are listed below.

r_s	$\nu_1\nu_2\nu_3$
-1	4321
-0.8	4231,4312,3421
-0.6	3412
-0.4	4132,4213,3241,2431
-0.2	2341,4123
0	3142,2413
0.2	1432,3214
0.4	2314,3124,1423,1342
0.6	2143
0.8	1243,2134,1324
1.0	1234

The permutations are equally likely under H_0. Therefore the distribution of r_s under H_0 is

r_s	-1	-0.8	-0.6	-0.4	-0.2	0	0.2	0.4	0.6	0.8	1
Prob.	$\frac{1}{24}$	$\frac{3}{24}$	$\frac{1}{24}$	$\frac{4}{24}$	$\frac{2}{24}$	$\frac{2}{24}$	$\frac{2}{24}$	$\frac{4}{24}$	$\frac{1}{24}$	$\frac{3}{24}$	$\frac{1}{24}$

11

Further Hypothesis Testing

Exercises 11.1 χ^2 Goodness of Fit Test

1. The number of insects of a certain type found on the underside of a leaf is thought to have the distribution
$$p_x = 2^{-(x+1)} \quad \text{if } x=0,1,2,\ldots$$
The numbers of insects on 32 randomly selected leaves were as follows.

0,1,2,0,3,1,4,2,5,0,1,0,2,0,0,1,2,3,2,2,0,2,3,3,0,1,0,0,2,0,3,0.
Are these data consistent with the above distribution? Use a 5% significance level.

¶ If the number of insects on a leaf has the given distribution then the expected number of leaves out of a sample of 32 having i insects on them, e_i, is given by
$$e_i = 32p_i = \frac{32}{2^{i+1}} \quad (i=0,1,2,3,\ldots).$$

The situation is summarised in the following table:

Number of insects (i)	Observed frequency (f_i)	Expected frequency (e_i)
0	12	16
1	5	8
2 or more	15	8

Here we have formed the combined class '2 or more' to ensure that all the expected frequencies exceed 5.

Then
$$\chi^2 = \sum \frac{(f_i - e_i)^2}{e_i}$$
$$= \frac{(12-16)^2}{16} + \frac{(5-8)^2}{8} + \frac{(15-8)^2}{8}$$
$$= 8.25.$$

Using Table 4, the χ^2 critical value corresponding to a 5%
significance level with 3 classes is

$$\chi^2_{.95}(2) = 5.991.$$

The computed value exceeds this and is therefore significant.
We conclude that the data are not consistent with the given
distribution.

2. Check that the random sample 0.43980, 0.25863,...,0.16977
formed from the first ten rows of Table 11 can be regarded
as a random sample from a uniform distribution on [0,1].
Apply a χ^2 test using a 5% significance level and (a) the
5 intervals [0,0.2), [0.2,0.4),...,[0.8,1.0], (b) the 10
intervals [0,0,1), [0.1,0.2),...,[0.9,1.0].

¶ (a) Using the five intervals, we have the following table

Interval	Observed frequency (f_i)	Expected frequency (e_i)
[0,0.2)	12	20
[0.2,0.4)	27	20
[0.4,0.6)	25	20
[0.6,0.8)	17	20
[0.8,1.0]	19	20

For this table

$$\chi^2 = \sum \frac{(f_i - e_i)^2}{e_i}$$

$$= \frac{1}{20}(8^2 + 7^2 + 5^2 + 3^2 + 1^2)$$

$$= 7.4.$$

Using Table 4, the critical value at the 5% significance
level based on 5 classes is

$$\chi^2_{.95}(4) = 9.488.$$

The computed value is therefore not significant and there
is no reason to doubt that the given numbers are uniformly
distributed on [0,1].

(b) Using the ten intervals, we have the following table.

Interval	Observed Frequency (f_i)	Expected Frequency (e_i)
[0,0.1)	5	10
[0.1,0.2)	7	10
[0.2,0.3)	14	10
[0.3,0.4)	13	10
[0.4,0.5)	15	10
[0.5,0.6)	10	10
[0.6,0.7)	8	10
[0.7,0.8)	9	10
[0.8,0.9)	12	10
[0.9,1.0)	7	10

For this table,

$$\chi^2 = \sum \frac{(f_i - e_i)^2}{e_i}$$

$$= \frac{1}{10} \, (5^2 + 3^2 + 4^2 + 3^2 + 5^2 + 0^2 + 2^2 + 1^2 + 2^2 + 3^2)$$

$$= 10.2 \, .$$

The critical value at the 5% significance level based on 10 classes is

$$\chi^2_{.95}(9) = 16.919 \, .$$

Again the computed value is not significant so that there is no reason to doubt that the given numbers are uniformly distributed on [0,1].

3. A random sample of size 50 is taken from the distribution of a positive random variable X. The results are as follows:

0.542 3.344 1.709 1.989 0.718 0.767 1.795 0.077 2.076 0.977
1.894 0.504 3.024 0.012 2.259 0.067 2.052 0.840 1.759 0.266
0.530 0.505 3.895 1.965 0.475 2.319 0.167 0.340 0.038 0.283
0.487 0.072 0.388 0.339 0.044 0.181 1.244 1.234 2.940 0.370
1.460 1.173 0.387 2.938 0.596 0.090 0.710 1.462 0.622 1.186

It is claimed that X has the probability density function

$$f(x) = e^{-x} \quad \text{if } x \geq 0,$$
$$= 0 \quad \text{otherwise.}$$

(i) Assuming that X has this distribution, find numbers a,b,c and d such that

$$P(X < a) = P(a \leq X < b) = P(b \leq X < c) = P(c \leq X < d)$$
$$= P(X \geq d).$$

(ii)   Use the intervals $[0,a)$, $[a,b)$, $[b,c)$, $[c,d)$, $[d,\infty)$ to test the claim at the 10% significance level.

¶   If X has the given distribution,

$$P(X < a) = \int_0^a e^{-x}\, dx = 1 - e^{-a}.$$

We require

$$1 - e^{-a} = \frac{1}{5},$$

$$a = -\log_e\left(\frac{4}{5}\right) = 0.2231.$$

Similarly,

$$P(X < b) = 1 - e^{-b} = \frac{2}{5},$$

$$b = -\log_e\left(\frac{3}{5}\right) = 0.5108.$$

Also,

$$P(X < c) = 1 - e^{-c} = \frac{3}{5},$$

$$c = -\log_e\left(\frac{2}{5}\right) = 0.9163.$$

Finally,

$$P(X < d) = 1 - e^{-d} = \frac{4}{5},$$

$$d = -\log_e\left(\frac{1}{5}\right) = 1.6094.$$

If X does have the given distribution, then each of the 5 intervals has an expected frequency of 10. We therefore have the following table.

Interval	Observed Frequency (f_i)	Expected Frequency (e_i)
$[0, 0.2231)$	9	10
$[0.2231, 0.5108)$	11	10
$[0.5108, 0.9163)$	8	10
$[0.9163, 1.6094)$	7	10
$[1.6094, \infty)$	15	10

For this table,

$$\chi^2 = \sum \frac{(f_i - e_i)^2}{e_i}$$

$$= \frac{1}{10}\left(1^2 + 1^2 + 2^2 + 3^2 + 5^2\right)$$

$$= 4.$$

Using Table 4, the critical value at the 10% significance level based on 5 classes is

$$\chi^2_{0.9}(4) = 7.779.$$

The computed value is therefore not significant. The data are consistent with the claim that X has the given distribution.

4. A company has three factories, A, B and C, which make large numbers of the same item. They produce $\frac{1}{2}$, $\frac{1}{3}$ and $\frac{1}{6}$ of the company's total output respectively. In a random sample of 486 items which were returned as defective by customers over a twelve month period, 300 were made by factory A, 122 by factory B and the remainder by factory C. Could the probability that an item is returned as defective be the same for all three factories? Use a χ^2 test and a significance level of 1%.

¶ The expected numbers of defectives out of 486 produced by factories A,B,C under the hypothesis that the probabilities of returning items as defective are equal, are respectively $486 \times \frac{1}{2}$, $486 \times \frac{1}{3}$ and $486 \times \frac{1}{6}$, i.e. 243, 162 and 81.

We therefore have the following table:

Factory	Observed Frequency (f_i)	Expected Frequency (e_i)
A	300	243
B	122	162
C	64	81

For these data,

$$\chi^2 = \sum \frac{(f_i - e_i)^2}{e_i}$$

$$= \frac{57^2}{243} + \frac{40^2}{162} + \frac{17^2}{81}$$

$$= 26.815.$$

Using Table 4, the critical value at the 1% significance level based on 3 classes is

$$\chi^2_{0.99}(2) = 9.210.$$

We conclude that the computed value is significant at this level so that the probability of being defective is not constant over the 3 factories.

5. The sales of an item in a supermarket were recorded on 100 consecutive Mondays and are summarised below

Number sold	0	1	2	3	4	5	6	7
Number of Mondays	8	22	37	15	14	2	1	1

Test at the 10% level of significance the hypothesis that sales on Mondays have a Poisson distribution.

¶   The sample mean is given by

$$\bar{x} = \frac{(1\times22)+(2\times37)+(3\times15)+(4\times14)+(5\times2)+(6\times1)+(7\times1)}{100}$$

$$= 2.2.$$

With this mean, the expected number e_i of Mondays on which i items are sold is given by

$$e_i = 100 \times \frac{2.2^i\, e^{-2.2}}{i!}.$$

Pooling the values 5,6,7 to ensure that all expected frequencies exceed 5, we have the following table:

No. sold (i)	Observed Frequency (f_i)	Expected Frequency (e_i)
0	8	11.08
1	22	24.38
2	37	26.81
3	15	19.66
4	14	10.82
5 or more	4	7.25

Note that the expected frequency for the class '5 or more' was found by subtracting the sum of the other expected frequencies from 100.

For these data,

$$\chi^2 = \sum \frac{(f_i - e_i)^2}{e_i}$$

$$= \frac{(8-11.08)^2}{11.08} + \frac{(22-24.38)^2}{24.38} + \ldots + \frac{(4-7.25)^2}{7.25}$$

$$= 8.458.$$

Using Table 4, the critical value at the 10% level with 4 degrees of freedom (i.e. one less than the number of classes minus one for estimating the mean) is

$$\chi^2_{0.9}(4) = 7.779$$

and we reject, at the 10% level of significance, the hypothesis that sales on Mondays have a Poisson distribution.

6. When an automatic bottle filler is working properly, the volumes
    of fluid released are normally distributed with mean 10.25 cl and
    standard deviation 0.075 cl, successive deliveries being indepen-
    dent. The amounts (in cl) put into 50 bottles are as follows.

    10.28 10.26 10.33 10.26 10.30 10.03 10.24 10.27 10.19 10.60
    10.35 10.11 10.16 10.24 10.22 10.20 10.48 10.34 10.19 10.33
    10.06 10.12 9.99 10.34 10.08 10.06 10.31 10.32 10.47 10.07
    10.27 10.17 10.14 10.37 10.05 10.13 10.24 10.14 10.03 10.20
    10.42 10.32 10.28 9.96 10.35 10.24 10.16 10.42 10.24 10.08

    (i) Is the bottle filler working properly? Use a χ^2 test and
         a 5% significance level.

    (ii) Calculate the mean and standard deviation of the sample
         and test the hypothesis that the volumes are normally
         distributed, using a 5% significance level.

    Comment on your results.

¶   (i) Taking, for example, five intervals whose expected
         frequencies are equal if the volumes are normally
         distributed with mean 10.25 and standard deviation
         0.075, we obtain the following table.

Interval	Observed Frequency (f_i)	Expected Frequency (e_i)
$(-\infty, 10.187)$	18	10
$[10.188, 10.231)$	5	10
$[10.231, 10.269)$	7	10
$[10.269, 10.313)$	6	10
$[10.313, \infty)$	14	10

    We find that,
    $$\chi^2 = \frac{64+25+9+16+16}{10} = 13.$$

    Using Table 4, the critical value at the 5% level with
    4 degrees of freedom is

    $$\chi^2_{0.95}(4) = 9.488.$$

    As the computed values of χ^2 exceeds this value we
    conclude that the bottle filler is not working properly.

    (ii) The sample mean is 10.2282 and the sample standard devia-
         tion is 0.13569. Taking these estimates to be the mean
         and standard deviation of the hypothesised normal distri-
         bution and again taking five intervals with equal expected

frequencies, we obtain the following table:

Interval	Observed Frequency (f_i)	Expected Frequency (e_i)
$(-\infty, 10.114)$	11	10
$[10.114, 10.194)$	9	10
$[10.194, 10.263)$	10	10
$[10.263, 10.342)$	12	10
$[10.342, \infty)$	8	10

This time

$$\chi^2 = \frac{1+1+0+4+4}{10} = 1$$

but, subtracting two degrees of freedom for the estimated parameters, the critical value is

$$\chi^2_{0.95}(2) = 5.991$$

and the hypothesis that the volumes are normally distributed is not rejected. Considering the values of the estimates of the mean and standard deviation, we conclude that the null hypothesis in (i) was rejected because the standard deviation of the volumes delivered is greater than 0.075 cl.

7. A computer program allegedly generates random variables which are normally distributed. The following frequency table summarises the results obtained by generating 1000 such numbers.

Range	1-2	2-3	3-4	4-5	5-6	6-7	7-8
Frequency	20	181	302	279	112	56	50

Plot these data on normal probability paper. Do you think that the computer program does what it is supposed to do? Carry out a χ^2 test of fit and comment on the result.

¶ We first derive the relative cumulative frequency table

Value	Cumulative Frequency	Relative Cumulative Frequency
2	20	0.020
3	201	0.201
4	503	0.503
5	782	0.782
6	894	0.894
7	950	0.950
8	1000	1.000

The graph on page 294 shows these data plotted on normal probability paper. The points do not lie on a straight line so that it is doubtful that the data come from a normal distribution.

In order to apply a χ^2 test, we need to estimate μ and σ^2 from the data using the sample mean and variance. We find that

$$\hat{\mu} = \frac{(20\times1.5)+(181\times2.5)+\ldots+(50\times7.5)}{1000}$$

$$= 4.15,$$

$$\hat{\sigma}^2 = \frac{(20\times1.5^2)+(181\times2.5^2)+\ldots+(50\times7.5^2)}{999} - \frac{1000}{999} \times 4.15^2$$

$$= 1.8714$$

whence $\hat{\sigma} = 1.368$.

Using these estimated values the expected number e_i in the range $(i,i+1]$ $(i=2,3,\ldots,6)$ is given by

$$e_i = 1000\left[\Phi\left(\frac{i+1-4.15}{1.368}\right) - \Phi\left(\frac{i-4.15}{1.368}\right)\right]$$

We need to take care in the two tails where 1-2 and 7-8 are changed to $(-\infty,2]$ and $(7,\infty)$. This allows for the fact that the normal distribution is defined over the range $(-\infty,\infty)$. Thus, for $(-\infty,2]$

$$\text{Expected frequency} = 1000\ \Phi\left(\frac{2-4.15}{1.368}\right) = 58.02,$$

and for $(7,\infty)$

$$\text{Expected frequency} = 1000\ [1-\Phi\left(\frac{7-4.15}{1.368}\right)] = 18.61.$$

Interval	Observed Frequency (f_i)	Expected Frequency (e_i)
$(-\infty,2]$	20	58.02
$(2,3]$	181	142.26
$(3,4]$	302	256.07
$(4,5]$	279	276.47
$(5,6]$	112	179.05
$(6,7]$	56	69.52
$(7,\infty)$	50	18.61

Using these data

$$\chi^2 = \sum \frac{(f_i-e_i)^2}{e_i} = 124.4.$$

There are 4 degrees of freedom (i.e. one less than the number of classes minus the 2 parameters being estimated).

Normal plot, Exercise 7.

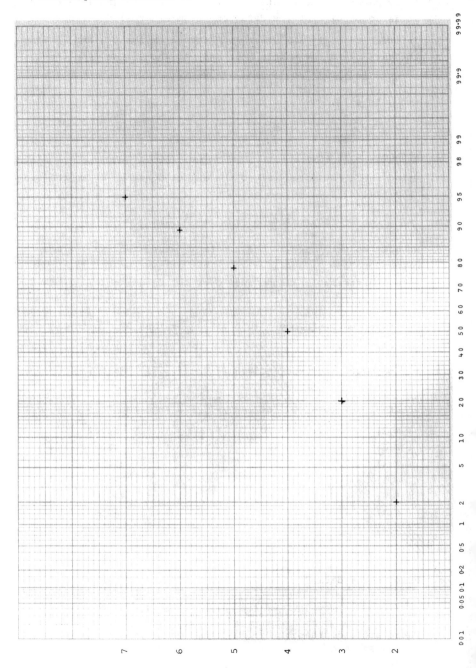

Using a 1% significance level,

$$\chi^2_{.99}(4) = 13.277.$$

The computed value is therefore highly significant, confirming that the data are not normal.

8. The volumes of wine contained in 25 randomly chosen bottles of a certain 'Riesling' were measured (in cl) as follows:

71.1, 69.9, 70.4, 71.3, 70.7, 71.5, 70.9, 70.2, 71.9, 72.1, 72.4, 71.6, 72.0, 72.8, 70.8, 71.4, 70.6, 72.6, 71.8, 72.3, 71.7, 71.3, 71.2, 71.0, 73.1.

Plot these data on normal probability paper. (Arrange the data in ascending order and plot the proportion $\leq$ x against x for x = 69.9, 70.2, ..., 72.8.) Draw a line by eye and estimate (i) the mean volume, (ii) the inter-quartile range, (iii) the probability that the volume in a randomly selected bottle is less than 70 cl.

¶ Ranking the data, we obtain the following:

69.9, 70.2, 70.4, 70.6, 70.7, 70.8, 70.9, 71.0, 71.1, 71.2, 71.3, 71.3, 71.4, 71.5, 71.6, 71.7, 71.8, 71.9, 72.0, 72.1, 72.3, 72.4, 72.6, 72.8, 73.1.

Plotting the points (69.9,0.04), (70.2,0.08), (70.4,0.12),... on normal probability paper, we obtain the plot shown on page 296. The linearity of the points suggests that the data are normally distributed.

Using the graph,

(i)   Mean $\approx$ 71.4,

(ii)   Inter-quartile range $\approx$ 71.97−70.83

$$= 1.14,$$

(iii) $P(V < 70) \approx 0.0475$.

9. A class of 20 pupils sits examinations in Mathematics and English and the marks are as follows:

Pupil	1	2	3	4	5	6	7	8	9	10
Mathematics	43	65	73	48	60	68	52	80	53	57
English	60	61	54	70	56	68	51	55	58	62
Pupil	11	12	13	14	15	16	17	18	19	20
Mathematics	39	76	46	63	50	66	70	53	56	59
English	67	49	65	52	47	53	57	64	66	71

Normal plot, Exercise 8.

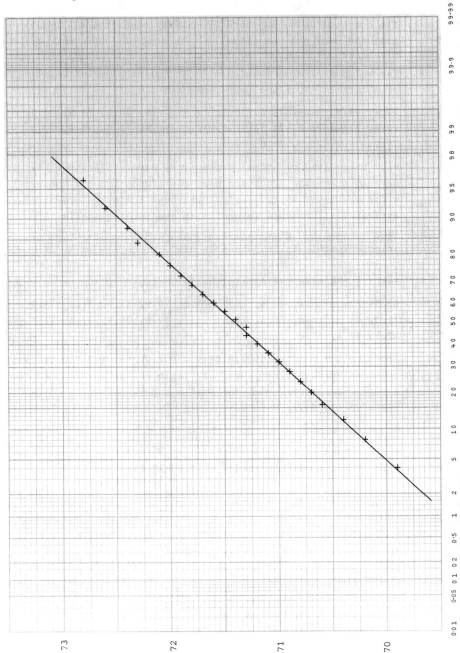

Plot the English and Mathematics marks separately on the same sheet of normal probability paper and explain why your plots suggest that the marks are normally distributed. Estimate the means and standard deviations of marks in English and Mathematics and compare these with the usual estimates.

¶ Ranking the data, we obtain

Mathematics

39, 43, 46, 48, 50, 52, 53, 53, 56, 57, 59, 60, 63, 65, 66, 68, 70, 73, 76, 80.

English

47, 49, 51, 52, 53, 54, 55, 56, 57, 58, 60, 61, 62, 64, 65, 66, 67, 68, 70, 71.

Plotting the Mathematics data $(39, 0.05)$, $(43, 0.1)$,... and the English data $(47, 0.05)$, $(49, 0.1)$,... on normal probability paper, as shown on page 298, we see that the points lie approximately on two straight lines. This suggests that the marks are normally distributed.

Using these plots, we obtain the following estimates of the means and standard deviations.

Mathematics

$$\text{Mean} \approx 58$$

$$\text{Standard deviation} \approx (69.5 - 46.5) = 11.5.$$

English

$$\text{Mean} \approx 59$$

$$\text{Standard deviation} \approx (66.5 - 51.5) = 7.5.$$

The usual estimates are as follows:

Mathematics $\hat{\mu} = \dfrac{(39+43+\ldots+80)}{20} = 58.5$

$\hat{\sigma}^2 = \dfrac{1}{19} (39^2 + 43^2 + \ldots + 80^2 - 20 \times 58.5^2)$

whence $\hat{\sigma} = 11.22.$

English $\hat{\mu} = \dfrac{(47+49+\ldots+71)}{20} = 59.3$

$\hat{\sigma}^2 = \dfrac{1}{19} (47^2 + 49^2 + \ldots + 71^2 - 20 \times 59.3^2)$

whence $\hat{\sigma} = 7.18.$

Normal plot, Exercise 9.

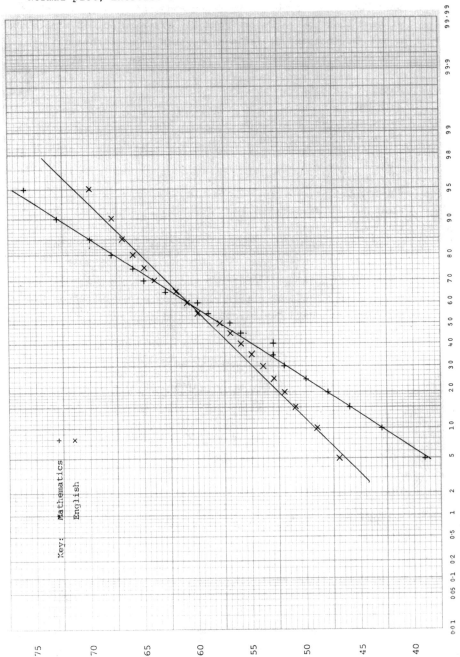

10. A research worker types a 200 page thesis. When he checks his typing for mistakes, he finds that the situation is as follows:

Number of errors on a page	0	1	2	3	4	5	6	≥7
Frequency	10	46	71	49	20	3	1	0

Plot these data on Poisson probability paper and state whether or not your plot suggests that the number of mistakes on a page is a Poisson distributed random variable.

¶ The data can be presented as follows:

Number of errors	Frequency	Proportion	Proportion of at least
0	10	0.05	1.0
1	46	0.23	0.95
2	71	0.355	0.72
3	49	0.245	0.365
4	20	0.1	0.12
5	3	0.015	0.02
6	1	0.005	0.005
≥7	0	0	0

These data are plotted on Poisson probability paper as shown on page 300.   The points do not lie on a vertical straight line, suggesting that the data are not Poisson distributed.

11. Plot the sales data of Exercise 5 on Poisson probability paper and comment on the result.

¶ The data can be represented as follows:

Number sold	Frequency	Proportion	Proportion of at least
0	8	0.08	1.00
1	22	0.22	0.92
2	37	0.37	0.70
3	15	0.15	0.33
4	14	0.14	0.18
5	2	0.02	0.04
6	1	0.01	0.02
7	1	0.01	0.01
≥8	0	0	0

Poisson plot, Exercise 10.

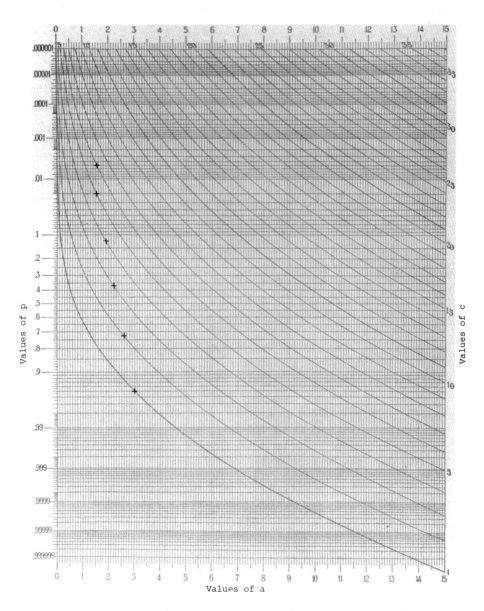

Poisson probability curves of mean a showing P(X≥c)

Poisson plot, Exercise 11.

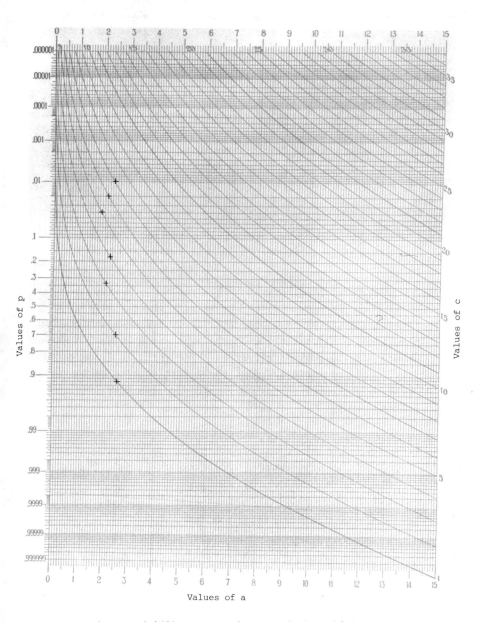

Poisson probability curves of mean a showing P(X≥c)

These data are plotted on Poisson probability paper, as shown on page 301.   The result is rather inconclusive.   This is consistent with the χ^2 test of Exercise 5 where the hypothesis that sales have a Poisson distribution is rejected at the 10% level but not at the 5% level.

12. The pupils in a statistics class are given a project in which they keep a record of the number of letters delivered daily to their homes over a period of approximately 6 months from March to September.   One of the pupils, Kenneth, produces the following frequency table from his records.

Number of letters delivered	Frequency
0	77
1	52
2	35
3	12
4	3
5	1
≥ 6	0

Plot these data on Poisson probability paper.   In a class discussion, it was subsequently discovered that Kenneth had included in his table 30 Sundays and Bank Holidays on which there were no postal deliveries.   Remove these 30 days from the frequency table and plot the resulting data on Poisson probability paper.   What conclusions do you draw from your plots?

¶ Consider the data in the following form:

Number of letters	Frequency	Proportion	Proportion of at least
0	77	0.428	1.000
1	52	0.289	0.572
2	35	0.194	0.283
3	12	0.067	0.089
4	3	0.017	0.022
5	1	0.005	0.005
≥ 6	0	0	0

Removing the 30 zeros, the data become

Poisson plot, Exercise 12 - Sundays and Bank Holidays included.

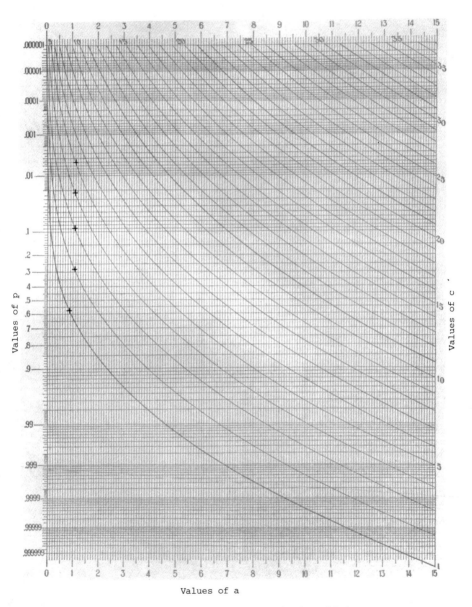

Values of a

Poisson probability curves of mean a showing P(X≥c)

Poisson plot, Exercise 12 - Sundays and Bank Holidays excluded.

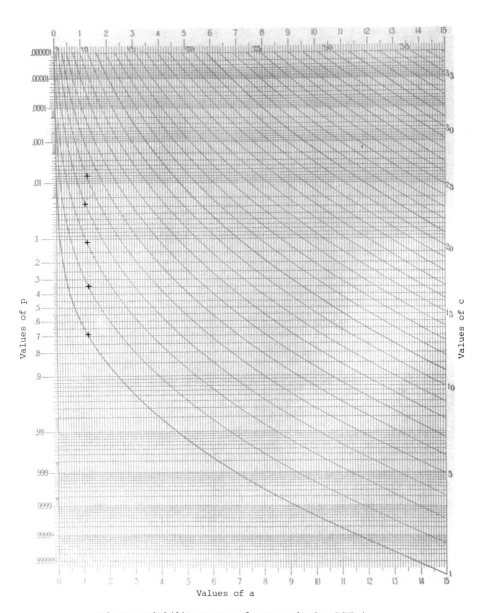

Poisson probability curves of mean a showing P(X≥c)

Number of letters	Frequency	Proportion	Proportion of at least
0	47	0.313	1.000
1	52	0.347	0.687
2	35	0.233	0.340
3	12	0.080	0.107
4	3	0.020	0.027
5	1	0.007	0.007
≥ 6	0	0	0

The two sets of data are plotted on Poisson probability paper as shown on pages 303 and 304. We see that removing Sundays and Bank Holidays from the data causes the points to lie on a vertical straight line, suggesting that the number of letters delivered daily has a Poisson distribution.

Exercises 11.2 Contingency Tables

1. A random sample of voting intentions was taken in a constituency. The following table was produced from the replies obtained.

	Men	Women
Conservative	65	51
Labour	63	44
Alliance	32	45

Test at the 5% level the hypothesis that voting intention is independent of sex.

¶ The observed frequencies and marginal totals are

	Men	Women	
Conservative	65	51	116
Labour	63	44	107
Alliance	32	45	77
	160	140	300

On the assumption of independence, the expected frequencies are

	Men	Women	
Conservative	61.86	54.13	116
Labour	57.06	49.93	107
Alliance	41.06	35.93	77
	160	140	300

For example, the top left-hand entry is obtained as

$$300 \times \frac{116}{300} \times \frac{160}{300} .$$

From these tables,

$$\chi^2 = \frac{(65-61.87)^2}{61.87} + \frac{(51-54.13)^2}{54.13} + \ldots + \frac{(45-35.93)^2}{35.93}$$

$$= 5.951.$$

There are $(3-1) \times (2-1)$, i.e. 2 degrees of freedom and

$$\chi^2_{0.95}(2) = 5.991.$$

The computed value is therefore not significant at the 5% level and the hypothesis of independence is not rejected.

2. The members of a random sample of 35 year old male graduates were classified according to the class of their degree and their current annual income. The results were as follows.

		Annual income (£)		
		<12000	12000-17000	>17000
Class of Degree	1	7	6	12
	2	19	24	17
	3	13	7	5

Test at the 5% level the hypothesis that income is independent of degree classification.

¶   The observed frequencies and marginal totals are

		Annual income (£)			
		<12000	12000-17000	>17000	
Class of Degree	1	7	6	12	25
	2	19	24	17	60
	3	13	7	5	25
		39	37	34	110

On the assumption of independence, the expected frequencies (to two decimal places) are

		Annual income (£)			
		<12000	12000-17000	>17000	
Class of Degree	1	8.86	8.41	7.73	25
	2	21.27	20.18	18.55	60
	3	8.86	8.41	7.73	25
		39	37	34	110

From these tables,

$$\chi^2 = 7.67 .$$

There are $(3-1) \times (3-1)$, i.e. 4 degrees of freedom, and

$$\chi^2_{0.95}(4) = 9.488.$$

The computed value is therefore not significant at the 5% level and there is no reason to suppose that salary depends upon degree classification.

3. Three hundred people were asked if they were afraid of heights (this condition is called acrophobia). The results were as follows:

	Yes	No
Male	31	134
Female	24	111

Test at the 10% level the hypothesis that the condition of acrophobia is independent of sex.

¶ The observed data are

	Yes	No	
Male	31	134	165
Female	24	111	135
	55	245	300

On the assumption of independence, the expected frequencies are.

	Yes	No	
Male	30.25	134.75	165
Female	24.75	110.25	135
	55	245	300

From these tables, using Yates' correction,

$$\chi^2 = \frac{(|31-30.25|-\frac{1}{2})^2}{30.25} + \frac{(|134-134.75|-\frac{1}{2})^2}{134.75}$$

$$+ \frac{(|24-24.75|-\frac{1}{2})^2}{24.75} + \frac{(|111-110.25|-\frac{1}{2})^2}{110.25}$$

$$= 0.0056.$$

There are $(2-1) \times (2-1)$, i.e. 1 degree of freedom and

$$\chi^2_{0.9}(1) = 2.706.$$

The computed value is therefore not significant at the 10% level and there is no reason to suppose that the condition of acrophobia is sex dependent.

4. A survey was carried out on the incidence of dental caries in twelve year old children in three towns, A, B and C. The concentrations of fluoride in the drinking water of the three towns were, respectively, 'high', 'medium' and 'low'. The following results were obtained

	A	B	C
With caries	77	103	92
Without caries	42	38	20

Is the apparent negative association between the incidence of dental caries and the concentration of fluoride significant at the 5% level?

¶ The observed data are

	A	B	C	
With caries	77	103	92	272
Without caries	42	38	20	100
	119	141	112	372

On the assumption of independence, the expected frequencies are

	A	B	C	
With caries	87.01	103.10	81.89	272
Without caries	31.99	37.90	30.11	100
	119	141	112	372

From these tables

$$\chi^2 = \frac{(77-87.01)^2}{87.01} + \frac{(103-103.10)^2}{103.10} + \ldots + \frac{(20-30.11)^2}{30.11}$$

$$= 8.927.$$

There are $(3-1) \times (2-1)$, i.e. 2 degrees of freedom and

$$\chi^2_{0.95}(2) = 5.991.$$

The computed value is therefore significant at the 5% level.

5. The flowers of the Lesser Celandine (*Ranunculus ficaria* L.) can be divided into two types, A and B. Flowers of type A have 8 petals. Flowers of type B have some other number of petals. (The most common number of petals is 8 but each flower can have as few as 7 petals or as many as 13.) A botanist examined flowers at four different sites and obtained the following data.

	Site 1	Site 2	Site 3	Site 4
Type A	275	155	445	69
Type B	148	24	116	14

Is the probability that a flower has 8 petals the same for all sites?

¶   The observed data are

	Site 1	Site 2	Site 3	Site 4	
Type A	275	155	445	69	944
Type B	148	24	116	14	302
	423	179	561	83	1246

Under the hypothesis of equal probability p of type A for all sites, p can be estimated by

$$\hat{p} = \frac{944}{1246}.$$

The expected frequencies (to two decimal places) are

	Site 1	Site 2	Site 3	Site 4	
Type A	320.48	135.61	425.03	62.88	944
Type B	102.52	43.39	135.97	20.12	302
	423	179	561	83	1246

For example, the top left-hand entry is

$$423 \; \hat{p} = 423 \times \frac{944}{1246}$$

and the bottom right-hand entry is

$$83(1-\hat{p}) = 83 \times (1 - \frac{944}{1246}).$$

From these tables

$$\chi^2 = \frac{(275-320.48)^2}{320.48} + \ldots + \frac{(14-20.12)^2}{20.12}$$

$$= 44.384.$$

There are 3 degrees of freedom (i.e. 1 less than the number of binomial distributions being compared) and taking the significance level to be, for example, 1%,

$$\chi^2_{0.99}(3) = 11.345.$$

The computed value is highly significant and we conclude that the probabilities of type A flowers are not equal across the 4 sites.

6. A driving test centre has three examiners. The numbers of candidates passed and failed by each examiner in a particular week are given in the table below.

	Philip	Alan	John
Passed	28	38	35
Failed	20	10	15

Is the apparent variation in pass rates, significant at the 5% level?

¶ The observed data are

	Philip	Alan	John	
Passed	28	38	35	101
Failed	20	10	15	45
	48	48	50	146

Under the hypothesis of equal pass rates, which is equivalent to equal probabilities p of passing for the 3 examiners, we estimate p by

$$\hat{p} = \frac{101}{146}.$$

The expected frequencies (to two decimal places) are

	Philip	Alan	John	
Passed	33.21	33.21	34.59	101
Failed	14.79	14.79	15.41	45
	48	48	50	146

From these tables,

$$\chi^2 = \frac{(28-33.21)^2}{33.21} + \ldots + \frac{(15-15.41)^2}{15.41}$$

$$= 4.909.$$

There are 2 degrees of freedom and

$$\chi^2_{0.95}(2) = 5.991.$$

The computed value is therefore not significant at the 5% level.

7. In a survey, people in the North and South East of England were asked if they read a certain national newspaper. The results are summarised below.

	North	South East
Yes	20	13
No	83	73

Is there a difference in readership between the two regions? State your conclusion carefully.

Suppose, instead, that a more extensive survey was carried out and that the results were as follows:

	North	South East
Yes	200	130
No	830	730

What is your conclusion now?

¶   The observed data are

	North	South East	
Yes	20	13	33
No	83	73	156
	103	86	189

On the assumption of independence, the expected frequencies (to two decimal places) are

	North	South East	
Yes	17.98	15.02	33
No	85.02	70.98	156
	103	86	189

Using Yates' correction,

$$\chi^2 = \frac{(|20-17.98|-\frac{1}{2})^2}{17.98} + \frac{(|83-85.02|-\frac{1}{2})^2}{85.02}$$

$$+ \frac{(|13-15.02|-\frac{1}{2})^2}{15.02} + \frac{(|73-70.98|-\frac{1}{2})^2}{70.98}$$

$$= 0.34.$$

There are $(2-1) \times (2-1)$, i.e. 1 degree of freedom and taking, for example, a significance level of 5%,

$$\chi^2_{0.95}(1) = 3.841.$$

The computed value is not significant at this level and we cannot conclude that there is a difference in readership of this particular newspaper between the two regions.

The modified data are

	North	South East	
Yes	200	130	330
No	830	730	1560
	1030	860	1890

On the assumption of independence, the expected frequencies (to two decimal places) are

	North	South East	
Yes	179.84	150.16	330
No	850.16	709.84	1560
	1030	860	1890

Using Yates' correction,

$$\chi^2 = \frac{(|200-179.84|-\frac{1}{2})^2}{179.84} + \frac{(|830-850.16|-\frac{1}{2})^2}{850.16}$$

$$+ \frac{(|130-150.16|-\frac{1}{2})^2}{150.16} + \frac{(|730-709.84|-\frac{1}{2})^2}{709.84}$$

$$= 5.722$$

As before, there is 1 degree of freedom, and

$$\chi^2_{0.95}(1) = 3.841.$$

The computed value is now significant at the 5% level even though the estimated proportions for the North (0.194) and the South East (0.151) are unchanged. This is because the sample sizes are much larger than before. Consequently there is much stronger evidence that the apparent difference between the North and the South East is real and not the result of sampling error.

8.   Two independent sequences of Bernoulli trials are carried out with respective success probabilities p_1 and p_2. In the first sequence there are n_1 trials in all and f_1 successes and, in the second, n_2 trials in all and f_2 successes.

Writing

$$\hat{p}_1 = \frac{f_1}{n_1} \, , \quad \hat{p}_2 = \frac{f_2}{n_2} \, , \quad \hat{p} = \frac{f_1+f_2}{n_1+n_2} \, ,$$

the statistic

$$Z = \frac{\hat{p}_1-\hat{p}_2}{\sqrt{\hat{p}(1-\hat{p})(\frac{1}{n_1} + \frac{1}{n_2})}}$$

can be used to test $H_0 : p_1 = p_2$ against $H_1 : p_1 \neq p_2$. The corresponding chi-square statistic is

$$\chi^2 = \sum_{i=1}^{2} (f_i - n_i\hat{p})^2 \left(\frac{1}{n_i\hat{p}} + \frac{1}{n_i(1-\hat{p})}\right) \, .$$

Show that $Z^2 = \chi^2$ and deduce that the chi-square test (without Yates' correction) is equivalent to the test based on Z.

N.B.   The square of a N(0,1) random variable has a chi-square distribution with 1 degree of freedom - see Chapter 4, Miscellaneous Problem 7.

¶   Consider

$$Z^2 = \frac{(\hat{p}_1-\hat{p}_2)^2}{\hat{p}(1-\hat{p})(\frac{1}{n_1} + \frac{1}{n_2})} = \frac{(n_2f_1-n_1f_2)^2}{(f_1+f_2)(n_1-f_1+n_2-f_2)} \left(\frac{1}{n_1} + \frac{1}{n_2}\right) \, .$$

Now

$$\chi^2 = (f_1-n_1\hat{p})^2 \left(\frac{n_1+n_2}{n_1}\right)\left(\frac{1}{f_1+f_2} + \frac{1}{n_1-f_1+n_2-f_2}\right)$$

$$+ (f_2-n_2\hat{p})^2\left(\frac{n_1+n_2}{n_2}\right)\left(\frac{1}{f_1+f_2} + \frac{1}{n_1-f_1+n_2-f_2}\right)$$

$$= (n_1+n_2)\left(\frac{1}{f_1+f_2} + \frac{1}{n_1-f_1+n_2-f_2}\right)\left[\frac{(f_1-n_1\hat{p})^2}{n_1} + \frac{(f_2-n_2\hat{p})^2}{n_2}\right] \, .$$

But $\quad f_1 - n_1 \hat{p} = \dfrac{n_2 f_1 - n_1 f_2}{n_1 + n_2}$

and $\quad f_2 - n_2 \hat{p} = \dfrac{n_1 f_2 - n_2 f_1}{n_1 + n_2}$.

Therefore

$$\chi^2 = \frac{(n_1 + n_2)^2}{(f_1 + f_2)(n_1 - f_1 + n_2 - f_2)} \left[\frac{(n_2 f_1 - n_1 f_2)^2}{n_1 (n_1 + n_2)^2} + \frac{(n_1 f_2 - n_2 f_1)^2}{n_2 (n_1 + n_2)^2} \right]$$

$$= Z^2$$

as required.

The critical region of the level α test of H_o against H_1 based on χ^2 is $\chi^2 > \chi^2_{1-\alpha}(1)$, as there is one degree of freedom. Since H_1 is two-sided the critical region for the level α test based on Z is $|Z| > z_\gamma$, where $\Phi(z_\gamma) = \gamma$ and $\gamma = 1 - \tfrac{1}{2}\alpha$, an equivalent critical region being $Z^2 > z_\gamma^2$. It follows that the two tests are equivalent since $Z^2 = \chi^2$ and $z_\gamma^2 = \chi^2_{1-\alpha}(1)$.

Exercises 11.3 Non-parametric Methods

1. Steel girders produced by a certain foundry are claimed to have a median breaking strength of 1000 tons. Nine girders were tested to destruction and the maximum loads, in tons, were

    910, 980, 1020, 900, 950, 1010, 960, 850, 975.

    Test the claim against the alternative that the median breaking strength is less than 1000 tons. Use the Sign test and a 10% level of significance.

¶   The null hypothesis H_o is that the median is 1000 tons and the alternative H_1 is that the median is less than 1000 tons. Let V denote the number of values less than 1000. Then the appropriate critical region is

$$C = \{v : v \geqslant k\},$$

where k is a suitably chosen constant. The significance level α is given by

$$\alpha = P(V \geqslant k \,|\, H_o \text{ true}) = \sum_{r=k}^{9} {}^9C_r \left(\tfrac{1}{2}\right)^9 .$$

We find that $\alpha = 0.08984$ if $k = 7$ but $\alpha = 0.25391$ if $k = 6$. Thus, since a 10% significance level is specified, we take $k = 7$ and

$$C = \{v : v \geqslant 7\}.$$

Examining the data, we find that $v = 7$. The claim is therefore rejected at the 8.984% level of significance and so is certainly rejected at the 10% level.

2. Each child in a class was asked to perform two tasks, each being marked on a scale from 0 to 100. The marks were as follows

Child	1	2	3	4	5	6	7	8	9
Task A	76	49	57	80	67	67	60	67	68
Task B	50	56	60	59	45	54	51	51	48
Child	10	11	12	13	14	15	16	17	18
Task A	80	74	59	58	56	55	67	58	71
Task B	70	79	53	60	32	70	66	44	52

Test the null hypothesis that the tasks are equally difficult. Use the Sign test and a 10% significance level.

¶   The null hypothesis H_0 is that the median difference between the two marks is zero and the alternative H_1 is that the median difference is not zero. Let V denote the number of positive differences. Then an appropriate two-sided critical region is

$$C = \{v : v \leqslant k \text{ or } v \geqslant 18-k\}$$

where k is a constant. The significance level α is given by

$$\alpha = P(V \leqslant k \text{ or } V \geqslant 18-k \mid H_0 \text{ true})$$

$$= \sum_{r=0}^{k} {}^{18}C_r (\tfrac{1}{2})^{18} + \sum_{r=18-k}^{18} {}^{18}C_r (\tfrac{1}{2})^{18}$$

$$= 2 \sum_{r=0}^{k} {}^{18}C_r (\tfrac{1}{2})^{18}.$$

We find that $\alpha = 0.0963$ if $k = 5$ but $\alpha = 0.2379$ if $k = 6$. Thus, since a 10% significance level is specified, we take $k = 5$ and

$$C = \{v : v \leqslant 5 \text{ or } v \geqslant 13\}.$$

Subtracting mark B from mark A, the observed differences are

26, -7, -3, 21, 22, 13, 9, 16, 20, 10, -5, 6, -2, 24, -15, 1, 14, 19.

Thus v = 13. This value lies in the critical region and the null hypothesis that the tasks are equally difficult is rejected at the 10% level of significance.

(Note that if the differences had been obtained by subtracting mark A from mark B then v = 5 and the same conclusion would have been reached.)

3. In a study of the effect of a drug, the body temperatures of 14 guinea pigs were taken immediately before treatment with the drug and again 24 hours later. The results (in degrees Centigrade) were as follows:

Guinea pig	1	2	3	4	5	6	7
Before	38.1	38.3	38.4	37.9	38.6	38.5	38.2
After	38.8	38.7	38.4	38.4	38.5	39.0	38.5

Guinea pig	8	9	10	11	12	13	14
Before	38.5	37.9	38.1	38.1	38.5	38.3	38.3
After	38.2	38.2	38.6	38.4	38.9	38.1	38.6

Use the Sign test at the 10% level of significance to test the hypothesis that the median temperature is increased by 0.2°C at most against the alternative that it is increased by more than 0.2°C.

¶ Take the null hypothesis H_0 to be that the median temperature increase is 0.2°C at most and the alternative H_1 that the median temperature increase is more than 0.2°C. Let V denote the number of differences ('after' minus 'before') exceeding 0.2. Then the appropriate critical region is
$$C = \{v : v \geqslant k\},$$
where k is a suitable constant. As H_0 is composite, the significance level α is the largest Type I error probability. Thus

$$\alpha = P(V \geqslant k \mid V \text{ is } B(14,\tfrac{1}{2})) = \sum_{r=k}^{14} {}^{14}C_r (\tfrac{1}{2})^{14}.$$

We find that α = 0.0898 if k = 10 but α = 0.2120 if k = 9. Therefore
$$C = \{v : v \geqslant 10\}.$$

The observed differences are

0.7, 0.4, 0, 0.5, −0.1, 0.5, 0.3, −0.3, 0.3, 0.5, 0.3, 0.4, −0.2, 0.3.

Thus $v = 10$ and the null hypothesis that the median temperature increase is 0.2°C at most is rejected at the 10% level of significance.

4.   A random variable X has a $N(\mu,1)$ distribution and it is required to test the hypotheses

$$H_o: \mu=0; \quad H_1: \mu=0.5.$$

A random sample of size 9 is taken from this distribution and the number Y of positive values is counted. The Sign test which rejects H_o if Y exceeds 6 and accepts H_o otherwise is used to test H_o. Find the Type I and Type II error probabilities of this procedure.

Construct a test based on the sample mean $\bar{X}$ which has the same significance level as the above Sign test. Find the Type II error probability of this procedure. Why is it smaller than the Type II error probability of the Sign test?

¶   We note first that, under H_o,

$$P(X > 0) = 0.5.$$

Also, under H_1,

$$\begin{aligned}
P(X > 0) &= 1-P(X \leq 0) \\
&= 1-\Phi(-0.5) \\
&= \Phi(0.5) \\
&= 0.69146.
\end{aligned}$$

Thus, under H_o, Y is $B(9,\frac{1}{2})$ and the Type I error probability is

$$\alpha = \sum_{r=7}^{9} {}^9C_r (\tfrac{1}{2})^9 = 0.08984.$$

Under H_1, Y is $B(9,0.69146)$ and the Type II error probability is

$$\beta = \sum_{r=0}^{6} {}^9C_r (0.69146)^r (0.30854)^{9-r} = 0.560.$$

The appropriate critical region based on $\bar{X}$ is

$$C = \{\bar{x} : \bar{x} > k\}$$

where k is a constant. For this procedure,

$$\begin{aligned}
\alpha &= P(\bar{X} > k | \bar{X} \text{ is } N(0,\tfrac{1}{9})) \\
&= 1-\Phi(3k).
\end{aligned}$$

Taking α = 0.08984,

$$\Phi(3k) = 0.91016$$

so that

$$3k = 1.342$$
$$or \quad k = 0.4473.$$

Thus

$$\beta = P(\bar{X} \leqslant 0.4473 | \bar{X} \text{ is } N(0.5, \tfrac{1}{9}))$$
$$= \Phi(3(0.4473-0.5))$$
$$= \Phi(-0.158)$$
$$= 0.437.$$

This is less than the previous value of β because the Sign test does not use all the available information and so is less powerful than the parametric test.

5. The data below constitute a random sample of size 12 from a distribution whose median is m:

$$50.1, \ 50.3, \ 49.5, \ 50.6, \ 50.8, \ 48.9,$$
$$51.2, \ 51.3, \ 48.3, \ 51.8, \ 52.0, \ 52.1.$$

Use the Wilcoxon signed-rank test to test the hypotheses

$$H_0: m=50; \quad H_1: m>50$$

at the 10% level of significance.

¶   Let $$D_i = X_i - 50,$$
where X_i is the ith observation. The values of the D's are

$$0.1, \ 0.3, \ -0.5, \ 0.6, \ 0.8, \ -1.1, \ 1.2, \ 1.3, \ -1.7, \ 1.8, \ 2.0, \ 2.1.$$

We note that these values are arranged in ascending order of magnitude. The value of the Wilcoxon statistic W is the sum of the ranks of the positive values. Thus

$$W = 1+2+4+5+7+8+10+11+12 = 60.$$

Using Table 9, the one-tailed critical region with a significance level of (approximately) 10% is

$$C = \{w : w \geqslant 56\}.$$

The observed value of W lies within the critical region and we reject H_0.

6. The data below constitute a random sample from a symmetric distribution with mean μ:

97.9, 111.4, 97.7, 112.6, 98.8, 114.0, 98.7, 101.4, 98.9, 115.2, 97.4, 117.9, 118.6, 113.0, 97.0, 97.8, 97.6, 97.5, 110.9, 110.7, 112.5, 97.3, 97.2, 110.8, 102.9.

Use both the Sign test and the Wilcoxon signed-rank test to test the hypotheses

$$H_0: \mu = 100; \quad H_1: \mu \neq 100$$

at the 5% level of significance and comment.

¶ Let V denote the number of observations greater than 100. Then the appropriate critical region is

$$C = \{v : v \leqslant k \text{ or } v \geqslant 25-k\}$$

where k is a constant. The significance level is

$$\alpha = \sum_{r=0}^{k} {}^{25}C_r (\tfrac{1}{2})^{25} + \sum_{r=25-k}^{25} {}^{25}C_r (\tfrac{1}{2})^{25}$$

$$= 2\sum_{r=0}^{k} {}^{25}C_r (\tfrac{1}{2})^{25}.$$

We find that $\alpha = 0.0433$ if k = 7 but $\alpha = 0.1078$ if k = 8. The critical region of the Sign test with a 5% significance level is therefore

$$C = \{v : v \leqslant 7 \text{ or } v \geqslant 18\}.$$

For these data, v = 13 and H_0 is not rejected by the Sign test.

To apply the Wilcoxon signed-rank test, let

$$D_i = X_i - 100,$$

where X_i is the ith observation. The values of the D's arranged in ascending order of magnitude are

−1.1, −1.2, −1.3, 1.4, −2.1, −2.2, −2.3, −2.4, −2.5, −2.6, −2.7, −2.8, 2.9, −3.0, 10.7, 10.8, 10.9, 11.4, 12.5, 12.6, 13.0, 14.0, 15.2, 17.9, 18.6.

The sum of the ranks of the positive values is

$$w = 4+13+15+\ldots+25 = 237.$$

Using Table 9 with n=25, the two-tailed critical region with a significance level of (approximately) 5% is

$$C = \{w : w \leqslant \tfrac{1}{2} \times 25 \times 26 - 235 \text{ or } w \geqslant 235\}$$

$$= \{w : w \leqslant 90 \text{ or } w \geqslant 235\}.$$

The computed value lies in the critical region so that H_0 is rejected by the Wilcoxon signed rank test at the 5% level.

Approximately half the observations have values less than 100 but not much below. On the other hand, most of the values greater than 100 are considerably greater. Unlike the Sign test, the Wilcoxon test takes this into account and so rejects H_0.

7. Apply the Wilcoxon signed-rank test to the data of Exercise 1
    of this section.   Use a $2\frac{1}{2}$% significance level.

¶   With H_0 and H_1 as in Exercise 1, let
$$D_i = X_i - 1000,$$
where X_i is the ith observation.   Arranging the D's in
ascending order of magnitude, we obtain
         10, -20, 20, -25, -40, -50, -90, -100, -150
The sum of the ranks of the positive values is
              w = 1+2.5 = 3.5.
Using Table 9 with n = 9, the one-tailed critical region
with a significance level of (approximately) $2\frac{1}{2}$% is
$$C = \{w : w \leqslant \tfrac{1}{2} \times 9 \times 10\text{-}39\}$$
$$= \{w : w \leqslant 6\}.$$
The computed value lies in the critical region and H_0 is
rejected in favour of H_1.

8. Apply the Wilcoxon signed-rank test to the data of Exercise 2
    of this section.   Use a 1% significance level.

¶   Arranging the differences between the two marks in ascending
order of magnitude, we obtain
              1, -2, -3, -5, 6, -7, 9, 10, 13,
              14, -15, 16, 19, 20, 21, 22, 24, 26.
The sum of the ranks of the positive values is
              w = 1+5+7+...+18 = 145.
Taking H_0 and H_1 as in Exercise 2 and using Table 9 with
n = 18, the two-sided critical region with a significance
level of (approximately) 1% is
              $$C = \{w : w \leqslant 28 \text{ or } w \geqslant 143\}.$$
The computed value lies in C and H_0 is rejected at the 1%
level of significance.

9. A study of the effect of mothers' smoking on babies' birth-
    weights involved 12 pairs of mothers - one smoker and one
    non-smoker in each pair.   The mothers in each pair were chosen
    to be as similar as possible with respect to factors, other
    than smoking, which might affect birthweight.   The birth-
    weights (in kilograms) of the mothers' babies were as
    follows.

Pair	1	2	3	4	5	6
Smoker	3.00	4.27	3.95	3.32	2.51	2.77
Non-smoker	3.22	4.48	3.90	3.47	3.07	3.23

Pair	7	8	9	10	11	12
Smoker	4.02	3.41	3.39	3.88	3.18	4.37
Non-smoker	4.25	3.31	3.33	3.78	3.18	4.60

Do babies of mothers who smoke tend to have smaller birth-weights? Use the Wilcoxon signed-rank test and a 5% significance level.

¶ Arranging the differences between each pair of birthweights in ascending order of magnitude, we obtain

0, −0.05, −0.06, −0.10, −0.10, 0.15, 0.21, 0.22, 0.23, 0.23, 0.46, 0.56.

Counting the zero as $\frac{1}{2}$, the sum of the ranks of the positive values is

$$w = \frac{1}{2} + 6 + 7 + 8 + 9\frac{1}{2} + 9\frac{1}{2} + 11 + 12 = 63.5.$$

Let the null hypothesis H_0 be that the median difference is zero and the alternative H_1 be that the median difference is greater than zero. Using Table 9 with $n = 12$, the one-tailed critical region with a significance level of (approximately) 5% is

$$C = \{w : w \geqslant 61\}.$$

The computed value lies in C so that H_0 is rejected at the 5% level. There is evidence at this level that babies of mothers who smoke tend to have smaller birthweights.

10. A wholesale greengrocer decides to buy a field of winter cabbages if he can convince himself that their median weight exceeds 1.2 kg. Accordingly he cuts 12 cabbages at random and weighs them with the following results (in kg):

1.26, 1.19, 1.17, 1.24, 1.23, 1.25,
1.20, 1.18, 1.23, 1.21, 1.19, 1.17.

Should the greengrocer buy the cabbages? Use an appropriate non-parametric test and a 10% significance level.

¶ We use the Wilcoxon signed-rank test.

Let $D_i = X_i - 1.2$,

where X_i denotes the weight of the ith cabbage. The values

of the D's arranged in ascending order of magnitude are
    0, -0.01, 0.01, -0.01, -0.02, -0.03,
    0.03, 0.03, -0.03, 0.04, 0.05, 0.06.
Let the null hypothesis H_o be that the median weight is
1.2 kg and the alternative H_1 be that the median weight
exceeds 1.2 kg.

The sum of the ranks of the positive values is
    $w = \frac{1}{2} + 3 + 7\frac{1}{2} + 7\frac{1}{2} + 10 + 11 + 12 = 51.5.$
Using Table 9 with n = 12, the one-tailed critical region
with a significance level of (approximately) 10% is
    $C = \{w : w \geq 56\}.$
As the computed value does not lie in the critical region,
the greengrocer should not buy the cabbages.
(See Question 3, Exercises 9.5 for the parametric version
of this problem.)

11. In a test on two different models of 1300 cc cars, the
     following distances, in kilometres, were travelled using
     10 litres of petrol:
          Model 1 : 126.2, 126.7, 128.3, 125.8, 130.5.
          Model 2 : 130.2, 128.1, 131.4, 127.8, 129.6.
     What evidence is there that Model 2 is more economical than
     Model 1? Use an appropriate non-parametric test and a 5%
     significance level.

¶ Since the two samples are independent we use the Mann-Whitney
   test. Let x_i, y_j denote respectively the distances travelled
   by the ith car of Model 1 and the jth car of Model 2. (For
   example, x_1 = 126.2 and y_4 = 127.8.)   Examining the data,
   we find that

   $$x_4 < x_1 < x_2 < y_4 < y_2 < x_3 < y_5 < y_1 < x_5 < y_3.$$

   Let z_j equal the number of x's less than y_j (j=1,...,5).
   Then the value of the Mann-Whitney statistic U is

   $$u = \sum_{j=1}^{5} z_j = 4 + 3 + 5 + 3 + 4 = 19.$$

   Alternatively, the sum of the ranks of the y's in the
   pooled sample is 34 so that

   $$u = 34 - \frac{1}{2} \times 5 \times 6 = 19 \text{ (see Exercise 17 below).}$$

Take the null hypothesis H_o to be that the two models are
equally economical on average and the alternative H_1 to be
that Model 2 is more economical on average than Model 1.
There will be a tendency for the y's to be greater than the
x's if H_1 is true. Thus we expect u to be large if H_1 is
true. Using Table 10 with m=n=5 the appropriate one-tailed
critical region with a significance level of (approximately)
5% is

$$C = \{u : u \geq 21\}.$$

The observed value of the Mann-Whitney statistic is 19.
This does not lie in the critical region and it cannot be
concluded that Model 2 is more economical than Model 1 at
this level of significance.

12. Ten light bulbs of brand A and ten light bulbs of brand B
were selected at random. The following sequence shows the
order in which the bulbs failed:

A,A,A,B,A,B,A,A,A,B,B,A,B,A,B,A,B,B,B,B.

Using an appropriate non-parametric procedure, test at the 5%
level of significance the null hypothesis that the mean lifetimes of bulbs of the two brands are equal against the
alternative that they are not.

¶ We use the Mann-Whitney test. Letting z_j equal the number
of A's to the left of the jth B in the sequence, the value
of the Mann-Whitney statistic U is

$$u = \sum_{j=1}^{10} z_j = 3+4+7+7+8+9+10+10+10+10 = 78.$$

Using Table 10 with m=n=10, the two-sided critical region
with a significance level of (approximately) 5% is

$$C = \{u : u \leq 10 \times 10 - 76 \text{ or } u \geq 76\}$$
$$= \{u : u \leq 24 \text{ or } u \geq 76\}.$$

As the computed value lies in C we reject the null hypothesis
that the mean lifetimes are equal.

13. A Statistics class contains 6 girls and 8 boys. They all
sit an examination at the end of term and their marks are as
follows:

    Girls: 64, 72, 69, 82, 59, 76,
    Boys: 63, 49, 58, 75, 70, 68, 55, 66.

Use the Mann-Whitney statistic to test at the 5% level the hypothesis that boys and girls are equally good at Statistics.

¶   Arranging the pooled data in ascending order and using an obvious notation, we have

49	55	58	59	63	64	66	68	69	70	72	75	76	82
B	B	B	G	B	G	B	B	G	B	G	B	G	G

Let z_j be the number of B's to the left of the jth G. Then the value of the Mann-Whitney statistic is

$$u = \sum_{j=1}^{6} z_j = 3 + 4 + 6 + 7 + 8 + 8 = 36.$$

Using Table 10 with m = 6 and n = 8, the two-sided critical region with a significance level of (approximately) 5% is

$$C = \{u : u \leqslant 8 \times 6 - 40 \text{ or } u \geqslant 40\}$$
$$= \{u : u \leqslant 8 \text{ or } u \geqslant 40\}.$$

The computed value does not lie in C and there is no evidence at this level of a difference in ability between boys and girls.

14.   A dyeing process is assessed by measuring the variation in colour-density along a 1 metre length of material. The smaller the variation, the better the dyeing process. Two dyeing processes, A and B, are compared by examining a number of randomly chosen 1 metre lengths from both processes. The results (in suitable units) are as follows:

Process A: 2.3, 4.0, 2.6, 2.8, 3.7, 3.8, 2.7, 3.1, 2.8, 2.5, 3.4.
Process B: 3.3, 4.0, 4.5, 2.1, 4.3, 4.2, 3.5, 3.6.

Test a claim that process A is better than process B using a 5% significance level.

¶   Take H_0 to be that the processes are equally good and H_1 to be that process A is better than process B. Arranging the pooled data in ascending order we have

2.1	2.3	2.5	2.6	2.7	2.8	2.8	3.1	3.3	3.4
B	A	A	A	A	A	A	A	B	A

3.5	3.6	3.7	3.8	4.0	4.0	4.2	4.3	4.5
B	B	A	A	A	B	B	B	B

The value of the Mann-Whitney statistic is

$$u = 0 + 7 + 8 + 8 + 10\tfrac{1}{2} + 11 + 11 + 11 = 66.5.$$

We now wish to find the one-tailed critical region with significance level closest to 5%. If process A is better than process B, then the A values will tend to be less than the B values, leading to a large value of the Mann-Whitney statistic. The relevant tail for the critical region is therefore the upper tail. So we obtain from Table 10 the critical region

$$C = \{u : u \geqslant 64\}.$$

The computed value lies in the critical region so that we reject H_o. There is evidence that process A is better than process B.

15. Apply the Mann-Whitney test to the birthweight data of Exercise 9 of this section, treating the birthweights of babies with mothers who smoke and the birthweights of babies with mothers who do not smoke as two independent samples. Comment on your result.

¶ Arranging the pooled data in ascending order and underlining the birthweight of the babies of the mothers who smoke, we obtain

2.51	2.77	3.00	3.07	3.18	3.18	3.22	3.23
3.31	3.32	3.33	3.39	3.41	3.47	3.78	3.88
3.90	3.95	4.02	4.25	4.27	4.37	4.48	4.60

The value of the Mann-Whitney statistic is

$$u = 3 + 3\tfrac{1}{2} + 4 + 4 + 4 + 5 + 7 + 7 + 8 + 10 + 12 + 12 = 79.5.$$

Using Table 10 with m=n=12, the appropriate 5% critical region for testing the null hypothesis that smoking does not affect birthweight against the alternative that it decreases birthweight is

$$C = \{u : u \geqslant 101\}.$$

The computed value does not lie in the critical region and, in contrast to Exercise 9, the null hypothesis is not rejected. The reason is that the variation between pairs is much greater than the variation within pairs. Consequently the effect of smoking on birthweight is not detectable when we ignore the pairing.

16. With the usual notation for the Mann-Whitney statistic, show that under the null hypothesis,

$$E(Z_{ij}) = \tfrac{1}{2}$$

and hence that

$$E(U) = \frac{mn}{2} .$$

Explain why Var(U) cannot be found using the same approach.

¶ Given the samples $X_1, X_2, \ldots, X_m$ and $Y_1, Y_2, \ldots, Y_n$ we define

$$\begin{aligned} Z_{ij} &= 1 \quad \text{if } X_i < Y_j, \\ &= 0 \quad \text{if } X_i > Y_j. \end{aligned}$$

The Mann-Whitney statistic is defined by

$$U = \sum_{j=1}^{n} \sum_{i=1}^{m} Z_{ij}$$

Now, under the usual null hypothesis H_o that the X_i's and Y_j's come from the same distribution,

$$P(X_i < Y_j) = P(X_i > Y_j) = \tfrac{1}{2} \quad \text{for all } i,j.$$

It follows that under H_o,

$$E(Z_{ij}) = \tfrac{1}{2} \times 1 + \tfrac{1}{2} \times 0 = \tfrac{1}{2}$$

Thus

$$E(U) = E \left| \sum_{j=1}^{n} \sum_{i=1}^{m} Z_{ij} \right|$$

$$= \sum_{j=1}^{n} \sum_{i=1}^{m} E(Z_{ij})$$

$$= \sum_{j=1}^{n} \sum_{i=1}^{m} \tfrac{1}{2}$$

$$= mn/2 .$$

Note that, even though the Z_{ij}'s are not independent, we can reverse the order of E and Σ.

Consider now

$$\text{Var}(U) = \text{Var} \left(\sum_{j=1}^{n} \sum_{i=1}^{m} Z_{ij} \right)$$

We cannot reverse the order of Var and Σ since this is valid only if the random variables being summed are uncorrelated. This is not the case here, e.g. Z_{11} and Z_{12} are correlated since they both involve X_1. The calculation of Var(U) therefore involves covariance terms and is algebraically tedious.

17. Establish the formula
$$U = R - \frac{n(n+1)}{2}$$
for the Mann-Whitney statistic, where R is the sum of the ranks assigned to $Y_1, Y_2, \ldots, Y_n$.

¶ Suppose that we have the two random samples $X_1, X_2, \ldots, X_m$ and $Y_1, Y_2, \ldots, Y_n$. Further suppose, without loss of generality, that the Y's are labelled in such a way that $Y_1, Y_2, \ldots, Y_n$ are arranged in ascending order. When the X and Y samples are pooled and ranked, we obtain a sequence such as

$$X X Y_1 X Y_2 X X Y_3 \ldots \quad .$$

Let

$$R_j = \text{the rank of } Y_j,$$
$$Z_j = \text{the number of X's less than } Y_j.$$

Then the Mann-Whitney statistic is given by

$$U = \sum_{j=1}^{n} Z_j .$$

Also

$$R = \sum_{j=1}^{n} R_j .$$

Now, inspecting the sequence above, we see that

$$R_1 = Z_1 + 1,$$
$$R_2 = Z_2 + 2$$

and, in general,

$$R_j = Z_j + j.$$

Summing over $j = 1$ to n,

$$\sum_{j=1}^{n} R_j = \sum_{j=1}^{n} Z_j + \sum_{j=1}^{n} j$$

or

$$R = U + \frac{n(n+1)}{2},$$

whence

$$U = R - \frac{n(n+1)}{2} .$$

18. Calculate the value of the Mann-Whitney statistic U for each of the 20 arrangements of the letters xxxyyy and deduce the distribution of U under the null hypothesis that these arrangements are all equally likely.

¶   The possibilities are as follows:

Arrangement	Value of U
xxxyyy	9
xxyxyy	8
xxyyxy	7
xxyyyx	6
xyxxyy	7
xyxyxy	6
xyxyyx	5
xyyxxy	5
xyyxyx	4
xyyyxx	3
yxxxyy	6
yxxyxy	5
yxxyyx	4
yxyxxy	4
yxyxyx	3
yxyyxx	2
yyxxxy	3
yyxxyx	2
yyxyxx	1
yyyxxx	0

It follows that the distribution of U under the null hypothesis is

u	0	1	2	3	4	5	6	7	8	9
Prob	$\frac{1}{20}$	$\frac{1}{20}$	$\frac{2}{20}$	$\frac{3}{20}$	$\frac{3}{20}$	$\frac{3}{20}$	$\frac{3}{20}$	$\frac{2}{20}$	$\frac{1}{20}$	$\frac{1}{20}$

.

Table 1.   The Normal Cumulative Distribution Function

The function tabulated is $\Phi(x) = \dfrac{1}{\sqrt{2\pi}} \displaystyle\int_{-\infty}^{x} e^{-y^2/2}dy = P(X \le x)$,

where X is normally distributed with zero mean and unit
variance.   The value of the function $\Phi(x)$ corresponds to
the shaded area.   For negative x the relation $\Phi(x)=1-\Phi(-x)$ should be used.

x	.00	.01	.02	.03	.04	.05	.06	.07	.08	.09
0.0	0.50000	0.50399	0.50798	0.51197	0.51595	0.51994	0.52392	0.52790	0.53188	0.53586
0.1	0.53983	0.54380	0.54776	0.55172	0.55567	0.55962	0.56356	0.56749	0.57142	0.57535
0.2	0.57926	0.58317	0.58706	0.59095	0.59483	0.59871	0.60257	0.60642	0.61026	0.61409
0.3	0.61791	0.62172	0.62552	0.62930	0.63307	0.63683	0.64058	0.64431	0.64803	0.65173
0.4	0.65542	0.65910	0.66276	0.66640	0.67003	0.67364	0.67724	0.68082	0.68439	0.68793
0.5	0.69146	0.69497	0.69847	0.70194	0.70540	0.70884	0.71226	0.71566	0.71904	0.72240
0.6	0.72575	0.72907	0.73237	0.73565	0.73891	0.74215	0.74537	0.74857	0.75175	0.75490
0.7	0.75804	0.76115	0.76424	0.76730	0.77035	0.77337	0.77637	0.77935	0.78230	0.78524
0.8	0.78814	0.79103	0.79389	0.79673	0.79955	0.80234	0.80511	0.80785	0.81057	0.81327
0.9	0.81594	0.81859	0.82121	0.82381	0.82639	0.82894	0.83147	0.83398	0.83646	0.83891
1.0	0.84134	0.84375	0.84614	0.84849	0.85083	0.85314	0.85543	0.85769	0.85993	0.86214
1.1	0.86433	0.86650	0.86864	0.87076	0.87286	0.87493	0.87698	0.87900	0.88100	0.88298
1.2	0.88493	0.88686	0.88877	0.89065	0.89251	0.89435	0.89617	0.89796	0.89973	0.90147
1.3	0.90320	0.90490	0.90658	0.90824	0.90988	0.91149	0.91309	0.91466	0.91621	0.91774
1.4	0.91924	0.92073	0.92220	0.92364	0.92507	0.92647	0.92785	0.92922	0.93056	0.93189
1.5	0.93319	0.93448	0.93574	0.93699	0.93822	0.93943	0.94062	0.94179	0.94295	0.94408
1.6	0.94520	0.94630	0.94738	0.94845	0.94950	0.95053	0.95154	0.95254	0.95352	0.95449
1.7	0.95543	0.95637	0.95728	0.95818	0.95907	0.95994	0.96080	0.96164	0.96246	0.96327
1.8	0.96407	0.96485	0.96562	0.96638	0.96712	0.96784	0.96856	0.96926	0.96995	0.97062
1.9	0.97128	0.97193	0.97257	0.97320	0.97381	0.97441	0.97500	0.97558	0.97615	0.97670
2.0	0.97725	0.97778	0.97831	0.97882	0.97932	0.97982	0.98030	0.98077	0.98124	0.98169
2.1	0.98214	0.98257	0.98300	0.98341	0.98382	0.98422	0.98461	0.98500	0.98537	0.98574
2.2	0.98610	0.98645	0.98679	0.98713	0.98745	0.98778	0.98809	0.98840	0.98870	0.98899
2.3	0.98928	0.98956	0.98983	0.99010	0.99036	0.99061	0.99086	0.99111	0.99134	0.99158
2.4	0.99180	0.99202	0.99224	0.99245	0.99266	0.99286	0.99305	0.99324	0.99343	0.99361
2.5	0.99379	0.99396	0.99413	0.99430	0.99446	0.99461	0.99477	0.99492	0.99506	0.99520
2.6	0.99534	0.99547	0.99560	0.99573	0.99585	0.99598	0.99609	0.99621	0.99632	0.99643
2.7	0.99653	0.99664	0.99674	0.99683	0.99693	0.99702	0.99711	0.99720	0.99728	0.99736
2.8	0.99744	0.99752	0.99760	0.99767	0.99774	0.99781	0.99788	0.99795	0.99801	0.99807
2.9	0.99813	0.99819	0.99825	0.99831	0.99836	0.99841	0.99846	0.99851	0.99856	0.99861
3.0	0.99865	0.99869	0.99874	0.99878	0.99882	0.99886	0.99889	0.99893	0.99896	0.99900
3.1	0.99903	0.99906	0.99910	0.99913	0.99916	0.99918	0.99921	0.99924	0.99926	0.99929
3.2	0.99931	0.99934	0.99936	0.99938	0.99940	0.99942	0.99944	0.99946	0.99948	0.99950
3.3	0.99952	0.99953	0.99955	0.99957	0.99958	0.99960	0.99961	0.99962	0.99964	0.99965
3.4	0.99966	0.99968	0.99969	0.99970	0.99971	0.99972	0.99973	0.99974	0.99975	0.99976
3.5	0.99977	0.99978	0.99978	0.99979	0.99980	0.99981	0.99981	0.99982	0.99983	0.99983
3.6	0.99984	0.99985	0.99985	0.99986	0.99986	0.99987	0.99987	0.99988	0.99988	0.99989
3.7	0.99989	0.99990	0.99990	0.99990	0.99991	0.99991	0.99992	0.99992	0.99992	0.99992
3.8	0.99993	0.99993	0.99993	0.99994	0.99994	0.99994	0.99994	0.99995	0.99995	0.99995
3.9	0.99995	0.99995	0.99996	0.99996	0.99996	0.99996	0.99996	0.99996	0.99997	0.99997

Table 2. Percentage Points of the Normal Distribution

The table gives the value of z_p satisfying $\Phi(z_p)=p$, for various values of p.

If $p<0.5$, the relation $z_p=-z_{1-p}$ should be used.

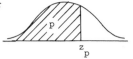

p	.00	.01	.02	.03	.04	.05	.06	.07	.08	.09
0.50	0.00000	0.02507	0.05015	0.07527	0.10043	0.12566	0.15097	0.17637	0.20189	0.22755
0.60	0.25335	0.27932	0.30548	0.33185	0.35846	0.38532	0.41246	0.43991	0.46770	0.49585
0.70	0.52440	0.55339	0.58284	0.61281	0.64335	0.67449	0.70630	0.73885	0.77219	0.80642
0.80	0.84162	0.87790	0.91537	0.95417	0.99446	1.03643	1.08032	1.12639	1.17499	1.22653
0.90	1.28155	1.34076	1.40507	1.47579	1.55477					

p	.000	.001	.002	.003	.004	.005	.006	.007	.008	.009
0.95	1.64485	1.65463	1.66456	1.67466	1.68494	1.69540	1.70604	1.71689	1.72793	1.73920
0.96	1.75069	1.76241	1.77438	1.78661	1.79912	1.81191	1.82501	1.83842	1.85218	1.86630
0.97	1.88079	1.89570	1.91104	1.92684	1.94313	1.95996	1.97737	1.99539	2.01409	2.03352
0.98	2.05375	2.07485	2.09693	2.12007	2.14441	2.17009	2.19729	2.22621	2.25713	2.29037
0.99	2.32635	2.36562	2.40891	2.45726	2.51214	2.57583	2.65206	2.74777	2.87816	3.09022

Table 3. **Percentage Points of the Student's t Distribution**

The table gives the value of $t_p(m)$ satisfying $P(T \leq t_p(m)) = p$,
for various values of p and m, where T has Student's t
distribution with m degrees of freedom.
If $p < 0.5$, the relation $t_p(m) = -t_{(1-p)}(m)$ should be used.

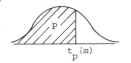

p m	0.9	0.95	0.975	0.99	0.995	p m	0.9	0.95	0.975	0.99	0.995
1	3.078	6.314	12.706	31.820	63.656	29	1.311	1.699	2.045	2.462	2.756
2	1.886	2.920	4.303	6.965	9.925	30	1.310	1.697	2.042	2.457	2.750
3	1.638	2.353	3.182	4.541	5.841	31	1.309	1.696	2.040	2.453	2.744
4	1.533	2.132	2.776	3.747	4.604	32	1.309	1.694	2.037	2.449	2.738
5	1.476	2.015	2.571	3.365	4.032	33	1.308	1.692	2.035	2.445	2.733
6	1.440	1.943	2.447	3.143	3.707	34	1.307	1.691	2.032	2.441	2.728
7	1.415	1.895	2.365	2.998	3.499	35	1.306	1.690	2.030	2.438	2.724
8	1.397	1.860	2.306	2.896	3.355	36	1.306	1.688	2.028	2.434	2.719
9	1.383	1.833	2.262	2.821	3.250	37	1.305	1.687	2.026	2.431	2.715
10	1.372	1.812	2.228	2.764	3.169	38	1.304	1.686	2.024	2.429	2.712
11	1.363	1.796	2.201	2.718	3.106	39	1.304	1.685	2.023	2.426	2.708
12	1.356	1.782	2.179	2.681	3.055	40	1.303	1.684	2.021	2.423	2.704
13	1.350	1.771	2.160	2.650	3.012	45	1.301	1.679	2.014	2.412	2.690
14	1.345	1.761	2.145	2.624	2.977	50	1.299	1.676	2.009	2.403	2.678
15	1.341	1.753	2.131	2.602	2.947	55	1.297	1.673	2.004	2.396	2.668
16	1.337	1.746	2.120	2.583	2.921	60	1.296	1.671	2.000	2.390	2.660
17	1.333	1.740	2.110	2.567	2.898	65	1.295	1.669	1.997	2.385	2.654
18	1.330	1.734	2.101	2.552	2.878	70	1.294	1.667	1.994	2.381	2.648
19	1.328	1.729	2.093	2.539	2.861	75	1.293	1.665	1.992	2.377	2.643
20	1.325	1.725	2.086	2.528	2.845	80	1.292	1.664	1.990	2.374	2.639
21	1.323	1.721	2.080	2.518	2.831	85	1.292	1.663	1.988	2.371	2.635
22	1.321	1.717	2.074	2.508	2.819	90	1.291	1.662	1.987	2.368	2.632
23	1.319	1.714	2.069	2.500	2.807	95	1.291	1.661	1.985	2.366	2.629
24	1.318	1.711	2.064	2.492	2.797	100	1.290	1.660	1.984	2.364	2.626
25	1.316	1.708	2.060	2.485	2.787	125	1.288	1.657	1.979	2.357	2.616
26	1.315	1.706	2.056	2.479	2.779	150	1.287	1.655	1.976	2.351	2.609
27	1.314	1.703	2.052	2.473	2.771	∞	1.282	1.645	1.960	2.326	2.576
28	1.313	1.701	2.048	2.467	2.763						

Table 4. Percentage Points of the Chi-Square Distribution

The table gives the value of $\chi^2_p(m)$ satisfying $P(X \leq \chi^2_p(m)) = p$, for various values of p and m, where X has the chi-square distribution with m degrees of freedom.

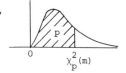

m \ p	0.9	0.95	0.975	0.99	0.995
1	2.706	3.841	5.024	6.635	7.879
2	4.605	5.991	7.378	9.210	10.597
3	6.251	7.815	9.348	11.345	12.838
4	7.779	9.488	11.143	13.277	14.860
5	9.236	11.070	12.833	15.086	16.750
6	10.645	12.592	14.449	16.812	18.548
7	12.017	14.067	16.013	18.475	20.278
8	13.362	15.507	17.535	20.090	21.955
9	14.684	16.919	19.023	21.666	23.589
10	15.987	18.307	20.483	23.209	25.188
11	17.275	19.675	21.920	24.725	26.757
12	18.549	21.026	23.337	26.217	28.300
13	19.812	22.362	24.736	27.688	29.819
14	21.064	23.685	26.119	29.141	31.319
15	22.307	24.996	27.488	30.578	32.801
16	23.542	26.296	28.845	32.000	34.267
17	24.769	27.587	30.191	33.409	35.718
18	25.989	28.869	31.526	34.805	37.156
19	27.204	30.144	32.852	36.191	38.582
20	28.412	31.410	34.170	37.566	39.997
21	29.615	32.671	35.479	38.932	41.401
22	30.813	33.924	36.781	40.289	42.796
23	32.007	35.172	38.076	41.638	44.181
24	33.196	36.415	39.364	42.980	45.559
25	34.382	37.652	40.646	44.314	46.928
26	35.563	38.885	41.923	45.642	48.290
27	36.741	40.113	43.195	46.963	49.645
28	37.916	41.337	44.461	48.278	50.993
29	39.087	42.557	45.722	49.588	52.336
30	40.256	43.773	46.979	50.892	53.672
32	42.585	46.194	49.480	53.486	56.328
34	44.903	48.602	51.966	56.061	58.964
36	47.212	50.998	54.437	58.619	61.501
38	49.513	53.384	56.896	61.162	64.181
40	51.805	55.759	59.342	63.691	66.766
45	57.505	61.656	65.410	69.957	73.166
50	63.167	67.505	71.420	76.154	79.490
60	74.397	79.082	83.298	88.379	91.952
70	85.527	90.531	95.023	100.425	104.215
80	96.578	101.879	106.629	112.329	116.321
90	107.565	113.145	118.136	124.116	128.299
100	118.498	124.342	129.561	135.807	140.169

Table 5. Critical Values of the Sample Correlation Coefficient

The table gives critical values of the sample correlation coefficient r for various significance levels and sample sizes n.

One tail Two tails n	10% 20%	5% 10%	2.5% 5%	1% 2%	0.5% 1%
4	0.8000	0.9000	0.9500	0.9800	0.9900
5	0.6870	0.8054	0.8783	0.9343	0.9587
6	0.6084	0.7293	0.8114	0.8822	0.9172
7	0.5509	0.6694	0.7545	0.8329	0.8745
8	0.5067	0.6215	0.7067	0.7887	0.8343
9	0.4716	0.5822	0.6664	0.7498	0.7977
10	0.4428	0.5494	0.6319	0.7155	0.7646
11	0.4187	0.5214	0.6021	0.6851	0.7348
12	0.3981	0.4973	0.5760	0.6581	0.7079
13	0.3802	0.4762	0.5529	0.6339	0.6835
14	0.3646	0.4575	0.5324	0.6120	0.6614
15	0.3507	0.4409	0.5140	0.5923	0.6411
16	0.3383	0.4259	0.4973	0.5742	0.6226
17	0.3271	0.4124	0.4821	0.5577	0.6055
18	0.3170	0.4000	0.4683	0.5425	0.5897
19	0.3077	0.3887	0.4555	0.5285	0.5751
20	0.2992	0.3783	0.4438	0.5155	0.5614
21	0.2914	0.3687	0.4329	0.5034	0.5487
22	0.2841	0.3598	0.4227	0.4921	0.5368
23	0.2774	0.3515	0.4132	0.4815	0.5256
24	0.2711	0.3438	0.4044	0.4716	0.5151
25	0.2653	0.3365	0.3961	0.4622	0.5052
26	0.2598	0.3297	0.3882	0.4534	0.4958
27	0.2546	0.3233	0.3809	0.4451	0.4869
28	0.2497	0.3172	0.3739	0.4372	0.4785
29	0.2451	0.3115	0.3673	0.4297	0.4705
30	0.2407	0.3061	0.3610	0.4226	0.4629
32	0.2327	0.2960	0.3494	0.4093	0.4487
34	0.2254	0.2869	0.3388	0.3972	0.4357
36	0.2187	0.2785	0.3291	0.3862	0.4238
38	0.2126	0.2709	0.3202	0.3760	0.4128
40	0.2070	0.2638	0.3120	0.3665	0.4026
45	0.1947	0.2483	0.2940	0.3457	0.3801
50	0.1843	0.2353	0.2787	0.3281	0.3610
n>50	$\dfrac{1.282}{\sqrt{n-1}}$	$\dfrac{1.645}{\sqrt{n-1}}$	$\dfrac{1.960}{\sqrt{n-1}}$	$\dfrac{2.326}{\sqrt{n-1}}$	$\dfrac{2.576}{\sqrt{n-1}}$

Table 6. Critical Values of the Spearman Rank Correlation Coefficient

The table gives critical values of the Spearman rank correlation coefficient r_s for various significance levels and sample sizes n.   Note that exact significance levels cannot, in general, be achieved.   The critical values given are those whose significance levels are nearest to the stated values.

One tail	10%	5%	2.5%	1%	0.5%
Two tails	20%	10%	5%	2%	1%
n					
4	1.0000	1.0000	1.0000		
5	0.7000	0.9000	0.9000	1.0000	1.0000
6	0.6571	0.7714	0.8286	0.9429	0.9429
7	0.5714	0.6786	0.7857	0.8571	0.8929
8	0.5476	0.6429	0.7381	0.8095	0.8571
9	0.4833	0.6000	0.6833	0.7667	0.8167
10	0.4424	0.5636	0.6485	0.7333	0.7818
11	0.4182	0.5273	0.6091	0.7000	0.7545
12	0.3986	0.5035	0.5874	0.6713	0.7273
13	0.3791	0.4780	0.5604	0.6484	0.6978
14	0.3670	0.4593	0.5385	0.6220	0.6747
15	0.3500	0.4429	0.5179	0.6000	0.6536
16	0.3382	0.4265	0.5029	0.5824	0.6324
17	0.3271	0.4124	0.4821	0.5577	0.6055
18	0.3170	0.4000	0.4683	0.5425	0.5897
19	0.3077	0.3887	0.4555	0.5285	0.5751
20	0.2992	0.3783	0.4438	0.5155	0.5614
21	0.2914	0.3687	0.4329	0.5034	0.5487
22	0.2841	0.3598	0.4227	0.4921	0.5368
23	0.2774	0.3515	0.4132	0.4815	0.5256
24	0.2711	0.3438	0.4044	0.4716	0.5151
25	0.2653	0.3365	0.3961	0.4622	0.5052
26	0.2598	0.3297	0.3882	0.4534	0.4958
27	0.2546	0.3233	0.3809	0.4451	0.4869
28	0.2497	0.3172	0.3739	0.4372	0.4785
29	0.2451	0.3115	0.3673	0.4297	0.4705
30	0.2407	0.3061	0.3610	0.4226	0.4629
32	0.2327	0.2960	0.3494	0.4093	0.4487
34	0.2254	0.2869	0.3388	0.3972	0.4357
36	0.2187	0.2785	0.3291	0.3862	0.4238
38	0.2126	0.2709	0.3202	0.3760	0.4128
40	0.2070	0.2638	0.3120	0.3665	0.4026
45	0.1947	0.2483	0.2940	0.3457	0.3801
50	0.1843	0.2353	0.2787	0.3281	0.3610
n > 50	$\dfrac{1.282}{\sqrt{n-1}}$	$\dfrac{1.645}{\sqrt{n-1}}$	$\dfrac{1.960}{\sqrt{n-1}}$	$\dfrac{2.326}{\sqrt{n-1}}$	$\dfrac{2.576}{\sqrt{n-1}}$

Table 7. The Fisher z-Transformation

The function tabulated is

$$z(r) = \tanh^{-1}r = \frac{1}{2} \log_e \left(\frac{1+r}{1-r}\right) .$$

If $r < 0$, then $z(r) = -z(-r)$.

r	.00	.01	.02	.03	.04	.05	.06	.07	.08	.09
0.00	0.0000	0.0100	0.0200	0.0300	0.0400	0.0500	0.0601	0.0701	0.0802	0.0902
0.10	0.1003	0.1104	0.1206	0.1307	0.1409	0.1511	0.1614	0.1717	0.1820	0.1923
0.20	0.2027	0.2132	0.2237	0.2342	0.2448	0.2554	0.2661	0.2769	0.2877	0.2986
0.30	0.3095	0.3205	0.3316	0.3428	0.3541	0.3654	0.3769	0.3884	0.4001	0.4118
0.40	0.4236	0.4356	0.4477	0.4599	0.4722	0.4847	0.4973	0.5101	0.5230	0.5361
0.50	0.5493	0.5627	0.5763	0.5901	0.6042	0.6184	0.6328	0.6475	0.6625	0.6777
0.60	0.6931	0.7089	0.7250	0.7414	0.7582	0.7753	0.7928	0.8107	0.8291	0.8480
0.70	0.8673	0.8872	0.9076	0.9287	0.9505	0.9730	0.9962	1.0203	1.0454	1.0714
0.80	1.0986	1.1270	1.1568	1.1881	1.2212	1.2562	1.2933	1.3331	1.3758	1.4219

r	.000	.001	.002	.003	.004	.005	.006	.007	.008	.009
0.900	1.4722	1.4775	1.4828	1.4882	1.4937	1.4992	1.5047	1.5103	1.5160	1.5217
0.910	1.5275	1.5334	1.5393	1.5453	1.5513	1.5574	1.5636	1.5698	1.5762	1.5826
0.920	1.5890	1.5956	1.6022	1.6089	1.6157	1.6226	1.6296	1.6366	1.6438	1.6510
0.930	1.6584	1.6658	1.6734	1.6811	1.6888	1.6967	1.7047	1.7129	1.7211	1.7295
0.940	1.7380	1.7467	1.7555	1.7645	1.7736	1.7828	1.7923	1.8019	1.8117	1.8216
0.950	1.8318	1.8421	1.8527	1.8635	1.8745	1.8857	1.8972	1.9090	1.9210	1.9333
0.960	1.9459	1.9588	1.9721	1.9857	1.9996	2.0139	2.0287	2.0439	2.0595	2.0756
0.970	2.0923	2.1095	2.1273	2.1457	2.1649	2.1847	2.2054	2.2269	2.2494	2.2729
0.980	2.2976	2.3235	2.3507	2.3796	2.4101	2.4427	2.4774	2.5147	2.5550	2.5987
0.990	2.6467	2.6996	2.7587	2.8257	2.9031	2.9945	3.1063	3.2504	3.4534	3.8002

Table 8.   **The Inverse Fisher z-Transformation**

The function tabulated is

$$r(z) = \tanh z = \frac{e^{2z}-1}{e^{2z}+1} .$$

If $r<0$, then $r(z)=-r(-z)$.

z	.00	.01	.02	.03	.04	.05	.06	.07	.08	.09
0.00	0.0000	0.0100	0.0200	0.0300	0.0400	0.0500	0.0599	0.0699	0.0798	0.0898
0.10	0.0997	0.1096	0.1194	0.1293	0.1391	0.1489	0.1586	0.1684	0.1781	0.1877
0.20	0.1974	0.2070	0.2165	0.2260	0.2355	0.2449	0.2543	0.2636	0.2729	0.2821
0.30	0.2913	0.3004	0.3095	0.3185	0.3275	0.3364	0.3452	0.3540	0.3627	0.3714
0.40	0.3799	0.3885	0.3969	0.4053	0.4136	0.4219	0.4301	0.4382	0.4462	0.4542
0.50	0.4621	0.4699	0.4777	0.4854	0.4930	0.5005	0.5080	0.5154	0.5227	0.5299
0.60	0.5370	0.5441	0.5511	0.5581	0.5649	0.5717	0.5784	0.5850	0.5915	0.5980
0.70	0.6044	0.6107	0.6169	0.6231	0.6291	0.6351	0.6411	0.6469	0.6527	0.6584
0.80	0.6640	0.6696	0.6751	0.6805	0.6858	0.6911	0.6963	0.7014	0.7064	0.7114
0.90	0.7163	0.7211	0.7259	0.7306	0.7352	0.7398	0.7443	0.7487	0.7531	0.7574
1.00	0.7616	0.7658	0.7699	0.7739	0.7779	0.7818	0.7857	0.7895	0.7932	0.7969
1.10	0.8005	0.8041	0.8076	0.8110	0.8144	0.8178	0.8210	0.8243	0.8275	0.8306
1.20	0.8337	0.8367	0.8397	0.8426	0.8455	0.8483	0.8511	0.8538	0.8565	0.8591
1.30	0.8617	0.8643	0.8668	0.8692	0.8717	0.8741	0.8764	0.8787	0.8810	0.8832
1.40	0.8854	0.8875	0.8896	0.8917	0.8937	0.8957	0.8977	0.8996	0.9015	0.9033
1.50	0.9051	0.9069	0.9087	0.9104	0.9121	0.9138	0.9154	0.9170	0.9186	0.9201
1.60	0.9217	0.9232	0.9246	0.9261	0.9275	0.9289	0.9302	0.9316	0.9329	0.9341
1.70	0.9354	0.9366	0.9379	0.9391	0.9402	0.9414	0.9425	0.9436	0.9447	0.9458
1.80	0.9468	0.9478	0.9488	0.9498	0.9508	0.9517	0.9527	0.9536	0.9545	0.9554
1.90	0.9562	0.9571	0.9579	0.9587	0.9595	0.9603	0.9611	0.9618	0.9626	0.9633
2.00	0.9640	0.9647	0.9654	0.9661	0.9667	0.9674	0.9680	0.9687	0.9693	0.9699
2.10	0.9705	0.9710	0.9716	0.9721	0.9727	0.9732	0.9737	0.9743	0.9748	0.9753
2.20	0.9757	0.9762	0.9767	0.9771	0.9776	0.9780	0.9785	0.9789	0.9793	0.9797
2.30	0.9801	0.9805	0.9809	0.9812	0.9816	0.9820	0.9823	0.9827	0.9830	0.9833
2.40	0.9837	0.9840	0.9843	0.9846	0.9849	0.9852	0.9855	0.9858	0.9861	0.9863
2.50	0.9866	0.9869	0.9871	0.9874	0.9876	0.9879	0.9881	0.9884	0.9886	0.9888
2.60	0.9890	0.9892	0.9895	0.9897	0.9899	0.9901	0.9903	0.9905	0.9906	0.9908
2.70	0.9910	0.9912	0.9914	0.9915	0.9917	0.9919	0.9920	0.9922	0.9923	0.9925
2.80	0.9926	0.9928	0.9929	0.9931	0.9932	0.9933	0.9935	0.9936	0.9937	0.9938
2.90	0.9940	0.9941	0.9942	0.9943	0.9944	0.9945	0.9946	0.9947	0.9949	0.9950
3.00	0.9951	0.9952	0.9952	0.9953	0.9954	0.9955	0.9956	0.9957	0.9958	0.9959
3.10	0.9959	0.9960	0.9961	0.9962	0.9963	0.9963	0.9964	0.9965	0.9965	0.9966
3.20	0.9967	0.9967	0.9968	0.9969	0.9969	0.9970	0.9971	0.9971	0.9972	0.9972
3.30	0.9973	0.9973	0.9974	0.9974	0.9975	0.9975	0.9976	0.9976	0.9977	0.9977
3.40	0.9978	0.9978	0.9973	0.9979	0.9979	0.9980	0.9980	0.9981	0.9981	0.9981
3.50	0.9982	0.9982	0.9982	0.9983	0.9983	0.9984	0.9984	0.9984	0.9984	0.9985
3.60	0.9985	0.9985	0.9986	0.9986	0.9986	0.9986	0.9987	0.9987	0.9987	0.9988
3.70	0.9988	0.9988	0.9988	0.9988	0.9989	0.9989	0.9989	0.9989	0.9990	0.9990
3.80	0.9990	0.9990	0.9990	0.9991	0.9991	0.9991	0.9991	0.9991	0.9991	0.9992
3.90	0.9992	0.9992	0.9992	0.9992	0.9992	0.9993	0.9993	0.9993	0.9993	0.9993

Table 9.   Critical Values of the Wilcoxon Signed Rank Statistic

The table gives critical values of the Wilcoxon signed rank statistic W
for various significance levels and sample sizes n.   Note that exact
significance levels cannot, in general, be achieved.   The critical values
given are those whose significance levels are nearest to the stated values.

| One Tail | 10% | 5% | 2.5% | 1% | 0.5% |
| Two Tails | 20% | 10% | 5% | 2.5% | 1% |
n					
3	6				
4	9	10			
5	13	14	15		
6	17	19	20	21	
7	22	24	26	28	28
8	28	30	32	34	36
9	34	37	39	42	43
10	41	44	47	50	52
11	48	52	55	59	61
12	56	61	64	68	71
13	65	70	74	78	81
14	74	79	84	89	92
15	83	90	95	100	104
16	94	100	106	112	117
17	104	112	118	125	130
18	116	124	131	138	143
19	128	136	144	152	158
20	140	150	158	167	173
21	153	163	172	182	188
22	167	178	187	197	204
23	181	193	203	214	221
24	196	208	219	231	239
25	211	224	235	248	257
26	227	241	253	266	275
27	243	258	271	285	294
28	260	276	289	304	314
29	278	294	308	324	335
30	296	313	328	345	356
32	333	353	369	387	400
34	373	394	412	433	446
36	416	438	458	480	495
38	460	485	506	530	546
40	506	533	556	582	599
45	632	664	691	722	743
50	771	809	841	877	902

For n > 50, the one-tail 100α% critical value w_α is given
approximately by

$$w_\alpha \approx \tfrac{1}{4}\, n(n+1) + z_{1-\alpha}\sqrt{\frac{n(n+1)(2n+1)}{24}}\,,$$

where z_p is the 100p'th percentile of the standard normal distribution.

Table 10.   Critical Values of the Mann-Whitney Statistic

The table gives critical values of the Mann-Whitney statistic U for various significance levels and sample sizes m and n.   Note that exact significance levels cannot, in general, be achieved.   The critical values given are those whose significance levels are nearest to the stated values.

One tail 2.5%   Two tails 5%

n \ m	1	2	3	4	5	6	7	8	9	10	11	12	13	14	15	16	17	18	19	20
1																				20
2					10	12	14	16	18	19	21	23	25	27	28	30	32	34	35	37
3				12	15	17	20	22	25	27	29	32	34	37	39	42	44	47	49	52
4			12	15	18	22	25	28	31	34	37	41	44	47	50	53	56	59	62	66
5		10	15	18	22	26	30	34	38	41	45	49	53	56	60	64	68	72	75	79
6		12	17	22	26	31	35	40	44	48	53	57	62	66	70	75	79	84	88	92
7		14	20	25	30	35	40	45	50	55	60	66	71	76	81	86	91	96	101	106
8		16	22	28	34	40	45	51	57	62	68	74	79	85	91	96	102	108	113	119
9		18	25	31	38	44	50	57	63	69	76	82	88	94	101	107	113	119	126	132
10		19	27	34	41	48	55	62	69	76	83	90	97	104	111	117	124	131	138	145
11		21	29	37	45	53	60	68	76	83	91	98	106	113	121	128	135	143	150	158
12		23	32	41	49	57	66	74	82	90	98	106	114	122	130	139	147	155	163	171
13		25	34	44	53	62	71	79	88	97	106	114	123	132	140	149	158	166	175	183
14		27	37	47	56	66	76	85	94	104	113	122	132	141	150	159	169	178	187	196
15		28	39	50	60	70	81	91	101	111	121	130	140	150	160	170	180	189	199	209
16		30	42	53	64	75	86	96	107	117	128	139	149	159	170	180	191	201	211	222
17		32	44	56	68	79	91	102	113	124	135	147	158	169	180	191	202	213	224	235
18		34	47	59	72	84	96	108	119	131	143	155	166	178	189	201	213	224	236	247
19		35	49	62	75	88	101	113	126	138	150	163	175	187	199	211	224	236	248	260
20	20	37	52	66	79	92	106	119	132	145	158	171	183	196	209	222	235	247	260	273

One tail 5%   Two tails 10%

n \ m	1	2	3	4	5	6	7	8	9	10	11	12	13	14	15	16	17	18	19	20
1										10	11	12	13	14	15	16	17	18	19	20
2			6	8	10	12	13	15	17	18	20	22	23	25	27	28	30	32	34	35
3		6	9	11	14	16	18	21	23	25	28	30	32	35	37	39	42	44	46	49
4		8	11	14	17	20	23	26	29	32	35	38	41	44	47	50	53	56	59	62
5		10	14	17	21	25	28	32	35	39	43	46	50	53	57	61	64	68	71	75
6		12	16	20	25	29	33	37	42	46	50	54	58	63	67	71	75	79	83	88
7		13	18	23	28	33	38	43	48	52	57	62	67	72	76	81	86	91	96	100
8		15	21	26	32	37	43	48	54	59	64	70	75	81	86	91	97	102	108	113
9		17	23	29	35	42	48	54	60	66	72	78	84	90	96	102	108	114	120	125
10	10	18	25	32	39	46	52	59	66	72	79	86	92	99	105	112	118	125	131	138
11	11	20	28	35	43	50	57	64	72	79	86	93	100	108	115	122	129	136	143	150
12	12	22	30	38	46	54	62	70	78	86	93	101	109	117	124	132	140	147	155	163
13	13	23	32	41	50	58	67	75	84	92	100	109	117	125	134	142	150	159	167	175
14	14	25	35	44	53	63	72	81	90	99	108	117	125	134	143	152	161	170	179	188
15	15	27	37	47	57	67	76	86	96	105	115	124	134	143	153	162	172	181	190	200
16	16	28	39	50	61	71	81	92	102	112	122	132	142	152	162	172	182	192	202	212
17	17	30	42	53	64	75	86	97	108	118	129	140	150	161	172	182	193	203	214	225
18	18	32	44	56	68	79	91	102	114	125	136	147	159	170	181	192	203	215	226	237
19	19	34	46	59	71	83	96	108	120	131	143	155	167	179	190	202	214	226	237	249
20	20	35	49	62	75	88	100	113	125	138	150	163	175	188	200	212	225	237	249	261

Table 11. **Random Digits**

The table gives 2500 random digits from 0 to 9, arranged for convenience
in blocks of five.

43980	25863	26439	96848	08808	32750	39157	21431	21197	62950
82570	23905	35993	89139	60589	84788	45431	11088	01163	98917
86570	38795	84683	00355	58478	22119	30796	42268	61817	58494
86204	32327	46960	31019	89194	31757	47078	83503	71038	65779
12949	66813	52110	86683	64116	63380	19737	27269	39312	47588
36327	78695	42302	74252	42403	99643	80113	22466	76965	73773
11115	79150	31849	90442	73575	96744	94050	40192	38292	79577
57252	32787	26543	13322	53020	16851	53913	22228	41267	25534
49019	58557	47837	75547	47908	81859	22262	83202	09860	57095
45769	51728	50109	64923	96849	28427	03235	43266	20044	16977
80783	24880	09609	18403	39091	95136	71859	10683	02516	58063
39706	03400	84512	33618	95642	32329	01747	03459	23185	01148
83671	15701	58406	62152	90917	74296	77591	51197	60797	02363
52143	47457	85125	57491	21576	66153	16699	55404	47795	84776
75534	73652	16161	68073	13448	28452	85854	01891	77223	16390
76046	98360	37690	96665	46669	75546	23459	38341	13905	36484
05176	24211	68844	76939	58384	19853	12196	38443	61689	47815
71183	84148	09761	43329	12934	05475	02297	79506	57089	63475
97846	23697	64406	03032	55860	16640	70986	85682	41660	90996
69296	23855	00451	86954	98693	74542	70272	05294	73389	51231
35027	89963	67316	94885	09603	24309	21988	34141	52246	75867
43200	21542	14528	48862	94144	37267	92356	31805	75656	55265
49171	48961	50622	94353	01366	44253	39414	58986	81876	76182
44592	19008	47954	90641	20609	65312	00491	38037	77548	64955
58433	07942	79251	19289	22703	22455	93278	60862	49645	50844
34966	28335	22446	55388	02075	19314	30049	06452	69955	72084
82538	56436	66377	99545	08196	81176	38375	14191	03926	89403
73087	65183	73496	56660	20365	62896	70951	78783	90373	47875
56524	30985	79833	07759	17041	75510	59221	47355	22331	07993
91641	75044	39946	56310	55033	46845	05126	03262	52106	32812
63212	46841	38718	34224	59000	30620	72120	05129	72859	19512
12902	24767	30553	33742	73867	46859	06518	93201	11402	29523
04159	68885	98881	35684	83865	61230	04848	30778	55043	68971
46158	26198	78286	83025	52959	51739	61351	03499	12572	09091
98255	90598	68914	09859	23299	60281	97239	22241	21424	39373
59515	62134	30752	66264	24339	48287	77888	89549	39831	10043
49185	21297	57814	91998	27879	15794	06048	03266	70816	58514
84778	13184	31122	74317	52715	97180	86360	73565	26108	91429
62917	93302	38860	22959	28666	02041	25665	68489	57059	45878
60210	92484	75692	59609	26977	73524	56787	63431	47108	38215
22944	38384	88480	06006	93570	98845	48765	89165	37967	41569
61670	71829	92667	49817	17472	39856	44656	90679	90218	61081
48656	81123	45138	97855	20095	73410	58308	11043	11880	98499
36256	26995	94766	64839	42232	83048	19981	81790	27308	72994
95500	37186	31550	87752	87971	19081	63875	33295	85733	99647
16902	12477	48924	05774	14255	85825	91343	11905	94075	50809
90391	79140	26965	72381	18633	22994	11752	58302	29197	46850
63689	07060	58802	07590	36533	95805	34765	35577	48545	28181
41664	95682	62795	05667	36222	43351	03542	86429	66816	59457
36433	66362	26482	22158	57380	33066	16389	84318	62887	08150

Titles in the RND Statistical Series:

Introductory Statistics　　　　　　　　*ISBN 0-9506719-1-6*
Volume 1 - Probability and Distribution Theory

**Worked Examples in Probability and
Distribution Theory**　　　　　　　　　　*ISBN 0-9506719-2-4*

Introductory Statistics　　　　　　　　*ISBN 0-9506719-3-2*
Volume 2 - Statistical Inference

Worked Examples in Statistical Inference　*ISBN 0-9506719-4-0*

Elementary Statistical Tables　　　　　*ISBN 0-9506719-5-9*

Specimen solutions to Advanced-level papers in Mathematics and Statistics set by several of the Examining Boards are also available from the Publishers. Further details can be obtained by writing to the address on page (ii).